Radar ornithology

ERIC EASTWOOD

Radar ornithology

METHUEN & CO LTD
11 NEW FETTER LANE · LONDON EC4

Distribution in the U.S.A.
by Barnes & Noble, Inc.

250958

Preface

When a book on the migration and flight behaviour of birds is offered by a physicist engaged on research in the electrical industry, perhaps a word of explanation is called for.

Radar was developed to meet the military need for surveillance of the air space, but the radio waves which are launched from a high-power, microwave radar to locate aircraft are also scattered back from droplets of rain, ice particles, birds, and even insects. The radar may indicate the presence of aircraft but it also displays echoes from these other occupants of the air space, and sometimes these unwanted 'angel' echoes can mask the very aircraft whose presence it is desired to detect.

In due course 'black boxes' were devised by the engineers and physicists engaged on radar research, and the operational difficulties occasioned by the reflection of radar waves from space clutter were overcome. The pursuit of this technical problem revealed that angels could often be equated with birds and it was apparent that radar could be of great assistance to the ornithologist studying the migrations of birds.

It was my privilege to be associated with radar research of this kind in the laboratories of the Marconi Company. When the engineering aspects of our particular clutter problems had been completed, however, it seemed a pity not to take advantage of the opportunity offered to obtain information on bird migration by securing film records of the p.p.i. displays simultaneously with the proving of valves and other components. It is a pleasure to thank the Chairman of the Marconi Company – Mr F. N. Sutherland – who gave his permission for a radar observational programme on bird echoes to be discharged in this way at the Bushy Hill Experimental Radar Station of the Marconi Company, and some of the results of this research work are described in the following pages.

In the years since the war, bird watching by radar has been pursued vigorously in Europe and America utilizing radar installations set up primarily for Military or Air Traffic Control duties. This research activity has created what is virtually the new and exciting science of RADAR ORNITHOLOGY, and so the time appears appropriate for a general review of the progress which has been made in this subject and the various observational techniques that have been employed. It is hoped that this little book will help to bridge the disciplines of Ornithology, Radar Engineering, and Physics and so will be of interest to the general reader attracted to the study of birds and their mysterious ways.

The writing of this book was prompted by the kind interest shown by Mr

PREFACE

R. D. N. Somerville and Mr F. Herrmann in a lecture on 'Radar and Birds' which I originally gave to the Royal Institution in 1962, and I am most grateful to them for their continued interest. I wish to thank Dr David Lack, one of the main architects of RADAR ORNITHOLOGY, for his encouragement and advice. He it was who introduced me to the study of bird migration and showed how radar could help with its problems.

I am grateful to Dr G. G. Macfarlane, formerly Director of the Royal Radar Establishment, for permission to quote some of the work of his engineers, also to Dr G. W. Schafer for kindly permitting me to reproduce Plate 3 (d, e) from his most recent work on wingbeat effects. I would like to thank the Editors of the Scientific Journals and the authors named in the text for permission to reproduce a number of figures whose source I have acknowledged fully in association with the individual drawings. My colleagues at Bushy Hill, Mr J. D. Bell and Mr J. Franklin, have given valuable assistance in the observational programme, and Mr G. C. Rider has collaborated with me in all phases of the work. To them I offer my grateful thanks, not least for reading the manuscript of this book and providing me with much useful comment. The technique of film recording employed at Bushy Hill was developed by Mr N. R. Phelp and it is a pleasure to acknowledge the beautiful radar photographs he has prepared to illustrate many of the types of bird movement I have described.

In preparing the text I have thought it better not to include the scientific names of all the birds mentioned but to place this information in the index. I hope that this arrangement will commend itself to the general reader while not impairing the scientific value of the book as a whole.

ERIC EASTWOOD

Contents

PLATES

Introduction

The general study of the behaviour of birds has been conducted through the years by field observers armed only with field glasses, cameras, and infinite patience. This devoted body of bird watchers, both amateur and professional, has slowly compiled a great volume of detailed information about the behaviour and habits of birds which complements the biochemical, physiological, and other more formal studies of the professional ornithologists. It is difficult to imagine how such problems as the distribution of bird population, the influence of toxic chemicals, the impact of the 1963 winter upon bird life and the subsequent recovery of various species could have been tackled without the massive support which amateur bird watchers, through their local Natural History and Ornithological Societies, have been able to mount. It is because the observations of bird watchers through the ages have been so detailed and valuable that it must be counted somewhat ironic that the exercise of that ability which so sharply distinguishes the bird from other vertebrate creatures – namely powered flight – tends to render its behaviour in the air comparatively inaccessible to the normal bird watcher. This deficiency has now been somewhat remedied by the use of radar; at the same time the ranks of the amateur ornithologists have been swelled by physicists and engineers using their radar equipments to help the eyes of the watchers in the field.

Many of the day flights of birds are performed within a few hundred feet of the ground and so can be observed through field glasses by the bird watcher, or better still, recorded by ciné camera. Bird flights, however, are often performed at altitudes substantially greater than 1,000 ft, and so are invisible to a ground observer. This is true, for example, of the migration flights of birds moving between the British Isles and the Continent. Such migratory flights, moreover, take place by night as well as by day, and so have been largely missed by the ordinary observer but they can now be detected, recorded, and studied in detail by radar. Indeed, it is only by the application of radar during recent years to the study of bird movements that the general pattern of migration to and from these islands has been traced in detail. Such studies are also contributing to the solution of that fascinating problem – how do birds navigate?

Any ordinary person can enjoy television without having detailed knowledge of the intricate electrical processes which are involved when the likeness of a distant scene is reproduced upon his own small screen. Nevertheless, some slight knowledge of radio principles and of the mode of operation of a television camera surely adds wonder to the spectacle. In like manner, it is unnecessary for the student of birds and their ways to possess close familiarity with the principles of radar engineering in order to follow the progress of radar ornithological research in various parts of the world. But the bird enthusiast wishes to assess critically the significance of the results achieved by this new type of bird watching, and so he will wish to acquire some understanding of radar principles – at least he will want to know how radar works and to appreciate both the advantages and limitations of this new method of bird study.

It is one of the purposes of this book to explain something of the principles and practice of microwave radar, and to show how radar equipments based upon these ideas have become powerful and indispensable aids to the modern ornithologist. It is well known that Radiolocation, as we in Britain termed the device that could detect and locate aircraft by radio, was a vital aid to the Royal Air Force during the Battle of Britain – it is less well known that geese and swans were detected by these same means as early as 1940. The association between radiolocation and the study of bird movements has thus been long established, but radiolocation has developed greatly since 1940, including the change of its name to radar, and modern equipments are now of such power that a single gull can be detected at a range of 50 miles, while bird heights have been measured up to 21,000 ft. We shall need to examine some of the main features of a modern radar station, and to appreciate how ciné films of radar displays have yielded new and exciting facts about the behaviour of migrating birds.

CHAPTER ONE

The principles of radar

Sound location

Any physically vibrating body such as the skin of a drum, the vocal chords of a human being, the string of a cello, or the column of air in an organ pipe, causes local pressure changes in the adjacent air. We may call such a pulsating source an 'acoustic transmitter', and the pressure changes it produces travel outwards through the air at a velocity of about 1,100 ft/s. When such a sound wave reaches the ear, the pressure fluctuations cause the eardrum to vibrate in sympathy; these movements are linked through the bones of the middle ear to the inner ear and ultimately excite the acoustic nerve. The ear constitutes an 'acoustic receiver'.

Sound waves are reflected from solid surfaces, and when an observer listens to the echo of his voice from a distant rock face he is operating a simple sound location system. A short cry or clap of the hands causes the emission or radiation of a short pulse of sound from his 'transmitter'. This pulse travels to the cliffs and is reflected back to the observer, whose ears form the acoustic receiver which records the return of the reflected signal or 'echo'. If he estimates the delay time of the echo as one second, for example, he will conclude that the signal has travelled 1,100 ft, and that the range of the cliff is 550 ft (Fig. 1.1).

The following three processes are fundamental to any echo ranging system:

(1) Transmission of a pulse or packet of waves.
(2) Reception of the reflected signal.
(3) Measurement of the delay time, which is the total propagation time for the round trip.

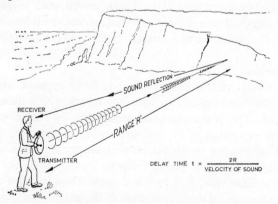

FIG. 1.1. Distance measurement by estimation of the time delay of a sound echo

3

In addition, the observer can derive information about the direction of arrival of the echo signal. This he normally does by turning his head until he is 'looking at the source of sound'; he is then reacting in response to the binaural effect, which states that the sound signals received by the ears separately are judged to be identical when the source is positioned in the direction at right angles to the line joining the ears. The student of bird song commonly makes use of a plastic or metal reflector in the form of a parabolic dish which he similarly 'points' at the bird whose song he wishes to record. Such a reflector constitutes an 'aerial' for sound waves and the observer adjusts the direction of the dish until the received

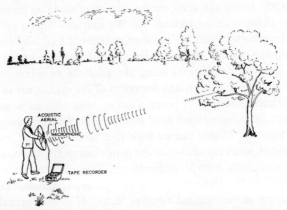

FIG. I.2. Acoustic direction finding as used to record the songs of birds

signal is a maximum; the bird or sound source then lies on the axis of the dish (Fig. I.2).

These familiar methods of locating a source of sound or an acoustic echo illustrate the basic principles of radar. Sound-radar or 'Sonar' techniques are widely employed in the steel industry to test for cracks in large forgings. Supersonic waves are generated by a piezo-electric crystal, such as quartz or barium titanate, and launched into the mass of steel; reflections from cracks and other discontinuities are collected by a second crystal acting as the receiver.

Optical location

That sound travels with a finite velocity is fairly apparent even to a casual observer; it is not so obvious that light also travels with a finite though much greater velocity. This is because phenomena involving the velocity of light are not within the experience of the ordinary terrestrial observer; this is what the great Galileo found when he tried to measure the speed of light with flashing oil lamps! It was the Danish astronomer Römer in 1675 who first enunciated the principle of the finite velocity of light and showed how its value could be estimated by measurements of the eclipse times of the satellites of Jupiter. This work was neglected until Bradley, the English Astronomer Royal, discovered the phenomenon of aberration in 1726. The positions of the so-called fixed stars were found to undergo small angular displacements or aberrations, whose value depended upon the position of the earth in its orbit. Bradley explained this effect in terms of the interaction between the velocity of the earth in its orbit and the finite velocity of light.

These astronomers had ingeniously made use of the vast dimensions of the solar system in order to reveal the fact that light does not travel at an infinite speed. Their measuring techniques, however, could not give an accurate value to this important universal constant of nature c, the velocity of light, since they were dependent upon the value of the solar parallax, or the angle subtended at the sun by the earth's radius, and this is still one of the most difficult measurements to make in practical astronomy.

The first accurate determination of the velocity of light by a terrestrial method was made by Fizeau in 1849 and this classic experiment is worth pausing over for a moment since it illustrates so neatly the basic principles of radar ranging. Fizeau's experimental arrangement is shown in Fig. 1.3. Light from a source

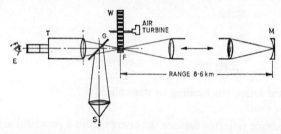

FIG. 1.3. Measurement of the velocity of light by Fizeau's pulse method

S was focused at a point F in the plane of the toothed wheel W before passing through the lens system to the distant concave mirror M 8·6 km away. The light was reflected from M back through the same optical system and through the inclined glass sheet G to the telescope. The observer could see the source, provided that a gap of the wheel were located at F, but as the wheel was slowly rotated the image was caused to flicker due to the passing teeth. As the speed of the wheel was increased this flickering ceased and the image became steady but of reduced intensity.

If the speed of the wheel were now increased to the point that the time taken for a tooth to replace the adjacent gap were equal to the transit time of the pulse of light from F to M and back again, then the returning pulse would be intercepted by the tooth and the source would be invisible. It is seen that measurement of the speed of the wheel will give the time t required for the pulse of light to travel the distance $2R$, and so yields the velocity of light. Throughout this book we shall take the value of c to be:

$$c = 3 \times 10^{10} \text{ cm/s or 186,000 miles/s}$$

Notice that the source and the toothed wheel together form a generator and

B

transmitter of optical pulses; similarly, the eye and the telescope together form an optical receiver, while the turbine and its tachometer form a timing system that permits the delay time t of the reflected echo pulse to be measured. The range R of the reflection point then follows from the relation, $R = \frac{1}{2} ct$. These principles of optical echo ranging apply in radar.

In order to determine direction in an optical location system, use is made of a lens or mirror, and the most obvious example of such a system is provided by the human eye. A single eye serves to provide direction, but the combination of the two eyes gives stereoscopic vision, i.e. actual location in space. The optical analogue to the radar case is provided by the old style military searchlight, in

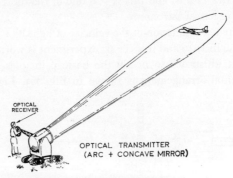

OPTICAL RECEIVER

OPTICAL TRANSMITTER (ARC + CONCAVE MIRROR)

FIG. I.4. Optical Direction Finding by searchlight

which the parabolic reflector focuses the energy from a powerful arc lamp into a sharp beam, which is swept over the sky and illuminates the clouds or aircraft, thus permitting the direction of a target to be found (Fig. 1.4).

Radiolocation

The close similarity between the acoustic and optical methods of echo location will be apparent, but neither of these techniques was capable of being developed into an aircraft detection and warning system that would possess military significance. It was the substitution of radio waves for the optical or acoustic waves that transformed the situation and so created the new technology of radar. Radiolocation, or radar, is the name given to the system which utilizes the reflection of radio waves in order to detect the presence of aircraft and, by providing measurements of both range and direction, serves to locate their positions.

It is rather a pleasing thought that a presentation of the simple principles of radar, intended to serve as an introduction to the contribution which radar studies have made to the understanding of bird flight behaviour, should really commence with another biological experiment, that of Galvani in 1792 when, in his famous 'frog's leg' experiment, he first stumbled upon the electric current. The sequence of electrical discoveries that led from Galvani to the present use of radar as a tool in ornithological research is graphically traced in Fig. 1.5.

Volta quickly invented his electric cell based upon Galvani's observation and

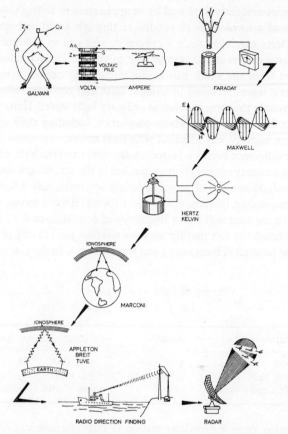

FIG. 1.5. The path of discovery from Galvani's 'frog leg' experiment to Radar Ornithology

Ampère showed that the electric current produced by a 'voltaic' cell produced a magnetic effect. The importance of this interrelation between electric and magnetic effects was recognized by Faraday and was embodied by him in his theories of electric and magnetic fields. His classic experiment of 1831 led him to the discovery of electromagnetic induction, i.e. the principle that a moving or changing magnetic field produces an associated electric field, which can most simply be detected as an electric current induced in a coil of wire. This is, of course, the principle of the dynamo, from which device modern electrical technology proceeds.

The mathematical investigation of Faraday's concept of the interrelated magnetic and electric fields was undertaken by Clerk-Maxwell, whose studies culminated in the electromagnetic theory of light which bears his name. According to this theory, light waves consist of associated oscillating electric and magnetic fields which are propagated through space with the finite velocity we have designated as c. Hertz immediately perceived that such an oscillating electric

7

field could be conveniently produced by an application of Kelvin's discovery that the discharge of a Leyden jar or condenser through a coil and spark gap was oscillatory. Hertz employed such a condenser and coil to produce a high frequency oscillatory current and he was able to show that electromagnetic waves were radiated from the spark gap in his circuit. He demonstrated that these electromagnetic waves travelled in straight lines and could be reflected and refracted in precisely the same manner as ordinary light waves. Hertz had, in fact, produced the first radio waves whose properties, including their speed of propagation, were in every way identical with light waves.

One major difference between Hertz's radio waves and the light waves familiar to us through ordinary optical phenomena, lies in the wavelength associated with them. Yellow light consists of waves of length approximately $5,890 \times 10^{-8}$ cm and the corresponding frequency is $5 \cdot 1 \times 10^{14}$ c/s. Hertz's waves, on the other hand, were 50 cm long and had a frequency of 600 Mc/s or 6×10^{8} c/s. This example illustrates the fact that for all wave motions the velocity of propagation is equal to the product of frequency f and wavelength λ. In the case of light waves we have:

$$\text{Velocity of light} = c = f.\lambda$$
$$\text{i.e. } 3 \times 10^{10} = f(c/s) \times \lambda(cm)$$

Radiation	λ (cm)	f (c/s)	c (cm/s)
X-rays	1×10^{-8}	3×10^{18}	3×10^{10}
Yellow light	$5,890 \times 10^{-8}$	$5 \cdot 1 \times 10^{14}$	3×10^{10}
Hertz's radio waves	50	600×10^{6}	3×10^{10}

The radiation from a broadcast station is monochromatic, i.e. it is of one wavelength only, as contrasted to the many colours, each of a different wavelength, contained in a beam of white light, and which are separated by refraction in a prism.

It was the recognition that these Hertzian radio waves offered a means of achieving communication between remote stations without the use of connecting wires that prompted the great upsurge of radio experiments which marked the close of the nineteenth century. Many famous scientists worked on radio phenomena during this period. Lodge, Campbell-Walker, Popoff, and many others made substantial contributions, but to Marconi belongs the distinction of being the first to achieve significant long-distance communication. Marconi's bridging of the Atlantic in 1907 marked the real commencement of the radio age, which has culminated in the wonder of television transmitted between remote points on the earth's surface via a communication satellite.

Marconi used long waves of frequency 20,000 c/s ($\lambda = 1,500$ m) in his Newfoundland–Cornwall experiment and it was the unexpected success of this work that led to the recognition that the earth's atmosphere must contain a layer, now termed the 'ionosphere', which was capable of reflecting the radio waves around

8

the bulge of the earth. Direct experimental demonstration of the presence of this reflecting layer was first made by Appleton in 1925, who launched radio waves vertically from the earth's surface to the ionosphere, where they were reflected back to the ground and could be received upon a separate aerial. It will be seen that the ionosphere was providing a radio echo and so the measurement of the time delay of the echo could provide a direct measurement of the height of the ionosphere. The ionospheric layer is located about 100 km above the earth's surface so that the time delay of the echo was approximately 2/3 of a millisecond (1 millisecond = 1/1,000 s, written 1 ms). This first radio ranging experiment serves to emphasize the fact that the echo times of even distant targets are very small and demand special methods for their measurement.

Appleton's work was quickly followed by the experiments of Breit and Tuve in which the transmitted radio wave was chopped into a series of short pulses precisely as in the Fizeau experiment described above. The electrical method of chopping used in place of the toothed wheel simply took the form of switching the transmitter on and off in rapid sequence. The delay time of the returned echo was measured by a cathode ray tube device as described in the next chapter, so that as early as 1925 there was in operation a pulse echo system of radiolocation for investigation of the ionized layers of the earth's upper atmosphere. This early research technique, however, falls short of a full radiolocation system since no direction was derived, the experiments being wholly concerned with vertically incident radio waves. Techniques to measure the direction of arrival of radio waves coming from a distant transmitter were, however, already well established and were in use on aircraft and on ships at sea. Such methods had, in fact, been developed during the closing phases of the First World War. The radio transmission from the ship or aircraft was picked up by the radio receiving station and the direction of arrival of the radio waves could be determined with the aid of an aerial having spaced elements capable of sampling the wave front at two points. In the case of medium frequencies, i.e. about 200 kc/s such as are used in ship communications, the normal form of directional aerial is a loop of wire which can be rotated about a diametral and vertical axis lying in the plane of the loop. The aerial is rotated for minimum signal. This occurs when its plane corresponds to the plane of the advancing radio-wave front, i.e. the direction of the source is at right angles to this plane.

Similar direction-finding techniques were applied in the early 1930s by Sir Robert Watson-Watt and his team to study the rate of occurrence and the direction of location of lightning discharges. Such a discharge of electricity from cloud to cloud or cloud to ground produces a short burst of radio noise that may be heard as an atmospheric in an ordinary sound radio. Since the discharge was of very short duration it was necessary that the direction-finding process should be accomplished within a very short space of time. The piece of apparatus developed to do this was a form of cathode ray tube display such as is now used in a television set. The same method could also be applied to determine the direction of arrival of any short duration radio signal so that, by 1932, the stage was set for

9

bringing together the techniques of radio echo-ranging and radio direction-finding in order to form the new technique of radiolocation.

The early workers in radiolocation were aware that radio waves could be reflected from aeroplanes as well as from the ionosphere but the radio echoes were very weak and difficult to detect. Nevertheless, it was clearly realized that if the echoes produced by a powerful pulse transmitter could be received and amplified then the range of the reflecting aircraft and its direction could be measured. It was also realized that such a perfected, non-co-operative method of detecting the presence of any aircraft in the air space and of radiolocating its position could be of vital importance in combating the air attacks that would inevitably be a major feature of any future war. The development and perfecting of radiolocation techniques were, therefore, undertaken with great vigour and in complete secrecy; the military success of the new weapon in the Second World War is well known.

Radiolocation has become a specialized and highly developed branch of modern radio engineering and so it was probably a happy idea of the Americans to give a new name 'Radar' to the new technology. The new word 'Radar' derives from the essential parts of the radiolocation process, i.e. *Ra*dio *De*tection *a*nd *R*anging, and it is used either as a noun or as an adjective. Thus we use a radar to observe migrating birds and we employ radar techniques to measure the density, altitude, and direction of flight of a stream of birds.

A modern radar station

It is not the purpose of this book to describe in detail the developments in radar technique which have taken place over the last thirty years; we may simply note that the aims of research over this period were to increase the detection range and to improve the accuracy of measurement. The military need to achieve these objectives has resulted in a progressive improvement in the power of the transmitter, in the sensitivity of the receiver and in the gain and resolution of the aerial systems that have been employed.

In the case of the transmitter a thousand-fold increase in pulse power has been obtained since 1939; the pulse powers of a few kilowatts only in 1939 have been converted to megawatts in the 1960s. The requirements for improved target resolution, coupled with high azimuthal accuracy, led to a movement away from the comparatively long radio wavelengths which were used in the first radar stations. Thus, in 1939, a wavelength of about 13 m (23 Mc/s) was employed for the Chain Home radars of the Royal Air Force, which existed as a belt of 'C.H.' stations round the coast of Britain. This wavelength was reduced to $1\frac{1}{2}$ m for the second chain of coastal stations, and radars with wavelengths of 50 cm, 10 cm and 3 cm respectively were later developed and brought into use with the Services. Modern equipments employ wavelengths in the band 50 cm–8 mm, the precise wavelength selected being dependent upon the operational role the radar is intended to fulfil. Thus, a 23-cm radar is commonly employed for long range warning or surveillance (up to 300 miles) but 3 cm or less is used for airborne radars. Radars operating in the waveband below 50 cm are usually termed 'microwave radars' and are characterized by the use of quasi-optical aerials, usually in the form of reflecting dishes. We shall be concerned exclusively with microwave radars in this book.

The requirement for good target resolution in range led to the use of shorter and shorter pulse lengths. Clearly, if the pulse length is 16 microseconds (16 millionths of a second, written 16 μs), the radio pulse packet occupies a length of approximately 3 miles. If two aircraft lying on the same radius from the radar are separated by less than half this length, they will not be recognized as two distinct targets because they will be contained within the same 'pulse packet'. For this reason radar pulse lengths were reduced progressively and it is now usual for a modern surveillance equipment to use a pulse length of $5/\mu$s. Short range sets commonly use 1 μs and in some ship applications even 0·1 μs is called for. Short though these pulses are, they are long compared to the time intervals of nano-

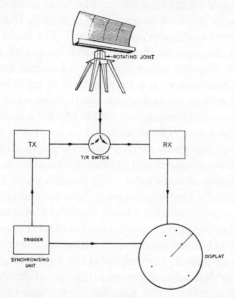

FIG. 1.6. The elements of a microwave radar

seconds encountered in modern computers. (1 nanosecond = 1 thousandth of 1 μs = 10^{-9}s).

The essential elements of a modern microwave radar station, as used for long-range observations of civil aircraft moving along airways may be described by reference to the Marconi experimental station shown in Plate 1 (a) and located on Bushy Hill in Essex, England. This is the station which has featured in a number of the researches described later in this book; it is also the source of most of the radar pictures here reproduced.

The radar consists of the following component sub-systems, shown diagrammatically in Fig. 1.6:

(1) Aerial – used both to transmit and receive.

(2) Transmitter (TX) – to produce a continuous succession of high powered, short duration pulses.

(3) Receiver (RX) – a very sensitive radio receiver to detect the feeble echoes.

(4) T-R Switch – An automatic device for isolating the receiver from the aerial during the transmission of the pulse.

(5) Display – a cathode ray tube device to measure both the delay time of the echo pulse and its direction of arrival.

(6) Sychronizing Unit or Trigger – to initiate the pulse train from the transmitter, and to trigger the time measuring circuits in the Display System.

Radar aerials

The prime purpose of the lens of a lighthouse lantern or the reflector of a motor-car headlamp is to bunch the optical energy of the lamp into a narrow beam in order to secure greater penetrating power. The radar aerial similarly serves to focus the radio energy delivered by the transmitter into a beam suitable for the illumination of aircraft at altitudes up to 50,000 ft. The Bushy Hill surveillance aerial is shown on the right of Plate 1 (a) and consists of a reflector in the form of a parabolic cylinder, rather similar to an electric fire, and measuring 75 ft × 25 ft. The radio energy at a wavelength of 23 cm is led from the transmitter via a copper tube or waveguide to a rotating joint which permits loss-free transmission of the energy to another waveguide which is attached to and revolves with the aerial on the gantry. This second guide is coupled to the aerial primary feed which is a slotted waveguide running the whole length of the array and occupying a position relative to the reflector identical to that of the heater element in an electric fire, i.e. it is located at the focus of the parabola which is the cross-section of the reflector (Fig. 1.7). The radiation pours from the slots of the feed guide and interacts with the reflector to form a beam whose width in the horizontal plane is only 0·8°. The shape of the beam in the vertical plane is asymmetric, as shown in Fig. 1.7. This form of beam is achieved by distorting the vertical section of the reflector from a true parabola. The purpose of this arrangement is to increase the proportion of energy radiated at angles lower than 10° of elevation, relative to the radiation at elevation angles higher than 30°; in this way the sensitivity of the radar is increased on distant aircraft flying below 50,000 ft.

The aerial is rotated on top of the gantry at 4 r.p.m. and so a fan beam of radio energy is swept like a lighthouse beam through 360° once every 15 s. Any object in the airspace, be it aircraft, cloud, or bird, is illuminated by this radio beam and scatters energy back to the radio aerial. In the case of an aircraft, at a range of 186 miles, the transit time for the double journey is 2 ms, and thus the returning pulse will find the bearing of the aerial substantially unchanged; actually it will be displaced about 3′. This received energy passes through the rotating joint and is routed to the receiver via the switch labelled 'T.R. Switch'.

The first radars employed two separate, static aerials in order to fulfil the transmit and receive functions respectively. Even the early 1½-m radars mentioned above, although of the rotating-beam type, still employed separate T and R arrays. The problem of ensuring that the receiver array (R) was suitably oriented to receive echoes from a target illuminated by the transmit aerial (T) was a difficult one, however, and was only ultimately overcome by combining the two aerials into one array – called a 'common T and R array'. This may seem an obvious solution to the alignment problem but it could only be applied if a method could be found for isolating the receiver from the aerial during the short transmission interval. Now the magnitude of the transmitted pulse from Bushy Hill radar is 2 MW, while the received echo pulse is in the order of 2×10^{-14} W. In order to employ a common T and R array, it is necessary to ensure that the receiver, so sensitive as to respond to an echo signal of 2×10^{-14} W, shall be completely isolated from the full blast of the outgoing transmitter pulse of 2×10^6 W. The ratio of these two pulses is about 10^{20}! The device which makes this possible is the T-R switch; it is an arrangement of gas discharge tubes which automatically conduct when the transmitter pulse occurs and so screen the entrance of the waveguide which leads to the receiver. When the echo pulse returns it is too feeble to re-strike the gas tubes, for these are no longer conducting due to the cessation of the transmitter pulse, and so the echo pulse passes straight to the receiver without attenuation. The T-R switch and the common aerial principle of radar which it makes possible were indeed wonderfully conceived.

Although the azimuthal beam width of the Bushy Hill radar is very narrow ($0.8°$), its spatial extent is obviously much greater than the aircraft or birds which it illumines, and so a number of echoes will be received from such objects during the transit of the beam over them. The radar emits 250 pulses per second and usually provides echo signals composed of eleven successive 'strikes' on the target. The narrowness of the beam, however, is more than adequate to ensure an accurate measurement of the bearing of the target. An electrical device, either a 'magslip' or 'selsyn', is geared to the array and relays the instantaneous bearing of the aerial to the radar display.

Although the aerial described provides a form of radiation pattern well suited to the surveillance role in civil or military operations, other forms of aerial radiation diagram are also needed and these special aerials can be extremely useful in certain forms of ornithological research. The aerial shown on the left of Plate 1 (a) is such an aerial; it is a steerable tracker which has been used to observe the movements of artificial satellites. This aerial consists of a 30-ft parabolic reflector set in an altazimuth mounting; it is fitted with two rotating joints to permit rotation of the dish about vertical and horizontal axes respectively.

At Bushy Hill the radio energy from the transmitter can be switched into the tracker as an alternative to the surveillance aerial and, after passage through the pair of rotating joints, is finally sprayed on to the reflector through a horn feed. The beam produced by the aerial is symmetrical about the dish axis and has an angular width of $1.8°$. This type of radar aerial is the complete radio analogue of the optical searchlight mentioned earlier and has to be steered to the correct azimuth and elevation so that the target lies on the axis of the reflector. Such an aerial is not suitable for monitoring the general movements of aircraft or birds, but it is extremely useful for the detailed examination of a single target and of the time variation of its echo.

It is interesting to note how fashion can operate even in such an unlikely subject as aerials for radar. In Britain there has been a tendency to design large surveillance aerials in the linear array form described above. In the U.S.A., on the other hand, designers have favoured the elliptical paraboloid which can be caused to produce an identical diagram by the use of a feed in the form of a stack of horns (see Fig. 1.7). The two types of aerial are completely equivalent but

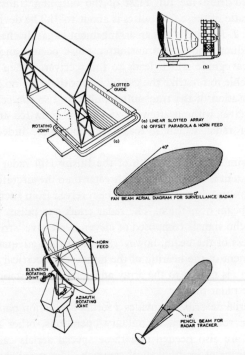

FIG. 1.7. Radar aerials and the radiation patterns which they produce

whatever kind of radar aerial is employed it is necessary to have detailed know-ledge of the characteristics of the radio beam which it is producing and of the position of the beam in relation to the aerial structure. This kind of information is calculable from the known geometry of the array and the wavelength of the radiation employed, but it is also desirable to check the results by measuring the magnitude of the signals picked up by the aerial from a remote transmitter of known power. In the case of the Bushy Hill aerials the most convenient source of radiation is the sun itself. The sun is a strong emitter of radio waves; it is also a source of small angular size (30') whose elevation and azimuth are accurately known at all times and so it is an ideal test source. Plate 14 shows how the sun's radio emission produces a radial white line upon the radar picture which accurately indicates the sun's bearing.

Aerial gain

The ability of an aerial to concentrate its radiation into a narrow beam is measured by a factor termed the aerial gain G. The gain of an aerial in a certain direction measures the ratio of the power per unit solid angle in that direction, compared to the power that would have been present if the same total power had been fed to a completely non-directional or 'isotropic' aerial. Clearly the gain must be less than unity in some directions, for example to the rear of the array, to make up for the concentration of energy in the forward direction. Usually we are most interested in the maximum gain along the principle axis of the array; in the case of the Bushy Hill aerials this is 20,000 for the surveillance set and 10,000 for the tracker. This definition of gain refers to the aerial as a transmitter but it applies equally to the same aerial when used as a receiver, rather as a lens may be used either in a projector (transmitter) or in a camera (receiver). The gain factor of the array is extremely important when considering the ranges at which targets of various sizes can be 'seen' by the radar; it is analogous to the power of a microscope, a quantity whose continuous improvement has been such an important factor in furthering biological research.

Polarization

Although radio waves and light waves both consist of travelling electric and magnetic fields, which are oscillating in time and space as shown in Fig. 1.5, the radio wave is usually simpler than the light wave in that it is 'Polarized'. In the case of an ordinary, monochromatic beam of yellow light, the electric field vector is oscillating randomly in all directions in the plane of the wavefront; such light is said to be unpolarized.

When the light beam is passed through certain crystals or a piece of 'polaroid', only the electric field components along a certain direction are transmitted and the light is now said to be polarized. It follows that if a second piece of polaroid is placed in the path of the beam, but with its polarization axis at right angles to that of the first polaroid, then no light will be transmitted even though the polaroids are separately transparent.

The field pattern shown in Fig. 1.5 corresponds to a plane polarized wave, because the electric field vector lies wholly in the wavefront and also in a plane through the axis of propagation which is itself at right angles to the wavefront. A high frequency oscillatory current in a straight wire produces such a radio wave, and the ordinary television aerial is a familiar example of a conductor picking up radio energy from the polarized electric field which is parallel to its length.

In the case of the C.H. stations the aerials consisted of horizontal wires which produced horizontally polarized waves. This polarization was selected because it

15

was considered that the metal wings and fusilages of aeroplanes would reflect horizontally polarized waves better than if vertically polarized radiation were employed. In this way a convention of using horizontal polarization was established which was carried over into the microwave era. Surveillance radars are usually horizontally polarized, although there is little difference in the microwave reflectivity of an aircraft to either polarization and, in fact, height finding radars usually employ vertical polarization as a simple consequence of the change of the axis of the aerial through 90°.

If the target is symmetrical no change in reflectivity occurs when the polarization is changed, and so a metal sphere shows no polarization effect. An asymmetric target, however, such as a length of metal rod, will reflect most strongly the radiation for which the polarization of the electric field corresponds to the long axis of the target. During the war use was made of this principle in order to interfere with enemy radars. False targets were produced by dropping strips of tinfoil – called 'Window' or 'Chaff'.

Advantage can also be taken of the polarization effect to reduce the strength of echoes from rain. Falling rain drops assume a spherical shape and so reflect vertically or horizontally polarized waves equally well. A device called a circular polarizer is fitted to the radar aerial which causes the echoes from rain to be reduced greatly in intensity compared to the echoes from polarization sensitive targets such as aircraft.

A radar producing a polarized beam can also be used to study the changes in symmetry of a target by examining the fluctuation in amplitude of the echo signal consequent upon the changed reflectivity of the target with respect to a polarized wave. An example of this phenomenon is the so-called 'propeller modulation' effect encountered with radar echoes from propeller aircraft. The amplitude of the signal is found to vary in synchronism with the rotation of the propellers, since a blade reflects the horizontally polarized radar wave better when it is in the horizontal position than when it is vertical. A similar effect can happen with birds due to the change in shape of the body from near spherical to ellipsoidal during wing flapping (Chapter Five).

Radar transmitters

The function of the radar transmitter is to produce a short duration burst of radio frequency oscillations. The Bushy Hill transmitter operates at a frequency of 1,305 Mc/s and a wavelength of 23 cm. The duration of a single pulse is 5 μs, so that during this time 6,525 complete waves are emitted from the aerial. Radar visibility of a distant object can only be secured by using strong illumination, i.e. by using pulses of high energy. In the case of Bushy Hill, this packet of energy is 10 J per pulse so that, to find the equivalent radio power of the transmitter, we must divide the pulse energy by the duration of the pulse and so the equivalent power appears as 2 MW. This radar power may be compared with the 40 kw of a television station.

In the early days of radar it was a difficult engineering task to produce high pulse power. Nevertheless, the C.H. stations were able to achieve 400 kw by the use of conventional valves. At microwave frequencies the problem of power development is complicated by the fact that the transit time of electrons between the electrodes in the tube begins to be comparable with the time of one cycle of the electrical oscillation. It was necessary to devote much research and ingenuity to overcome this fundamental difficulty both during the war and in the decade that followed. Two completely new types of radio transmitting valves emerged from this work and have been developed to a remarkable level of perfection. First the 'Magnetron' – this is a self oscillating device which, when fed with a high-voltage d.c. pulse, bursts into electrical oscillation of a frequency determined by the geometry of the valve. A substantial proportion of the Bushy Hill bird migration records have been taken with a 2 MW cavity magnetron of this type. A completely different principle of operation is used in the second type of high power microwave valve known as a 'Klystron'. This is a driven valve which accepts a radio-frequency pulse at the kilowatt level and amplifies it to the megawatt range. Its frequency is determined by the low level drive circuits and so it is a coherent radio system which may be held to a predetermined frequency. It is for this reason that the klystron is now finding wide application in ultra high-frequency television. The klystron has been used in certain forms of observation at Bushy Hill concerned with the velocities of aircraft and birds.

It will be appreciated that the magnetron or klystron generator must be fed with d.c. power from a modulator source which is then converted by the action of the tube into high frequency radio power. The engineering of the modulator is a very involved matter which it is not the purpose of this book to describe; the modulator functions as a precision switch which delivers 250 pulses of d.c. energy per second to the magnetron upon receipt of synchronizing pulses supplied from the trigger unit. The same pulse train is also supplied to the Display System described in the next chapter and initiates the range measuring process.

The receiver

High performance radio receivers are now commonplace 'pieces of furniture' in most homes, whether for television or sound radio. In principle, the radar receiver does not differ from these domestic units but, since it is required to respond to the very small signal power received as an echo by reflection from a distant target, it is necessary that the receiver shall be very sensitive. Now every radio receiver creates noise – this fact can readily be appreciated by turning up the volume control on a domestic set which has been detuned from any station and detached from an aerial; a loud hissing noise is produced which is an amplified version of the electrical noise developed in the first circuit of the receiver. Radio noise, in general, is partly received from the outside world via the aerial and is partly produced by the electronic components in the first circuit of the receiver. The purpose of a receiver is to amplify the signals received without distortion and without introducing additional radio noise for this will only confuse the signal detection process. A good receiver, therefore, is one which produces as little extra noise as possible and 'goodness' in this connexion is measured by the so-called Noise Figure. In radar work great effort has been devoted to producing receivers of low noise figure – a very difficult problem at microwave frequencies. It was first solved by reverting to the form of crystal receiver familiar in the early days of broadcasting. Crystal receivers are still employed in radar, especially in the modern form known as parametric amplifiers. Special valve receivers are also used and the Bushy Hill equipment employs such a receiver in the form of a low-noise travelling wave tube. This gives a noise figure of 6–9 db as compared to the 15–18 db of 1945. The search for better receiving techniques is well worth while since reduced noise figure in the receiver is just as effective as increased power from the transmitter in improving the radar performance; but the receiver method is much less expensive to achieve in terms of both apparatus and running costs.

The radar equation and the target 'echoing area'

The original purpose of a radar was to detect the presence of aircraft in the airspace and to give the earliest possible warning of their approach. In order to increase the warning time, and to have the defences in a state of readiness, the radar must detect the target at the greatest possible range. It is, therefore, necessary to understand how the maximum range of the radar is dependent upon the characteristics of the aerial and the transmitting and receiving equipment we have reviewed above. But the range is also affected by the size and nature of the target itself; in other words, it is much easier to see aircraft than birds. We will now examine, in a simple way, the relationship between the maximum range and the quantities which determine it, i.e. the power of the transmitter, sensitivity of the receiver, and the gain of the aerial.

We wish to calculate the power of the pulse finally presented to the receiver for recognition as an echo – let this quantity be P_r W.

If the pulse from the transmitter possesses a power P W, then the effective power of the pulse radiated from the aerial is PG, where G is the gain of the array.

Let the target be at a range r, then as the radio waves travel from the aerial they will be spread out over a greater and greater area and the power density will be attenuated according to the usual inverse square law. This law states that the power density at a range r is derived from that at the source by dividing by the area of the sphere – $4\pi r^2$.

We thus have an incident power density at the target of:

$$\frac{PG}{4\pi r^2} \text{ W/sq m}$$

Now a certain multiple A of this incident energy per unit area will be reradiated or scattered by the target back to the radar, i.e. the total power scattered by the target is

$$A \cdot \frac{PG}{4\pi r^2} \text{ W}$$

This re-radiated wave will again be attenuated by $4\pi r^2$ in its return to the aerial,

i.e. Power of echo pulse at the aerial $= \dfrac{1}{4\pi r^2} \cdot A \cdot \dfrac{PG}{4\pi r^2}$ W

Aerial theory shows that the fraction of this incident power which is made available to the receiver is

$$\frac{G\lambda^2}{4\pi}$$

where λ is the wavelength of the radiation employed.

$\therefore$ Power in the pulse presented to the receiver

$$= P_r = \frac{G\lambda^2}{4\pi} \cdot \frac{1}{4\pi r^2} \cdot A \cdot \frac{PG}{4\pi r^2} \text{ W}$$

$\therefore$

$$P_r = \frac{PG^2\lambda^2 A}{64\pi^3 r^4} \text{ W}$$

Now a target is at the limit of visibility when this power presented to the receiver is equal to a certain minimum, P_{min}, which is the power necessary to produce a detectable signal on the display. P_{min} is dependent upon the noise figure of the receiver and also upon the video bandwidth, the spot size of the cathode ray tube and the afterglow characteristic of the phosphor.

The maximum range, r_{max}, will be achieved by setting

$$P_r = P_{min}$$

i.e.

$$P_{min} = \frac{PG^2\lambda^2 A}{64\pi^3 r^4{}_{max}} \text{ W.}$$

i.e.

$$r_{max} = \sqrt[4]{\left(\frac{PG^2\lambda^2 A}{64\pi^3 P_{min}} \right)}$$

This expression, which is termed 'the Radar Equation', is of fundamental importance in the study of radar operations and shows how the maximum range varies, not only with the radar system parameters but also with the factor A which we have used to describe the scattering of energy from the target. The factor A is called the 'Echoing Area' of the target, or the 'Radar Cross Section' and is defined as follows:

The echoing area of a target is the area of the incident wave front which must be intercepted in order to yield the power which, if radiated uniformly in all directions, would produce the same signal at the aerial as is produced by the actual radio wave reflected from the target.

Echoing area is usually measured in square metres and has a value of 11 m² for a Canberra aircraft. The echoing areas of birds are quite small, as is to be expected from their small size; for comparison it may be noted that A for a starling is 0·0002 m² in head aspect! The ratio of the echoing area of a Canberra aircraft to that of a starling is, therefore, 55,000:1 but, surprisingly, the ratio of the ranges is only 15:1 – this is a consequence of the fourth power law!

The radar performance diagram

Although the radar equation is essential to a precise discussion of the design or performance of a radar system, its implications can be appreciated more readily when it is presented in graphical form. We notice that the radar equation tells us the maximum range at which a target of known echoing area will be seen by the radar whose characteristics P, λ, and P_{min} are fixed. The gain factor G of the array is also known but it is not a constant, being a function of the angle of elevation, i.e. the maximum range of the radar changes with the elevation. If the maximum range is plotted in polar co-ordinates against the angle of elevation then a closed curve of the form shown in Fig. 1.8 is obtained.

This figure presents the performance diagram of the Bushy Hill radar. The

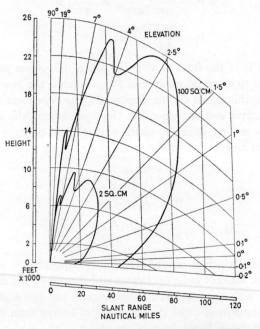

FIG. 1.8. Vertical Performance Diagram of the Bushy Hill surveillance radar against targets of echoing area 2 cm² and 100 cm² respectively

outer curve represents the limit of visibility of a target having an echoing area of 0·01 sq m, i.e. 100 cm² which is roughly the target that would be presented by a flock of about five lapwings. It will be noted that the curve of limiting visibility continues to negative angles of elevation; this is a consequence of the fact that the site height of the station is 250 ft above sea level and so many birds are visible at depression angles from the radar.

Another feature of the diagram to which reference will frequently be made in later chapters is the inclusion of lines of constant altitude. These curves have been calculated to take account both of the curvature of the earth and also of the bending of radio waves due to refraction in the earth's atmosphere. This diagram permits us to read off the range of disappearance of any target of known echoing area which has been flying at constant altitude, radially away from the station. Conversely, it marks the point of first appearance of such a target.

Single target radars

A modern high power microwave radar is capable of providing comprehensive cover for both airspace management and the close ground control of aircraft, either military or civil. Radars of this type are well suited to the study of broad-front bird migration over large areas, and the results of research work in which surveillance radars have been used in this way are described in later chapters.

From the earliest days of radar, however, it was realized that 'early warning' and defence by fighter interception had to be supplemented by ground defences – guns and rockets – and in order to use these weapons it was necessary to have precise knowledge of the position and movements of the aircraft to be engaged. Various radars were developed that would facilitate accurate gun laying and so they were termed G.L.-equipments, and were operated by Anti-Aircraft Units of the army. The first G.L.s operated on metric wavelengths, but the introduction of microwaves permitted the design of powerful 10-cm trackers of the radar searchlight type. The transmitter/receiver and display units of this type of fire-control radar were housed in a mobile trailer, on top of which was mounted the aerial, usually in the form of a parabolic reflector that could be moved freely in both elevation and azimuth. A beam width of about 4° was employed, which was sufficiently wide to allow acquisition of an aircraft target whose initial position and track had been defined by a medium-powered surveillance radar. After the target had been acquired it was possible to manipulate the aerial so that the target was held in the beam, no matter how it might manoeuvre to avoid attack. More sophisticated radars were equipped with a 'lock follow device' which performed the tracking function automatically and supplied very accurate range, bearing, and elevation information. A short pulse length was employed so that good range resolution could be obtained. Target tracking radars of this type are very useful for the examination of single bird targets.

Other forms of very short pulse, high resolution radars have also been used to study the behaviour of individual bird targets at ranges less than 10,000 ft, e.g. to measure altitudes, rates of climb, and speeds of flight. These equipments operate on a wavelength of 3 cm and include Air Interception Radars (AI) as used in military aircraft or as Weather Radars in civil airliners; the Precision Approach Radars of Civil Air Traffic Control Units and various adaptations of ship radiolocators.

It will be seen that there exists quite a variety of radars which the ornithologist could use with advantage in various types of research. To observe the progress of large scale migratory movements requires access to a high power surveillance radar. The flight behaviour of a single bird, however, is best studied with the aid of one of the forms of short range, high resolution radars. During the war these various types of radar were required to fulfil complementary roles and all were equally necessary to the defence. It is hardly surprising to find that this still holds good in the application of these radars to ornithological research – all are capable of supplying some new and valuable information about bird behaviour.

CHAPTER TWO

The extraction and display of radar information

In order to find the range of an aircraft, cloud, or bird which is reflecting a radio wave back to the aerial of a radar station it is necessary to measure the time taken by the radar pulse to travel to the target and back again. Since light travels 186,000 miles in 1 s this delay time is only 2 ms even for an aircraft 186 miles away, and so it is clear that normal timing methods dependent upon stopwatches and the like can have little relevance in radar. It was fortunate for the rapid development of radar that it occurred at a time when the cathode ray tube was already a well established tool in radio and electrical research, for this device immediately provided not only a perfected means of measuring the very small time delays encountered in radar ranging, but also offered a convenient method of displaying radar signals to the observer. The cathode ray tube was as important to radar as it was to television and the simultaneous emergence of practical radar and television systems in the 1930s was no coincidence – both techniques drew heavily upon the long and patient researches which had led to this ingenious exploitation of the low inertia and high speed of beams of electrons formed in a vacuum tube.

The cathode ray tube

It was the study, during last century, of electrical discharges through low pressure gases that led to the discovery of 'cathode rays'; this was the name given by Hittorf to the mysterious radiations which emanated from the cathode of a discharge tube and caused a green, fluorescent glow to appear on the glass at the far end of the tube. Hittorf showed that these rays travelled in straight lines by the simple observation that a sharp shadow was produced of an obstacle lying in the path of the rays, as in Fig. 2.1(a). In 1879 Crookes demonstrated that cathode rays could be deflected by a magnet, and so must be regarded as composed of negative electricity in motion (Fig. 2.1(b)). The story was completed by Thomson in 1897 when he proved that cathode rays were streams of swiftly moving negatively charged particles emitted by the cathode. These particles we now call 'electrons'. Thomson employed crossed electric and magnetic fields in his experiment shown in Fig. 2.1(c), in order to exert opposing forces on the moving electrons. The electric field deflected the cathode ray beam from its equilibrium position at O to the point A – the point of impact of the electrons being rendered visible by coating the end of the tube with a phosphor such as zinc sulphide in order to enhance the natural fluorescence of the glass. By adjustment of the magnetic field the deflected beam could be returned to O and comparison of the two fields

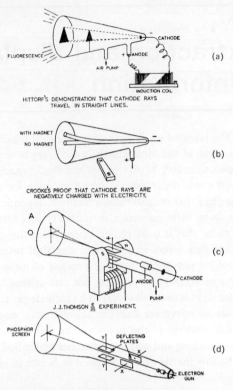

FIG. 2.1. The development of the cathode ray tube
(a) Cathode rays travel in straight lines
(b) Cathode rays are negative electrical charges in motion
(c) Thomson's experiment to prove that cathode rays are swift moving electrons
(d) An electrostatically deflected cathode ray tube

in this balanced state permitted Thomson to measure the ratio of the charge of an electron to its mass. The constancy of this ratio led to the recognition that the electron is a fundamental particle in atom building.

Thomson's experiment was a crucial one for the progress of atomic physics but its importance for the subjects of television and radar which developed forty years later was that it showed how the deflexion of high velocity electrons could be used to measure changes in electric and magnetic fields. Electrons possess very small mass, which means that they can be easily accelerated to velocities near the velocity of light, their low inertia also permits them to respond to rapid fluctuations in the deflecting fields applied to them. Fig. 2.1(d) represents a modern electrostatically deflected cathode ray tube and shows how little it has changed from Thomson's apparatus. The electrons are no longer derived from an electrical gas discharge but are produced thermionically from a heated cathode in an evacuated bulb. Acceleration and focusing of the electrons into a fine beam takes place in the 'electron gun', while deflexions in two directions at right angles are produced by the two pairs of deflexion plates. In a modern television set the deflexion of the electron beam is achieved magnetically, i.e., changing electric currents are passed through two orthogonal pairs of coils which are placed externally round the neck of the cathode ray viewing tube. The crossed coil technique of television is cheaper to apply and so is appropriate to a commercial industry, particularly as it allows brighter pictures to be produced. Electrostatic deflexion, on the other hand, in which varying voltages are applied to the two pairs of plates, requires a more expensive tube but is superior for measurement work. This superiority arises from the fact that higher rates of change of voltage than current can be observed, due to the limitation imposed by the self-inductance of the deflexion coils.

The cathode ray oscilloscope

In order to convert the cathode ray tube from the field-balancing device used by Thomson into an instrument for measuring rapidly fluctuating electrical voltages or currents, it is necessary to provide not only calibration of beam deflexion in terms of voltage applied, but also to arrange for a movement or sweep of the beam along the x-direction in a prescribed manner. It is usual to provide a voltage for application to the X-plate of the tube which increases in a linear fashion and so causes a steady, straight line progress of the spot of light across the phosphor screen of the tube. Special electronic circuits have been devised to provide the required uniformly increasing voltages and such circuits are usually termed 'time-base circuits' since they provide the basis of time measurement in a C.R.T. (cathode ray tube) instrument. Linear time bases are most commonly employed and controls are provided in the circuit which permit different speeds of sweep to be employed, i.e. to change the rate of motion of the spot across the tube. In addition, the time base is caused to deliver its sweep voltage in a cyclic or repetitive fashion. The rate of repetition of the sweep, or time base recurrence frequency as it is called, can be adjusted, and if this frequency is caused to coincide with the repetition rate of the phenomenon under observation on the Y-plates then a steady or locked pattern may be observed upon the screen. This is the manner in which a C.R.T. and its time base are used to examine repetitive events, such as an alternating current waveform in an electrical power circuit, or an electrical oscillation in radio engineering. When used in this way the C.R.T., together with its time bases and the associated X- and Y-input amplifiers, is known as a 'C.R.T. oscilloscope'. It was the C.R.T. in this form which played such a vital part in the early development of radar; it was used, not only as a test instrument, but also as the first radar display device for the measurement of range. When used in this way the C.R.T. oscilloscope is known as a 'Radar A-scope'.

The radar A-scope display

The arrangement of an A-scope, when used to measure the time delay of a radar echo, is shown in diagrammatic form in Fig. 2.2.

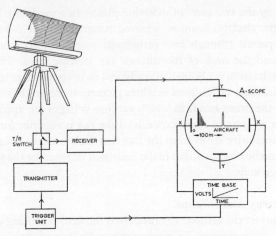

FIG. 2.2. The measurement of radar range using an A-scope

The trigger unit produces a continuous sequence of very short pulses (1 μs duration) which, in the case of Bushy Hill, are separated by intervals of 4 ms, i.e. the pulse recurrence frequency is 250 pulses per second. When such a synchronizing pulse is received by the time-base circuit, a steadily increasing voltage commences to be generated and is applied to the X-plates of the A-scope, and the spot begins to move steadily from left to right across the tube.

The same synchronizing pulse is applied to the transmitter, which is caused to fire, and so produces the radar pulse, which is immediately radiated from the aerial. Ground and other objects close to the aerial are illuminated by the radar pulse and scatter energy back to the aerial, so producing short-range echoes which are detected by the receiver, and the signals are applied to the Y-plates of the A-scope. These echo signal voltages cause vertical deflexion of the cathode ray beam simultaneously with its horizontal motion under the influence of the time base, and so the clutter of permanent echoes near zero range are produced, as shown in Fig. 2.2. Suppose a single aircraft at a range of 100 miles lies in the path of the radar beam, then a radar echo signal will be received 1·07 ms after the trigger pulse, and will produce the single vertical deflexion indicated. Clearly, it is more convenient to mark the x-deflexion axis of the tube in terms of miles of range rather than milliseconds of delay time, and the A-scope becomes a convenient device both to display echoes and to measure their ranges. Such an A-scope picture is shown in Plate 3.

When the aerial rotates so that the radar beam sweeps over the target, the echo signal increases to a maximum and then decreases to zero until the next revolution. The appearance of the A-scope under these conditions is shown in Plate 3. The successive traces of the time base have been staggered, so that the ten consecutive strikes on the target during transit of the beam are shown clearly. It will be appreciated that the range of the aircraft has not changed appreciably during the 4 ms that separate the pulses. This form of modified A-scope display is extremely useful when looking for very rapid changes in the signal from a bird flock.

The A-scope is not suitable for recording photographically the range changes of echoes supplied by a non-scanning radar with fixed beam; a modified form of the display has therefore been produced for this purpose. In this case the radar signal is not applied to the Y-plate of the C.R.T. but to the grid of the electron gun, as in a television set, and so produces brightness or intensity modulation of the time base trace. This may conveniently be described as Z-modulation. In other words, only a very feeble beam of electrons is allowed to produce the time base sweep, but when an echo is received the electron beam is brightened and so produces a bright spot on the trace. The arrangement is shown in Fig. 2.3. A

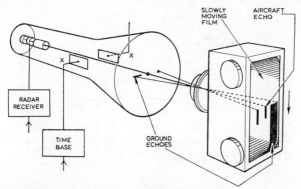

FIG. 2.3. Z-modulation display for use with a moving film to record the ranges of echoes and the times of occurrence

camera is used to focus an image of the intensity modulated trace upon a film which is slowly traversed by clockwork in the direction of its length. Steady echoes from permanent ground objects trace a continuous vertical line, but aircraft echoes which cross the beam at right angles produce temporary echoes only, which change little in range. Plate 3 shows an interesting example of such a Z-scan display, as it is sometimes termed – the track of a V_2 missile through a C.H. radar beam. In this case there was a rapid change of range and the echo from the missile was inclined to the time base; the short duration echoes on this picture were due to meteors.

This form of display is used in ionospheric research and also in the bird counting and altitude investigations described later. It is the form of display best suited for a fixed radar beam looking upwards; under these circumstances range and altitude become identical. Plate 23 shows the passage of birds through an X-band beam at Bushy Hill.

The plan position indicator

A rotating beam radar can provide both the range and bearing of a target. If an A-scope is used to measure the ranges of the echoes, however, it is necessary to use also an angle measuring device to give the bearings of the targets before their positions can be plotted upon a map of the area. It would be more convenient if a combined range and bearing measure device could be employed that would immediately locate a target in its correct position relative to the radar station. Such a device is the plan position indicator.

The main features of the plan position indicator display (p.p.i.) are shown in Fig. 2.4. The signal from the radar receiver is applied to the grid of the electron gun in order to produce an intensity modulated trace.

The time base of a p.p.i. is of the linear growth-of-current type, a process which is initiated by a synchronizing pulse from the trigger unit. The time-base

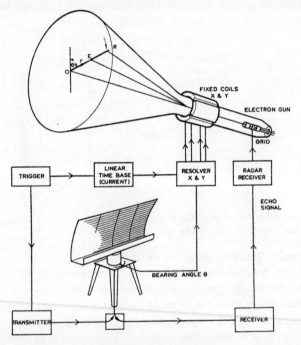

FIG. 2.4. The C.R.T. used as a Plan Position Indicator

current waveform is fed to the rotating coil of the resolver unit and induces currents in two pairs of coils at right angles. The central coil is linked to the aerial and rotates in synchronism with it. The currents derived from the crossed coils are applied to a corresponding pair of orthogonal fixed coils which envelop the neck of the tube and produce deflexions of the cathode ray beam such that the trace OR revolves about O like the spoke of a wheel, but in exact time and angle synchronism with the aerial. This method of applying brightness modulation to the scanning electron beam is identical to that used in television, as is also the magnetic method of moving the trace over the face of the tube. In television the time base trace moves parallel to itself, up and down the tube, during a single frame of the picture, but in the p.p.i. the range trace rotates about its zero range

28

end, in sympathy with the aerial's motion. As a consequence of the simultaneous presentation of both range OE, and the bearing angle θ, the position of the target at E is shown in its correct plan position. If a graticule of the map of the area is made on perspex and caused to overlay the p.p.i., then map references of targets such as E can immediately be read from the tube.

One curious feature of the p.p.i. display deserves special mention – the apparent lack of correlation between the size and brilliance of an echo 'paint', as it is termed, and the physical size of the target reflecting the radio wave. When the p.p.i. was developed it was realized that the signal power available from a target to drive the C.R.T. would depend upon the echoing area of the target and upon its range. This relationship is expressed by the Radar Equation. Expected variations in available power, in fact, could easily extend over a range of $10^{11} : 1$, a range so wide that it seemed at first to be impossible to design a display which could simultaneously present weak signals from small, remote targets, and strong signals from large aircraft close to the radar station. The trick which overcame these difficulties was to use a 'limiter'. This is a circuit device which allows a signal of up to about three times the noise level to be passed, but cuts all larger signals to just this level. In this way defocusing of the electron beam on strong signals is avoided, halation effects are reduced to a minimum and burning of the phosphor is prevented. But the price paid is substantial loss of information about the amplitudes of the echoes; however, this information can be found in other ways when it is required, as, for example, in counting birds by radar (Chapter Twelve).

Perception factor

The visibility of a signal upon a p.p.i. depends upon such factors as the characteristics of the phosphor, the spot size of the C.R.T., the area covered by the echo, the bandwidth of the video amplifiers, the level of ambient illumination in the operations room, and the general brightness level over the whole face of the p.p.i. due to random noise peaks. To discuss these matters fully would hardly be appropriate in this book, but it should be noted that their combined effect is to determine a quantity called the Perception Factor-Π, which measures the goodness of the display. Π is the ratio of signal power to noise power at the second detector that is required to produce a signal just detectable on the p.p.i.

Reference to the radar equation will show that the perception factor of the display must have a marked effect upon the value of $P_{min.}$, which was the power in the minimum signal presented to the aerial that could result in a detectable echo on the display. Π directly affects the range performance of the radar and its improvement by display designers in recent years has been of great importance.

The video map

So convenient and realistic did the p.p.i. prove for observing the movements of aircraft, that it was considered necessary to extend its usefulness still further by developing a device that would permit the direct presentation of fixed map features, such as the coastline, upon the face of the C.R.T. The device now employed for this purpose is called the video map; it is a flying spot scanner similar in principle to the film scanner used in television studios.

A slide is prepared which is a photographic negative of the lines of latitude and longitude, coast outline or airway boundaries which it is required to show as bright lines upon the p.p.i. This slide is illuminated by a radial time-base trace formed on the face of a small projection-type C.R.T. of high brilliance (Fig. 2.5). The time base is rotated in synchronism with the similar time base of the p.p.i. As the bright spot tracing the radial range line crosses each of the transparent lines on the slide, a light impulse is transmitted into a photocell, and so produces an electrical signal. This video signal is mixed with the radar signal applied to the grid of the p.p.i. Video signals corresponding to map details are thus produced

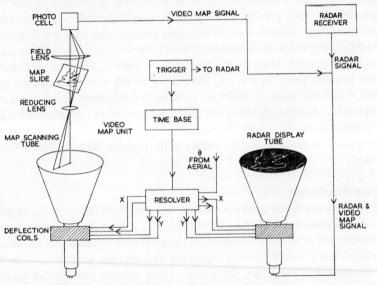

FIG. 2.5. The Video Map Unit which supplies mapping signals to the p.p.i.

simultaneously with the journeyings of the radar pulse through space and are also impressed upon the grid of the p.p.i., so that the rotating time base will paint the map lines of the area at the same time as the radar signals are painting the targets themselves. It will be appreciated that a large number of p.p.i.'s may be supplied with synchronized map signals from one video-map unit.

A typical picture of a Bushy Hill p.p.i. situation is shown in Plate 1(b); the positions of aircraft will be noted, also the video map traced on the p.p.i. When it is required to make range measurements only, the video map is suppressed and range rings are presented upon the p.p.i. instead, as in Plate 13. The rings correspond to successive 10-nautical-mile intervals, and it is convenient to enhance the brightness of the rings at 40, 80, and 120 n.m. in order to facilitate identification. Although the various signals shown on these p.p.i. pictures are painted only momentarily and have to await a complete rotation of the aerial before they can receive a further impulse from the cathode ray beam, the pictures on the tube are remarkably persistent due to the after-glow of the magnesium fluoride phosphor.

The appearance of a portion of the operations room at Bushy Hill may be gathered from Plate 2 which shows a group of p.p.i. consoles one of which is equipped with a camera recorder. Although the grid reference, or range and bearing, of an aircraft can be read from the p.p.i., this method is not usually sufficiently accurate for the computations and manipulation of the data which have to follow. Instead, the operator is provided with a joystick which permits him to control precisely the position of a ring strobe marker upon the face of the p.p.i. He first causes this marker to be centred accurately upon a selected target then, by pressing the appropriate button, the co-ordinates of the aircraft are passed into the store of the computer for subsequent processing. Such a ring marker is shown in Plate 21.

The radar microscope or B-scope display

It often happens that the observer wishes to examine a close grouping of aircraft or birds at a magnification much greater than is possible with the simple method of time-base switching described above. The Marconi Radar Microscope display was developed to fulfil this need and the facility which it provides is shown in Fig. 2.6.

The operator has on his display a bucket-shaped region formed by two rings at ranges r_1 and r_2, also two radial lines at bearings of θ_1 and θ_2. When he wishes to use the microscope, a switch brings the 'bucket' on to his display and at its centre is a ring marker whose position on the display can be selected by operating the joystick control. Moving the marker carries the 'bucket' with it. All signals

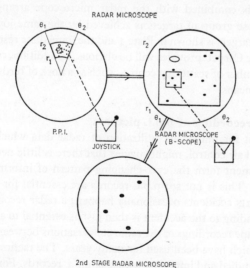

FIG. 2.6. The B-scope or Radar Microscope Display

contained within the 'bucket' now reappear on a second display tube; this second tube is identical to a p.p.i., but its associated circuits are so arranged that the polar plot of signals on the p.p.i. are reproduced in cartesian form on the microscope display. The X-axis of this latter display corresponds to the bearing θ, ranging from θ_1 to θ_2, and the tube can accept 20° of azimuthal cover. Range is presented on the Y-axis and covers 20 n.m. It follows that circles on the p.p.i. are changed into ellipses on the B-scope tube, as it is termed. A second stage of magnification is also provided so that by joystick manipulation of a ring marker on the B-scope a box measuring 5° × 5 miles can be selected for presentation on a third display. In Plate 4 a group of angel echoes will be seen within the 'bucket' located over the Straits of Dover. These echoes are shown magnified on the B-scope display Plate 4b. This form of display is ideal for counting echoes and its use is described in Chapter Twelve.

The 'Magic Carpet' display

A brief mention may be made here of one further type of display which has been employed in some of the investigations described later. We have seen that a form of A-scope giving the amplitudes of the group of pulses returned from a target when the radar beam passes over it can provide valuable information on the pulse-to-pulse signal variation. This was achieved by using a succession of A-scope traces, the consecutive members of which were displayed progressively displaced to the right on the C.R.T. If a compact group of targets is under investigation which differ only slightly in range and bearing, it is impossible to use the staggered A-scope method of sorting out the echoes. In the so-called 'Magic Carpet' display, range and bearing are separated by using a form of isometric display, but the A-scope presentation of amplitude of successive pulses is still retained.

This display is combined with the radar microscope arrangement, so that selection of a close group of targets is achieved by the same joystick operation. Such a group of targets is shown in Plate 4 and the immediate resolution of echoes which the 'Magic Carpet' provides will be obvious. In addition, composite targets made up of a number of scattering centres, such as a flock of birds, can be investigated by these means.

Photographic recording of p.p.i. pictures

The requirement for immediate utilization of radar data which exists in both military and civil air control, might suggest that there is little need for devices to record in permanent form the ever-changing pattern of information presented on a radar p.p.i. This is not so; p.p.i. records are essential for many purposes.

At large airports accidents occasionally happen; a radar record of the succession of events leading to the accident is then just as essential to an analysis of the incident as the tape recordings of the radio conversations between ground control and the pilot, which have been used for many years. The tactics of fighter interception can be studied and improved by use of p.p.i. records. For these and other reasons a number of special p.p.i. recording devices have been produced, but for the purpose of this book it will be sufficient to describe the system which has been developed for Bushy Hill.

Birds fly at comparatively slow speeds and with a p.p.i. adjusted to cover a range of 120 miles, such as is employed to observe the flight paths of migrants across the southern North Sea, it is difficult to trace the motions of the birds between successive sweeps of the aerial by direct observation of the tube. It is also tedious to make close observations of bird movements over periods of many hours, although this is necessary if the history of a movement is to be followed in detail and correct conclusions drawn as to the factors which have influenced the course of events. But in ornithological research it is not usually necessary to have the same immediate access to p.p.i. data as is required in aircraft operations. Indeed, it is preferable to have the information in a form which will permit repeated examination and measurement of a bird situation, as in the starling roosting movements discussed in Chapter Nine. The method of photographic recording adopted at Bushy Hill fulfils all these needs; it also permits the technique of Time Compression to be applied as explained below and makes bird research by radar economically possible. The operation of a powerful radar such as Bushy Hill is an expensive business, it could clearly not be maintained for ornithological research alone, but by the use of photographic recording it has proved to be possible to secure films of bird events simultaneously with the normal transmissions of the station, and without interference to its research programme.

Filming technique

Most radars employing p.p.i. presentation use aerial rotation rates lying between 2 and 20 r.p.m. Bushy Hill, being of the long range surveillance type, uses the comparatively slow speed of 4 r.p.m., and so every p.p.i. picture is built up in 15 s. During the 5 μs when the signal from a particular target is being received, the paint on the phosphor is very bright indeed. This paint will be repeated 1/250 of a second later if the pulse recurrence frequency is 250 per second and 10 strikes on the target are obtained at Bushy Hill. These 10 paints are almost superimposed on to one spot of the C.R.T. phosphor, but no further beam energy will be applied to this spot until one aerial revolution later, by which time the target will have moved slightly and the new paint will be displaced from its former position. In the case of a television tube a phosphor is necessary which decays rapidly after being energized, otherwise successive frames would be confused. Radar, on the other hand, requires a long decay or after-glow time so that the p.p.i. can show not only the present position of targets but also a history of the positions they have occupied during the previous few minutes. After excitation by the electron beam a target paint immediately begins to decay exponentially with a time constant of about 35 s and when looking at a p.p.i. it is seen that the most recent bright paint of a target is followed by a succession of progressively fainter paints which are the faded echoes of past positions of the target – the so-called after-glow tail. A curve showing the relationship between present brightness

33

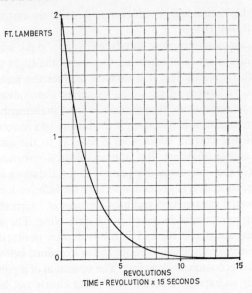

FT. LAMBERTS

REVOLUTIONS
TIME = REVOLUTION x 15 SECONDS

FIG. 2.7. Relationship between the brightness of a paint on the p.p.i. and the time elapsed since excitation

in footlamberts and elapsed time since initial excitation is given in Fig. 2.7 and shows that the brightness of an echo has decreased to one half its value after 20 s; 10 aerial revolutions later the brightness has fallen to one hundredth of its initial value. Plate 5 is a single short exposure of a p.p.i. after one complete revolution of the aerial and illustrates how the brightness decays.

The consequence of this fading of the paints is that if a ten-plot history of a track is required in the recording then a brightness range of several hundred to one can be involved. Recording such a range of density requires a fast negative material combined with a panchromatic response in order to respond to the orange colour of the phosphor. Kodak Tri-X negative has been found satisfactory at Bushy Hill but processing was only to a gamma of 0·4, so as to preserve a suitable density range in the negative and to allow some latitude in the exposure time.

In contrast to Plate 5 the aim in p.p.i. recording is to obtain as uniform a picture as possible of all the echoes received during one rotation of the aerial and, by taking a continuous sequence of such pictures, to obtain the complete and detailed record of all the movements of targets within the cover of the radar. Subsequent projection of such a film at 25 frames per second will give a 'time compressed' presentation of these events.

Most people are now familiar, through television, with the principle of time-lapse photography. Slowly occurring events, such as the growth and opening of a flower, can be presented in a dynamic and vivid manner by the projection of a ciné film whose consecutive frames are still photographs of the flower taken after the lapse of successive equal intervals of time, perhaps on consecutive days.

34

The whole process of eruption of the leaves and stem through the surface of the soil, the subsequent growth and ultimate flowering is then compressed from weeks into seconds and is seen as a smoothly flowing succession of events. Time-lapse photography records the state of the object observed at a number of selected instants of time equally separated from each other, but long compared to the frame separation time employed during subsequent projection. In the time-compression method of photographing the p.p.i., on the other hand, no information is lost, since no selection process is involved. The time taken to record one complete p.p.i. picture is 15 s, with the result that successive frames of the film record the positions of birds and aircraft at 15-s intervals. The ciné projector used in television projects 25 frames per second, so that the time-compression ratio is 375; aircraft are therefore seen to career across the screen at a disconcertingly high speed, while the complicated movements of birds in congested regions such as the Calais–Dover crossing, or the arrival of starlings to their roost in the evening, can be quickly traced in detail. This facility is invaluable when it is wished to measure the speed at which a flock of birds is flying; the speed of a whole migrating movement can be measured in the same way. Plate 5 illustrates the movement of a number of aircraft and was obtained by leaving the shutter of the camera open for ten successive revolutions of the aerial, with no transport of the film; this photograph gives some idea of the ease with which the movements of birds can be followed by the ciné time-compression method.

Time-compression photography requires the camera to be equipped with a means of taking a time exposure during the whole of the rotation period of the aerial, and then closing the shutter for a very short interval during which the film is transported rapidly to the next frame. A transport time of 60 ms is achieved in the cameras at Bushy Hill, so that the dead time corresponds to an aerial rotation angle of $1\cdot4°$, and only 15 pulses are 'lost'; in fact, radar information generated during the closed shutter period is by no means lost, for the long persistence of the phosphor ensures a level of density on the film only slightly less than that on the adjacent areas of the p.p.i. Evidence for the surprisingly low loss of information is provided by the various photographs in this book, on which it is extremely difficult to detect the point at which transfer of the frame took place.

The 'head' or last paint of an echo trail is emphasized in pictures much as Plate 5 partly because of increased film density due to the 'flash' or brilliance of the phosphor under direct electron excitation – an effect which is restricted by the characteristic curve of the film emulsion – and partly due to increased spot size on the C.R.T. Strong echoes, although subjected to top cut by the limiter, paint for a longer time, due to the shape of the horizontal polar diagram of the radar aerial; this effect is further increased in the negative by reflection and halation. It is not wholly disadvantageous to have bright echo heads, but the effect needs to be controlled by partial closing of the lens iris diaphragm. Too small an aperture, however, will limit the number of after-glow paints recorded, and a suitable compromise based upon Bushy Hill experience is to adjust the lens for about 10 paints. An aperture between f/4 and f/5·6 is suitable and, with a lens of ½-in. focus, good recording conditions with a camera distance of about 20 in. are obtained, as in Plate 2 which shows the mounting of a 16-mm camera in front of a p.p.i. console.

In order to obtain films free from interference which might prejudice interpretation of the pictures, it is necessary to operate the camera in synchronism with the radar aerial. Departure from synchronism means that a rotating sector of different density will be obtained on the projected picture which can be very distracting. Anticlockwise or clockwise rotation of this sector will occur, depending on whether the camera was taking pictures at a faster or slower rate respectively than the rate of rotation of the aerial. In the second case, two exposures per frame of the bright flash are possible; this is very objectionable, since not only is gross over-exposure of fixed targets then produced, but moving targets are provided with two bright heads, which is confusing to the interpretation. Synchronization is achieved by arranging for a pair of contacts on the aerial to close at some predetermined point – usually at a bearing which is of least interest – the electrical impulse closes the camera shutter, initiates operation of the transport mechanism, and reopens the shutter. Although such an automatic system can be very reliable, faults do occasionally occur and can be very exasperating if they happen at a moment when particularly interesting information is being recorded. A detailed discussion of the art of p.p.i. recording and the precautions necessary for success have been given by Phelp and Downie (1962) upon whose work at Bushy Hill this section is based.

The measurement of speed and direction of flight by radar

The p.p.i. is an ideal form of radar display, not only for the measurement of range and bearing of targets, but also for the extraction of speed and direction of flight. Two plots of an aircraft echo on the p.p.i., as produced by consecutive scans of the aerial, are sufficient to estimate roughly the speed and direction of flight of a fast target. For a jet airliner, travelling at a speed of 500 knots, the distance travelled in the 15-s interval which separates two successive sweeps of the aerial is about 2 miles and this quantity can easily be measured on the p.p.i. Birds move more slowly of course, and so it is necessary to wait for a correspondingly greater number of aerial transits before a reasonably accurate estimate of speed can be made from such simple range and time measurements.

The time compression method described above can be usefully applied to bird speed measurement, for by projection of the p.p.i. film the movements of slowly moving targets are not only greatly magnified but the eye is able to follow the track more effectively. It is also possible to use electronic devices coupled to the projector to measure the speed of targets more easily. After initial projection and selection of a particular angel track the speed is measured by counting the number of frames corresponding to 10 miles of track; this counting is conveniently achieved by fitting an electronic counter to the sprocket wheel of the projector. A pointer is used to follow the track of the echo on the screen and also to scribe the path so that true track distance can subsequently be measured. The act of applying the pointer to the screen may be arranged to switch on the counter; removal of the pointer likewise switches it off. In this way time and distance, even along a curvilinear track, can be measured with fair accuracy and the speed of flight calculated. Due to the slight movement of the film in the pro-

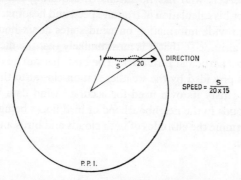

DIRECTION

SPEED $= \dfrac{S}{20 \times 15}$

P.P.I.

FIG. 2.8. Measurement of the speed of bird flight from plots on the p.p.i.

jector, however, there is a small shift of the image on the screen so that this method, though useful for quick estimates, does not give the most accurate results. It is best to make measurements on individual frames which carry range rings and some fixed targets for reference. In consequence, it is usually the average speed of bird echoes over a number of aerial sweeps which is measured as in Fig. 2.8.

Just as the association of two echo positions on the p.p.i. can yield the speed of a target so the join of the plots provides the direction of the track over the earth's surface. But aircraft and birds fly in the air and partake of the movement of that air, so the target velocity measured on the p.p.i. is actually the resultant of the true, still air velocity and the velocity of the wind. Velocities are compounded according to the Parallelogram Law and Fig. 2.9 shows that if the vector

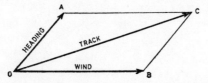

FIG. 2.9. Application of the Parallelogram Law to 'take out the wind'

OB represents the direction and speed of the wind, OA the heading and still air speed of the bird, then OC represents the track in both magnitude and direction. It is the speed and direction of the track which are measured on the p.p.i., and to derive the still air speed and heading of the bird it is necessary to 'take out the wind' by application of the Parallelogram Law. This assumes that we know the wind speed and direction at the point occupied by the bird or aeroplane.

D

Aircraft measure air speed by means of a pitot head; the navigator can also measure wind drift by direct observation of the ground or sea surface, or even by use of the Doppler Navigator, which is an airborne radar device. Whether the bird can detect and correct for drift is one of the fascinating questions which is discussed many times in this book; certainly, it cannot signal the information to the radar observer, who has no means of acquiring the wind information which he needs for his calculation of true air speed and heading. Synoptic weather stations usually provide information on wind states at six-hourly intervals, but wind varies with altitude so that it is most unlikely that the meteorological office data will apply to a particular bird track. The best that can be done is to take the wind at 900 m as provided by the weather station closest to the area of interest. Radar can often satisfy its own need for accurate wind data by measuring the movements of clouds in the neighbourhood of bird flocks being studied, but it is necessary to determine the altitudes of both clouds and birds and make allowance for the difference.

CHAPTER THREE

The interpretation of radar echoes

Radar echoes: real or spurious?

Although radar was devised in response to the urgent military need to have a means of warning against the approach of enemy aircraft during time of war, it was not at first apparent that radar might ultimately be capable of monitoring the total content of the airspace. Neither was it anticipated that radar echoes from the familiar occupants of the air – birds, rain, clouds, snow, ice crystals, dust storms, insects, and occasional high-altitude visitors such as meteors and aurora – might come to constitute such a clutter of echoes as to mask the very aircraft whose detection had been the original objective.

Perhaps the reason for this late recognition of the potential danger to radar from spurious echoes is to be found in the difficulties which had to be overcome by the first experimenters before they could obtain easily recognizable signals from aircraft at modest ranges of tens of miles only. It hardly seemed likely in those early days that transmitter power, receiver sensitivity, aerial gain, and resolving power would all be improved so greatly that even the flights of birds and insects would become accessible to the new radar technique. But the impossible happened and echoes from spurious targets became a major embarrassment.

It should be noted that the masking signals from unwanted targets were far from spurious; if a 'true' echo were one derived from an aircraft, then a 'spurious' echo was one which arose from a reflection or scattering mechanism not associated with an aircraft. Nevertheless, the radio energy thus received was real enough and means had to be devised for recognizing the 'true' echo from an aircraft in the presence of the interfering 'false' echoes.

Increased certainty of echo interpretation depended upon the gradual growth of knowledge of the types of interference which were experienced by the various types of radar equipment introduced to meet the changing operational need. We shall see that the form of the echo received from non-aircraft targets is greatly influenced by the wavelength of the radiation employed. Since radar has progressed by the introduction of shorter and shorter wavelengths an account of echo interpretation must trace briefly this path of radar system development. But this subject is wholly relevant to the purpose of this book, since it was the study of spurious echoes which led to the recognition of the part that radar could play in ornithological research.

Wartime metric radars and their echoes

As explained in Chapter One, the first radars which formed the Home Chain operated in the 20–30-Mc/s band of frequencies (wavelengths of 15–10 m) and used fixed radio beams formed by static aerials. The beam was very wide, about 120°, and extended seawards over the coast. This beam illuminated the ground and the sea in front of the station and so produced a bunch of strong, 'permanent' echoes extending from zero range on the A-scope trace to about 15 miles as shown in Fig. 2.2. Obscuration of echoes from aircraft flying within this permanent echo region was inevitable, but resulted in little operational disadvantage. Moreover, because the pattern of echoes produced by the ground returns was constant and characteristic of the station, it became familiar to the operators and very few problems of misinterpretation arose. The C.H. radar was, in fact, remarkably free from interference, and its relative immunity to spurious echoes from air-borne objects, such as rain and birds, was in the main attributable to the long wavelength of the radiation employed; low aerial gain and receiver sensitivity were also contributory factors. One interesting form of spurious echo which caused some trouble during 1944, when the C.H. radars were used for the detection of V_2 missiles, was found to arise from radar reflections from the tracks of meteors (Plate 3c).

The C.H. stations were soon supplemented by the so-called C.H.L. stations (Chain Home Low) and the ground control interception stations or G.C.I.'s. Both types of stations operated on a wavelength of $1\frac{1}{2}$ m and used a revolving aerial for both transmission and reception; the effective beam width was 16° and a p.p.i. display was employed. Although the wavelengths of the radiation used on these stations was only one-tenth of that employed on the C.H. stations echoes from rain, snow, and clouds were still a very rare occurrence for reasons which will be discussed later. Birds were seldom observed; nevertheless, it is to this type of radar that we must ascribe the distinction of being the first radar in Britain to detect and track a flight of birds. This occurred at the Royal Air Force C.H.L. station at Happisburgh in Norfolk in 1940 when the station staff were able to associate some radar echoes with the observed flights of geese.

Full advantage of the p.p.i. display for both the plotting of aircraft tracks and the control of intercepting fighters had to await the development of radars having narrow beams and high resolving power, for only in this way could the confusion arising from overlapping echoes of formations of aircraft be avoided. This need could only be fulfilled by the utilization of the shorter wavelengths and so the next major drop in wavelength was from $1\frac{1}{2}$ m down to 50 cm. This type of radar is now used to monitor the flow of aircraft along the airways of Britain. A wavelength of 50 cm is usually taken to mark the transition to the microwave family of radars in which both azimuthal resolving power and range can be substantially increased, but the penalty is greater susceptibility to interference from cloud and rain. Interference from weather occurs very infrequently with a 50-cm radar, for only the largest cumulus clouds produce detectable echoes; neither are birds frequently observed by this radar so that it would not give much help to ornithologists!

Microwave radars

Although the operational objective of the early radar development teams had been to supply a ground-based aircraft detection system capable of aiding Fighter Command in the air defence of Britain, it was realized that radar was required for mobile land forces, also for ships and for use in aeroplanes to provide radio eyes for the Night Fighters. These were some of the military needs that prompted microwave radar development. After the invention of the cavity magnetron, attention was concentrated on the development of radars operating in the 10-cm and 3-cm bands, and little attention was given to radar development in the 10–50-cm waveband. The concentration of effort on shorter wavelength systems in the S- and X-bands (10 cm and 3 cm respectively), instead of in the 'L' band (20–30 cm) caused radar development to be speeded up, because the technology of magnetrons, aerial structures, and microwave guides was easier at these shorter wavelengths.

An example of the p.p.i. picture which a modern medium powered S-band equipment can provide is shown in Plate 7 (*a*). The high resolution will be noted. Such a radar provides comprehensive cover on aircraft at altitudes up to 40,000 ft and its receiving power is adequate for most military and civil surveillance needs. But the reduction of wavelength from 50 cm to 10 cm has produced marked enhancement of the echoes from rain and detection of aircraft targets on the p.p.i. in the presence of widespread rain clouds can be very difficult.

Very high resolving power can be obtained by use of 3-cm wavelength and very compact radars of this type have been designed for use on aircraft and on board ships. A marine radiolocator of this type gives good warning of the approach of other ships and also greatly assists navigation in coastal waters. Rain echoes, however, are even more troublesome at 3 cm than 10 cm. X-band radars proved very successful in airborne and ship-board application but the high powers that would be necessary for success in a ground surveillance role against aircraft would be difficult to achieve at this wavelength, while the precipitation returns would provide a major operational problem. It is for these same reasons that X-band is not suited to long-range ornithological work, although it is ideal for the examination of single bird targets at short range.

In the years following the war it was realized that the pursuit of wavelengths shorter than 10 cm would be unlikely to provide the ideal military surveillance radar and from various theoretical studies it was concluded that the best compromise wavelength was likely to be about 25 cm. In these studies the operational objectives included:

(1) The need to achieve long range on small targets.
(2) Comprehensive cover in the vertical plane.
(3) Resolution of closely bunched targets.

(4) Minimization of echoes from precipitation or fixed targets.

(5) Ability to detect a moving target in clutter.

But these are just the desirable performance factors which would be requested by an ornithologist, and so in meeting the military need radar engineers have also created ideal instruments for ornithological research. The Bushy Hill radar is such an equipment; it provides long range combined with high resolution while interference from echoes from precipitation and the ground can be kept to a minimum by means of the special devices with which the radar is equipped and which are discussed below. In this way the interpretation of echoes displayed upon the p.p.i. is rendered much more certain; nevertheless, the problem of identifying the scattering object associated with any selected echo is not yet completely solved.

The scattering of radio waves: radar cross-section

Wreaths of smoke slowly curling upwards from a lighted cigarette appear blue, but the smoke issuing from the mouth of the smoker looks grey by comparison. What is the reason for this colour change?

It was shown by Lord Rayleigh that when a beam of light is incident upon an assembly of small particles whose dimensions are small compared to the wavelength λ, then light is scattered in all directions, and the intensity of this scattered radiation in a given direction varies as $1/\lambda^4$. This conclusion from theoretical physics means that the proportion of blue light in the scattered radiation is greatly increased as compared to the red component, since the wavelength of blue light is roughly half that of the red. The light scattered from the small particles which constitute the dry cigarette smoke, therefore, appears bluish – the blue of the sky in directions away from the sun is also attributable to the same effect, the scattering being produced by the molecules of the air. Conversely, the light which is transmitted through an assembly of scattering particles with its direction unchanged is impoverished at the blue end of its spectrum due to the scattering loss and so appears redder than the incident light. This is the reason why the sun and moon at low angles of elevation appear reddish, for under these circumstances the light is traversing longer path lengths in the atmosphere. When the smoke of the cigarette is inhaled the small particles act as nuclei for the condensation of the water vapour in the mouth and lungs and the size of the particle is increased accordingly. When the diameter of the droplets becomes more comparable to the wavelength then the scattering of the blue light is no longer favoured relative to the red and the bluish colour becomes much less pronounced, i.e. the exhaled cigarette smoke appears grey in comparison to the blue colour of the free rising smoke.

This same wave scattering phenomenon also occurs in radar. When a radio wave is incident upon any object or region of space whose refractive index differs from that of the surrounding air then a scattered secondary wave is produced as in Fig. 3.1. It is this scattered wave which returns to the radar aerial and produces

42

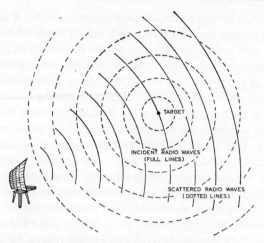

FIG. 3.1. The scattering of a radar wave from an object

the signal which ultimately paints an echo on the p.p.i. The amplitude of the scattered wave depends upon the material, size, and form of the scattering object and so the measurement of the magnitude of a radar signal can tell us something about the nature of the target, provided that certain rules of interpretation are carefully observed. This branch of radar has become a highly specialized science under the title 'Radar Signature Analysis'.

Now in Chapter One we mentioned that the ability of a target to produce a scattered or echo wave is measured by its so-called 'Echoing Area' or 'Radar Cross-section'. This is the area of the incident wave that would have to be intercepted in order to collect just the energy that would be required to be radiated in all directions uniformly from the target so as to yield the same signal in the radar receiver as is produced by the actual target. It is not always possible to relate the effective echoing area of target to its physical shape or dimensions. In one case only is this possible, namely, a spherical metal surface whose circumference is large compared to the wavelength of the radiation employed; in this case the echoing area is equal to the area πr^2 of the diametral plane. In the case of such a metal sphere there is no penetration of the electromagnetic wave into the body of the sphere as would occur with a sphere of water, for example, and by 'large' is meant a sphere in which the ratio of circumference to wavelength exceeds 10.

The scattering of waves from spheres has been examined in great detail, both experimentally and theoretically, and the conclusions are conveniently summarized in Fig. 3.2. In this figure the ordinate represents the effective echoing area A of the sphere measured in terms of the area of the diametral plane (πr^2); the abscissa corresponds to the number of wavelengths contained in the circumference, i.e. $2\pi r/\lambda$. Curve 1 corresponds to a metal sphere while curve 2 relates to a sphere of water. It is seen that when the circumference is much less than one wavelength then the echoing area falls rapidly and steadily below the πr^2 figure; this corresponds to the Rayleigh type scattering we have discussed above for the

43

optical case in order to explain the colour of cigarette smoke. When the length of the circumference lies between 1 wavelength and 10 wavelengths the value of the echoing area is seen to fluctuate between a value of $\frac{1}{4}\pi r^2$ up to $4\pi r^2$. For spheres with circumferences greater than 10λ the echoing area approximates to the projected area of the sphere, i.e. πr^2. If the sphere is composed of water then curve 2 applies and the same general variation of echoing area with wavelength is encountered as for the metal sphere, but the echoing area of the large sphere of water ultimately approximates to $0.56\pi r^2$ instead of πr^2 as in the metallic case.

Although the radar scattering behaviour of a sphere is a very special case it suggests the general conclusion that radar cross-sections of large metal targets such as aircraft will not change greatly for a wavelength change from 25 cm to 3 cm. On the other hand, the Rayleigh scattering behaviour of the small droplets of water which constitute a rain cloud will be much emphasized at a wavelength of 3 cm as compared to 25 cm. It is for these reasons that the longer wavelength is to be preferred for a long-range radar surveillance system, for then the scattering from raindrops and clouds is greatly reduced relative to the wanted echoes from aircraft.

Radar cross-sections of aeroplanes and birds

It will be appreciated from the above discussion of the scattering properties of a sphere that such a target provides the most accurate method of measuring the

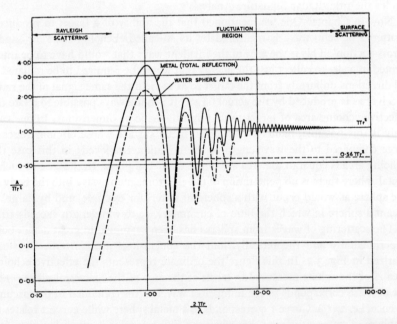

FIG. 3.2. The variation of the echoing area of a sphere with the wavelength of the incident radiation (Crown Copyright. Reproduced with the permission of The Controller H.M.S.O.)

performance of a radar. Not only is the radar cross-section of the target then calculable but it is obviously independent of the rotation of the sphere; this would not be the case for any other shape of body. The Royal Radar Establishment have made use of a spherical target in the form of a copper coated ping-pong ball in order to calibrate their satellite tracking radar which operates on a wavelength of 10 cm. When dropped from an aeroplane the ball fell at a speed of 14·2 m/s and could be observed at a range of 50 miles! A ping-pong ball has a diameter of 3·5 cm and a circumference of 11 cm which is roughly one wavelength long at this radar frequency. Curve 1 of Fig. 3.2 shows that the radar cross-section for the case is $3·7 \pi r^2$, i.e. 35·6 cm^2 or 0·0036 m^2. By contrast the moon has a radar cross-section of 5×10^{11} m^2, while the echoing area of a Canberra twin-engined aircraft has already been quoted as 11 m^2.

Now the radar cross-section of an aircraft is not constant but varies greatly with the aspect or direction from which the aircraft is observed. Fig. 3.3 illustrates how the radar cross-section of a typical aircraft varies with azimuth.

If every portion of the aircraft surface illuminated by the radar beam is regarded as an individual scattering centre then the various waves spreading outwards from this distribution of points will interfere with each other in accordance with the simple Huyghens theory, taking account of the amplitude and phase of each contributing wavelet. In this way the scattering curve of Fig. 3.3 may be approximately calculated, but it is usually determined more accurately and conveniently by experimental measurements. A metallized wooden model of the aircraft is suspended in the path of a microwave beam whose wavelength bears the same relation to the wingspan of the model that the actual radar wavelength bears to the wingspan of the true aircraft. The scattered power is measured for each aspect of the aircraft.

It will be noted that the maximum cross-section occurs when the fuselage

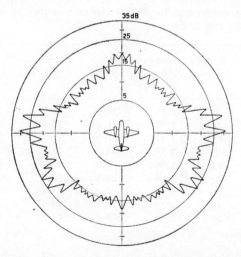

FIG. 3.3. The variation of the radar cross-section of an aircraft with azimuth

of the aircraft is broadside on to the direction of the radar beam. Under these circumstances the illuminated broadside section of the aircraft may be regarded as a radiating aerial of wide aperture, i.e. it possesses high gain, and so produces a narrow scattering beam pointing to the ground radar aerial.

When we consider the radar scattering properties of a bird we are faced with both similarities and differences as compared to the aircraft case. The symmetry of the bird is similar to that of the aircraft but only in the gliding posture with wings outspread. The dimensions of the bird in contrast to those of the aircraft are more nearly comparable to the 23-cm and 10-cm wavelengths commonly used in surveillance radars and so the echoing area may differ markedly from the simple optical cross-section of the bird. In addition, flesh, blood, and feathers would seem to be a poor substitute for aluminium sheets when the scattering of radio waves is in question. However, this last point is surprisingly at variance with the facts.

A simple approach to the problem of assessing the magnitude of the radar cross-section of a bird is to assume that the interaction of its body with the radio-wave produces the same effect as would a sphere of water of mass equal to the mass of the bird. Thus the average mass of a starling is 80 g and a sphere of water of this same mass would possess a cross-sectional area of 22·4 cm² and a circumference of 16·8 cm. Assuming radar wavelengths of 10 cm and 23 cm respectively, we obtain circumference to wavelength ratios of 1·68 and 0·73 respectively for these wavelengths, leading to cross-sections of 34 cm² at 10 cm and 29 cm² at 23 cm. For a wavelength of 3 cm the calculated echoing area is 10 cm².

Such a calculation can be expected to suggest only the order of magnitude of a bird's radar echoing area, but it shows that a very powerful radar will be required to detect a single bird at long range. We shall find later that the resultant radar

TABLE 3.1 *Average masses and calculated radar cross-sections of some familiar birds for wavelengths of 23 and 10 cm*

Bird	Average mass (g)	Radius of sphere (r cm)	πr^2 (cm²)	$2\pi r$ (cm)	Calculated radar cross-sections	
					23 cm	10 cm
Blackbird	100	2·88	26·0	18·1	42	8·7
Chaffinch	24	1·78	10·1	11·2	2·2	21
House sparrow	25	1·81	10·3	11·4	2·4	21
Lapwing	200	3·63	41·3	22·8	91	58
Robin	17	1·60	8·0	10·0	1·1	18
Song thrush	70	2·56	20·5	16·1	22	2·1
Starling	80	2·67	22·4	16·8	29	34
Swift	43	2·17	14·8	13·7	8·3	13
Warbler (large, garden warbler)	20	1·68	8·9	10·6	1·7	18
Warbler (small, chiff-chaff)	8	1·24	4·8	7·8	0·3	8·1

cross-section of a random grouping of birds to form a flock is the sum of the individual cross-sections, and so a flock of 16 birds is visible at $\sqrt[4]{16}$ or twice the range of a single bird. This surprising result is a consequence of the fourth power law involved in the Radar Equation. Table 3.1 shows the relative cross-sections of a number of birds.

Experimental determination of radar cross-sections of birds

The radar cross-sections of a number of birds have been measured experimentally by Edwards and Houghton (1959) using a method similar to that employed to estimate the cross-sections of aircraft with the aid of metal sprayed models. 3-cm radiation was used which was formed into a beam by means of a metal mirror and allowed to fall upon the body of the bird which was supported by nylon cord as shown diagrammatically in Fig. 3.4. Horizontal polarization of the beam was employed, since this electric field configuration is the one usually adopted in surveillance radars. By suspending the birds at heights such that the radar aerial was looking upwards at an angle of 18°, the errors from side lobe interference could be avoided and the overall sensitivity of the apparatus was such that radar cross-sections as low as 2×10^{-6} m^2 could be measured with an accuracy of ± 1 db. Calibration of the equipment was performed by replacing the bird by a metal sphere.

In order to study the variation of the radar cross-section of the bird with change of azimuthal aspect the bird could be rotated slowly through 360°, the radar aerial remaining stationary. In this way the scattering polar diagram of the bird could be recorded, and the results obtained for the pigeon, starling, and sparrow respectively are reproduced in Fig. 3.5. It will be seen that the maximum echoing areas for these birds occur for the azimuthal angles 65–115°, which corresponds to the radar beam striking the bird roughly in the broadside aspect. The radar cross-sections measured by Edwards and Houghton for these same

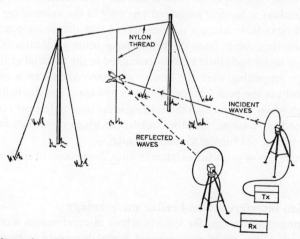

FIG. 3.4. Measuring the radar cross-section of a bird with the aid of a 3-cm radar

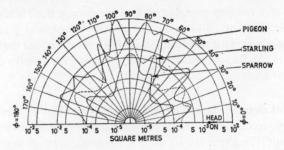

FIG. 3.5. Scattering polar diagrams of the Pigeon, Starling, and Sparrow (after Edwards and Houghton, *Nature*, 1959)

three species of birds in broadside, head, and tail aspects is given in Table 3.2. These figures may be compared with the values derived above by the simple theory of scattering applied to a sphere of water equal in mass to that of the bird in question.

TABLE 3.2   *Measured radar cross-sections*

	Broadside (cm²)	Head (cm²)	Tail (cm²)
Pigeon	30	1·5	1·1
Starling	11	2·0	1·3
House sparrow	5	0·3	0·2

These birds were measured in the fully feathered state but with wings closed and legs retracted. In order to examine the contribution made by the feathers, measurements were made separately on a plucked pigeon and also upon its feathers contained in a polythene bag. No significant difference was found between the cross-sections of the normal and the plucked bird while the echoing area of the feathers separately measured was only in the order of 0·5 cm². This result is understandable when it is remembered that the major contribution to the radar scattering comes from the highly polar water molecules of which the body is largely composed; little water is contained in the material of the feathers. Perhaps more surprising were the results of measurements on a rook. In the broadside position the peak echoing area was 250 cm². For the belly and back positions with wings outstretched the echoing areas were only 5 per cent different from the broadside position. In other words, the wings contribute very little to the echoing area of the bird as viewed by radar.

These results are of great importance in later discussions of bird counting by radar.

Precipitation interference and radar meteorology

It was mentioned above that for spheres whose circumferences were less than one wavelength of the radiation employed Rayleigh type of scattering was involved and only the initial part of the cross-section curve of Fig. 3.2 applied. Now the water droplets which compose visible but non-precipitating clouds usually possess diameters less than 20 μ (1 μ is 1/1,000 mm) while the greatest diameter a falling raindrop can attain in the atmosphere is 6 mm. It follows from these figures that for rain droplets the circumference/wavelength ratio for the usual radar wavelengths of 3 cm (X-band), 10 cm (S-band) and 23 cm (L-band) is less than unity and so we are always concerned with Rayleigh type scattering when estimating the radar returns from clouds and falling rain.

More detailed analysis of the shape of the first part of the Rayleigh scattering curve for a spherical particle of diameter d cm, for which the circumference πd is small compared to the wavelength λ, shows that the radar cross-section A is given by the formula:

$$A = \pi^5 \left(\left| \frac{\epsilon - 1}{\epsilon + 2} \right| \right)^2 \frac{d^6}{\lambda^4}$$

In this expression ϵ is the complex dielectric constant of the material of which the particle is composed and varies both with the wavelength and with the temperature. However, the variation of

$$\left| \frac{\epsilon - 1}{\epsilon + 2} \right|^2$$

is quite small over the wavelength range 3–25 cm and for temperatures around 0° C it is sufficiently accurate for all radar meteorological calculations to set it equal to 0·94. The echoing area of an atmospheric water droplet now appears as:

$$A_{\text{water}} = 288 \frac{d^6}{\lambda^4}$$

Ice particles are often present in clouds and in the upper atmosphere and can also produce interfering radar echoes upon the p.p.i. The value of ϵ for ice is much smaller than for water and

$$\left| \frac{\epsilon - 1}{\epsilon + 2} \right|^2$$

takes the value 0·18, being fairly constant over the wavelength band in question i.e.

$$A_{\text{ice}} = 55 \frac{d^6}{\lambda^4}$$

These expressions show that the echoing area of a droplet not only varies inversely with λ^4 in accordance with Rayleigh's scattering law, but also directly as d^6. This means that it is the larger droplets which contribute the major portion of rain echo signals.

When a radar beam sweeps over a cloud formation, a region of falling rain, or an assembly of ice particles, every droplet or particle illuminated by the beam scatters an echo signal back to the radar aerial. These individual echo points are not displayed as such upon the p.p.i., being too close together to permit resolution in either angle or range. If the time duration of the pulse radiated by the radar is τ, then all particles contained in a region of space $\tau c/2$ in thickness will be combined to yield one range echo point only on the p.p.i. This is because drops at ranges r and $r + \tau c/2$ will provide signals to the receiver within the same pulse interval τ. Similarly, only the particles contained within the beam contour can contribute to the resultant signal S, as shown in Fig. 3.6. In other words, all particles within the pulse volume provide scattered energy to make up the signal

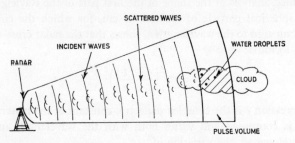

FIG. 3.6. The scattering of a radar wave from distribution of water droplets within the pulse volume

S, the pulse volume being $\tau c/2$ thick in the radial direction and having angular widths θ in azimuth and ϕ in elevation, where θ and ϕ are the horizontal and vertical beam widths respectively of the aerial.

The appearance of an extensive rain cloud upon the p.p.i. is shown in Plate 11; the difficulty of observing aircraft or bird echoes in the region occupied by the cloud will be apparent. It should be noted, however, that the obscuration produced by the cloud is not the result of the attenuation of the radio wave in passing through the cloud, but is due to the difficulty of detecting the small signal from the aircraft in the presence of the large signal provided by the return from the rain within a pulse volume at the same range as the aircraft and on the same bearing. The problem is further complicated by the fact that the p.p.i. is fed with limited signals as explained in Chapter Two and so the combined signal at any point on the tube suffers top cut and so the aircraft signal is in effect lost. What is required is a means of detecting the target in the presence of the interfering clutter signal. Such a means of achieving what is termed 'sub-clutter visibility' is provided by the Moving Target Indication system described below.

When receiving a so-called cloud echo upon the p.p.i. it is tempting to assume that its appearance is precisely what would be noted visually by a suitably located observer. Such a close correspondence may occasionally happen, but in general it will not, since the radar picture is so heavily dependent upon the size and number of the droplets per unit volume which constitute the cloud. A common value for the number of drops per cubic centimetre in a cloud is about one hundred, but of these, only a few will have diameters greater than 20 microns. Growth of raindrops occurs by coalescence of the smaller drops, but this takes place at the

50

expense of the total number of drops. Nevertheless, a fewer number of drops of larger diameter may result in an enhanced radar echo, due to the d^6 law mentioned above. Thus, if the drop diameter were doubled, the echoing area per unit volume of space would increase by $2^6 = 64$, assuming the number of drops to remain the same. If the volume of water were held constant during coalescence, the number of drops would fall by a factor of eight, i.e. the echoing area per unit volume would still be $64/8$, or eight times greater with water in the form of large drops, as compared to more numerous smaller drops of half the diameter.

If these factors which determine the radar scattering capability of a cloud are applied to the radar equation it is possible to show that the Bushy Hill radar would have little chance of seeing a non-precipitating cloud composed of droplets with a size distribution whose upper limit did not exceed 20 μ. If the cloud consisted of drops of precipitable size, i.e. 1 mm in diameter or greater, however, then detection at a range of 60 miles would be possible, even though there were only three such drops in every cubic metre. Radar is a very sensitive detector of falling rain or precipitation within clouds, even though such rain does not reach the ground, but it is much less capable of detecting ordinary clouds composed of non-precipitating small droplets.

Mention has been made of the much smaller dielectric constant of ice relative to that of water, and how this factor causes the radar echoing area of comparable shapes to be reduced when composed of ice. Experimental measurements confirm that the radar signals returned from regions of precipitation containing dry ice particles are much smaller than those yielded by falling rain. The distinction is not a clear one, however, for if the snow is wet, i.e. the temperature of the air through which the snow is falling is only 0° C or slightly above, then the snow flakes may be covered with a film of water, and so become powerful scatterers of radiation, being in effect composed of liquid water but of increased volume.

This short account of precipitation effects will have made it clear that radar is already a very important tool in meteorological research. It is the purpose of this chapter, however, to discuss meteorological effects only in so far as they affect the use of radar for detecting and tracing the movement of birds. One such meteorological phenomena is the occasional occurrence of a widespread temperature inversion; this calls for special comment since it can profoundly affect the performance of a radar, as this inversion can cause the so-called 'anomalous propagation' of radio waves.

Anomalous propagation of radio waves
Light waves travel in straight lines through homogeneous media such as air, glass, or water. If the characteristics of the propagating medium change suddenly at an interface, as when a ray of light passes from water into air, then the light ray is refracted or deviated at the surface of separation, and this is the reason why an oar appears bent at its point of entry in the water. This bending takes place in accordance with Snell's Law as in Fig. 3.7, and the index of refraction of the medium is measured by the ratio:

$$n = \frac{\text{sine angle of incidence}}{\text{sine angle of refraction}}$$

$n = 4/3$ for water and $3/2$ for glass, but for dry air at normal temperature and pressure it has the value of $1\cdot0000056$.

Sometimes the changes in refractive index which a light ray encounters in passing through a non-homogeneous, transparent medium occur continuously

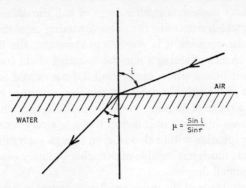

FIG. 3.7. Snell's Law of Refraction

instead of abruptly as in the example above. Thus a ray of light from the sun on entering the earth's atmosphere encounters successive layers of air in which the temperature and pressure are changing continuously. These factors affect the refractive index of the air; normally n increases as the earth's surface is approached with the result that the light ray is curved as shown in Fig. 3.8. In the optical case the bending of a ray of light near the horizon may be as much as $45'$, and it is for this reason that the rising sun is actually visible before it has climbed above the tangent plane which is the geometrical horizon.

Radio waves are electromagnetic waves just like light waves, and obey the same laws of refraction. The path of the ray which marks the progress of a radio wave through the atmosphere is normally curved downwards, just like the light ray, and the degree of curvature or refractive bending of the ray depends upon the rate of change of refractive index with altitude. In a normal atmosphere in which the temperature and density fall off with height the rate of refractive index change is commonly $1\cdot22 \times 10^{-8}$ per ft, and the curvature of the radio ray is about three-quarters of that of the earth itself. Aircraft seen by the radar will appear at apparently higher angles of elevation than is truly the case, and when calculating the altitude of an aircraft from radar observations it is necessary to allow for the refractive effect. It is usual to plot radar altitude elevation charts such as Fig. 1.8, as if the radio waves were travelling in straight lines above an earth whose radius is $4/3$ that of the true geometrical radius. This simple approach takes care of all the usual refraction effects (Fig. 3.8). A radio wave launched from an aerial at a height h ft above the earth's surface can in fact strike the earth at a point beyond the usual geometrical horizon limit. It is well known

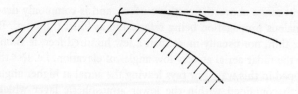

FIG. 3.8. Path of a radio wave through a normal atmosphere

that an approximate formula for this horizon distance is $\sqrt{(3h/2)}$ miles; the distance to the radio horizon however, is $\sqrt{(2h)}$ under the normal refractive conditions which are taken care of by assuming an effective earth's radius of $4/3\,R$.

Now the refractive index of the atmosphere for a radio wave depends upon the temperature and pressure of the air just as does a light wave, but in addition, humidity has a marked effect upon the radio refractive index, due to the polarizability of the water molecule at radio frequencies. It is possible under some meteorological circumstances for the normal lapse rate of radio refractive index to be greatly increased and if a value of 5×10^{-8} per ft is achieved then the curvature of the ray becomes equal to that of the earth itself, i.e. the ray would bend round the earth and remain parallel to it. Refractive index gradients of this value can be produced by temperature gradients alone, e.g. in the dense air just above the ground which has cooled off rapidly at night. Usually, the required critical

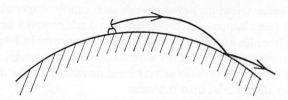

FIG. 3.9. Increase curvature of the path of a radio wave in an atmosphere having an abnormal lapse rate of refractive index (Anomalous Propagation)

value of refractive index gradient is more easily produced by a high humidity gradient, e.g. by the rapid night cooling of moist ground with the formation of a temperature inversion above it, also above the sea's surface. A combination of temperature inversion and the appropriate humidity gradient can in fact produce such a high lapse rate of refractive index that the curvature of a radio ray is greater than that of the earth as shown in Fig. 3.9. Under these circumstances, the ray actually curves round to meet the surface of the earth again, and so produces a permanent echo at a very distant point well below the geometrical horizon. It is possible for the ray to be reflected at the earth's surface, and to execute another 'hop' to an even more distant scattering point.

It will be apparent that unusually rapid rates of change of refractive index with height are required in order to produce this super-refraction or anomalous propagation effect. Such an exceptional atmospheric state only exists over a

E

limited height range above the earth's surface, and is commonly described as a 'duct', anomalous propagation being referred to as 'duct trapping'. Because the duct is quite thin, not usually more than a few hundred feet, it is only the rays which leave the radar aerial at very low angles of elevation, i.e. less than 1°, that become trapped in this way. For rays leaving the aerial at higher angles of elevation, the path contained within the lower atmospheric layer which possesses the high refractive index gradient is too short to curve the ray into the trapping configuration.

Most surveillance radars radiate a substantial amount of energy at angles below 1°, and so the performance of the radar can occasionally be affected by anomalous propagation when the required atmospheric conditions prevail. Plate 6 is a very impressive p.p.i. record of one such event which was photographed at Bushy Hill on 3 December 1962. The echoes from the Channel Islands and the Isle of Man will be noted; it was with some gratification, if not surprise, that they were seen to coincide with the video map positions! This occasion was also remarkable for the widespread distribution of the trapping duct; the anticyclonic subsidence inversion was accompanied by heavy fog.

In summertime the onset of anomalous propagation at Bushy Hill is most frequently signalled by the growth of permanent echoes along the Belgian and Dutch coasts where the radio path is largely over the sea. Under these conditions it is not unusual to observe birds flying around the mouth of the Scheldt and starling dispersals have been similarly observed both on the Continent and at a range of 70 miles (Newbury) even though such sunrise dispersals occur well below 300 ft (see Chapter Nine). Similarly, Dr Lack observed lapwing at the Dutch coast from his 10-cm radar station near Sheringham in Norfolk. Fortunately, anomalous propagation is not a common occurrence around the coasts of Britain. Its presence is also easily detected, and no mistakes in the interpretation of bird echoes should arise from this cause.

The suppression of permanent echoes: moving target indication

Plate 6 is an extreme and, fortunately, a very rare example of widespread ground or permanent echoes which can, as in this example, saturate the p.p.i. and so prevent the detection of aircraft. It is clearly desirable to have some means of suppressing such stationary echoes and to be able to present the desired moving echoes from aircraft free from interfering ground clutter.

We are all familiar with the apparent change in pitch of the sound emitted from the horn of a passing car. This is a consequence of a famous principle in acoustics enunciated by Doppler in 1863. According to this principle, the apparent frequency f' of a sound as heard by a stationary observer of a note of true frequency f emitted by a source moving with velocity v towards the observer is given by the expression:

$$f' = \frac{s}{s-v} \cdot f$$

where s is the velocity of sound.

It will be noticed that as v increases the apparent frequency f' rises; if the source is receding then v is negative and f' is reduced, i.e. the apparent pitch is reduced or the wavelength is increased (Fig. 3.10).

This same phenomenon is encountered in astronomy in the form of the so-called 'red-shift'. Certain stars show lines in their spectra which correspond to the characteristic spectrum lines of known terrestrial elements, but which are

FIG. 3.10. The Doppler Principle – the change in pitch of a sound from a moving source. Note the change in wavelength when the source passes the observer

slightly displaced in wavelength towards the red end of the spectrum. This displacement is attributed to the Doppler effect, arising from a recessional velocity of the star. Remembering that radio waves, electromagnetic waves, and light waves are all one, it is to be expected that the Doppler Principle will also apply in radar, and experiment proves this to be the case. If the frequency of the radiated wave is f, then the frequency f' of the wave reflected back from the target moving towards the radar with velocity v is:

$$f' = f \cdot \frac{c + v}{c - v}$$

where c is the velocity of light.

It follows that the frequency displacement Δf, or the Doppler frequency as it is usually termed, is given by:

$$\Delta f = f' - f = \frac{2v}{c - v} f$$

Since the velocity of light c is very great, then v may be neglected in comparison with c, and the expression becomes:

$$\Delta f = \frac{2v}{c} \cdot f = \frac{2v}{\lambda}$$

which shows that the Doppler frequency is proportional both to the frequency of the radar and to the velocity of the target.

For an aircraft moving at 300 knots, the Doppler frequency observed at Bushy Hill, with $f' = 1,300$ Mc/s, is about 1,100 c/s.

The important point to notice is that the echo from a moving target is displaced in frequency by an amount proportional to its velocity, while the frequency shift from a permanent echo is zero. It follows that if a special filter is designed

55

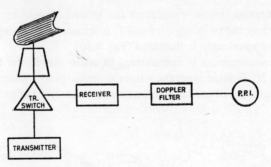

FIG. 3.11. The use of the Doppler Principle in radar to suppress echoes from stationary targets

to analyse the signals from the radar receiver as in Fig. 3.11, then it can be arranged that only the frequency shifted signals are allowed to pass on to the p.p.i., and the signals from permanent echoes are suppressed. Such a Doppler frequency sensitive radar receiver chain is termed a Moving Target Indicator. An M.T.I. system can be made extremely effective not merely for cancelling clutter but rather for enhancing the visibility of moving targets in the clutter region. Plate 7 illustrates the effect which is called 'improving the sub-clutter visibility'. Although the Doppler method is applicable to pulse radars, it is most conveniently applied to continuous-wave radars such as are used for target illumination in guided missile work. In fact, to prevent bird interference with this type of 3-cm radar, it is necessary to arrange for the removal of Doppler frequencies below about 1,200 c/s produced by birds flying into the beam; this cut-off frequency covers radial speeds up to 40 knots.

Flight direction indication by M.T.I.

In the above simple description of the radio Doppler effect it should be noticed that the shift in frequency is proportional not to the total velocity of the target but to its radial component relative to the observer. If an aircraft is flying along a track which does not pass over the radar station then at any point A or B (Fig. 3.12) the radial component of velocity relative to the radar is $v \sin \alpha$. When the aircraft has arrived at the position T, which is the foot of the perpendicular from the radar upon the aircraft's track, then the angle $\alpha = 0°$ and $\sin \alpha = 0$. At just this moment both the radial velocity and the Doppler frequency are zero and the radar signal from the aircraft being of the unchanged frequency f will be suppressed by the filter, i.e. targets moving tangentially with respect to the radar are momentarily invisible. By careful design of the receiver/filter chain the sensitivity can be such that the value of the radial velocity ($v \sin \alpha$) required to give a detectable signal may be kept as low as ± 3 knots. If the aircraft speed is 300 knots, then to give a radial component of 3 knots α is only 0·6°, or the total arc of invisibility 2α is 1·2°; this means that only one p.p.i. paint would be lost, which is insignificant. If the target is moving slowly, for example, when an extended

56

region of falling rain is moving transversely with a wind speed of say 15 knots, then $2\alpha = 23°$, and the arc of invisibility is comparatively wide as at AB in Fig. 3.12(a).

If a large assembly of birds are moving on parallel paths as in Fig. 3.12, those birds lying within the double wedge are invisible to the radar and the bright mass of echoes on the p.p.i. is crossed by two dark wedges. The bisector of the wedge

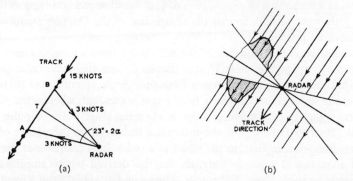

(a)   (b)

FIG. 3.12 (a). Suppression by the M.T.I. filter of the signal from a target flying tangentially

FIG. 3.12 (b). Determination of the average direction of flight of migrants by the M.T.I. wedge

angle is clearly at right angles to the direction of motion of the birds and although the wedges are diffuse it is not difficult to identify this axis of symmetry with considerable accuracy. Such a situation is illustrated in Plate 6b.

M.T.I. cancellation

Wedges of this form were noted by Sutter (1957b) as causing the invisibility of some of his migrating birds in Switzerland. The method has also been used by Drury and Nisbet (1964) to estimate the flight directions of migrants over New England. It will be seen that if the track of a migration is to be measured in this way it is necessary that a substantial portion of the wedge shall be covered by the migrating birds. This requires that the bird flock shall be of considerable extent. It is also necessary that the flight paths of the individual birds shall be closely parallel to each other, for if the orientations of the birds differ at random a simple wedge will not be formed and measurement of the average track by this method will not be possible. A following wind increases the ground speed of the birds, so reducing the angle of the wedge, and improves the accuracy of the measurement. Conversely, in the presence of headwinds and crosswinds the ground speed is reduced, also the parallelism of the tracks is disturbed and so the wedge becomes diffuse and wider, measurements are then much less certain.

Speed measurement by Doppler radar: rain echo cancellation

Although the description of the Doppler M.T.I. system given above is correct in principle it will be appreciated that the 'filter' box is really a rather complex

57

device whose mode of operation depends upon some involved radar theory. If the radar is of the continuous wave type then simple mixing of the received echo signal of frequency f' with the radiated frequency f does indeed permit immediate extraction of the Doppler frequency $\Delta f = 2v/\lambda$. This is the method used in the simple speed measuring radars used by the Road Police for traffic monitoring. In the case of a surveillance radar such as Bushy Hill, however, the radiation is in the form of a succession of pulses, each of 5 μs duration and occurring at the rate of 250 pulses per second, so that the recognition of the Doppler frequency is a more involved process.

Although the radio frequency of the echo pulse from a moving target is still displaced by the Doppler shift Δf, it is simpler to treat this pulse radar case as a phase shift problem rather than one of frequency displacement and to say that the phase of the signal returned from a fixed target is constant, whereas the phase of the echo signal from a moving target is changing from pulse to pulse by an amount $(2\pi v T)/\lambda$ (where T is the interpulse time). When the phases of these pulse returns are compared to the phase of a stable local oscillator at the radar, then a sequence of secondary signals may be derived whose amplitudes are determined by these phase differences. The secondary signal from a fixed target is therefore constant from pulse to pulse, and may be cancelled by subtraction of two consecutive pulses. The secondary signal from a moving target, on the other hand, changes from pulse to pulse due to the progressive change in phase and so by the subtraction process a residual signal is derived from two consecutive moving target pulses, and may be applied to the p.p.i. to paint a moving target echo. This simple treatment of pulse M.T.I. also uncovers another disadvantage of the Doppler system of moving target detection in addition to the tangential effect discussed above, for if the target moves exactly a distance $\lambda/2$ towards the radar between successive pulses, then the phase of the reflected wave is constant from pulse to pulse, and the target will be treated as a fixed target and suppressed. This special speed is termed the 'blind speed' of the radar. In the case of Bushy Hill with $\lambda = 23$ cm, and an interpulse time of 4 ms, then the blind speed is 58 knots or a multiple thereof. Techniques of multiple pulsing are available which can overcome any operational disadvantage that might result from this blind speed effect.

Although the subject is too technically involved for detailed discussion in a book primarily devoted to the ornithological applications of radar, it is important for what follows to mention that if the phase of the Stable Local Oscillator is shifted progressively between pulses by an amount $2\pi V' T/\lambda$, where V' is the radial velocity of a particular target, then the shift in phase of the reference oscillator exactly matches the phase change in the signal from the moving target due to its displacement during the interpulse period. In other words, the apparent phase of the target signal may be held constant and such a target will be treated as a fixed target by the filter and suppressed. This is the simple principle of Velocity Adjusted M.T.I. which may be used, not only to measure the speeds of selected targets such as aircraft or birds but also to effect cancellation of large areas of moving rainclouds, thereby permitting aircraft to be detected in the presence of rain. Similarly, birds can be seen flying below rain clouds if the radial velocity difference between birds and rain is sufficiently great. In order to permit this 'area cancellation' of rain to take place the phase of the Stable Local Oscillator has to be adjusted to correspond to the radial velocity of the rain cloud for each position of the aerial. By arranging for a phasing device in the Stable Local Oscillator circuit to be controlled continuously by a linkage to the aerial this requirement can be fulfilled. The operational advantages of this system will be obvious and this facility has been very valuable in many of the bird studies described later in this book.

The problem of identification

When the early experimenters had established the feasibility of locating aircraft by the reflection of radio waves it was quickly realized that before a comprehensive radar system could become operational in the military sense, it would be necessary to have some means of distinguishing between friendly aircraft and enemy aircraft. A radio method of identification was devised and embodied in the radar stations and was given the name 'I.F.F.' – Identification, Friend or Foe. All friendly aircraft were fitted with a 'black box' in the form of a small radio receiver/transmitter whose function was to receive the pulses from the ground radar station, amplify them, and re-transmit them back to the radar according to a coded pattern. The ground station received ordinary reflected radar signals from all aircraft, but the echoes from friendly aircraft were accompanied by an additional I.F.F. signal which served to identify them. This method of identification by interrogating a transceiver in the aircraft with a signal from the ground station is now used in civil air traffic operations under the title 'Secondary Radar'.

Unfortunately, secondary radar can hardly be used to identify scattering objects other than aircraft. In particular, the identification of the kinds of bird which are responsible for the various groups of echoes upon the film record of a p.p.i. is a problem which has not yet been fully solved. The pursuit of this problem involves an exhaustive search for clues and all the characteristics of the radar signals have to be investigated. Thus the time of occurrence, signal amplitudes, positions, speeds, altitudes, and directions of motion of echoes have to be recorded and analysed, seasonal and diurnal changes studied and correlations with the various weather factors looked for. All these features of the echoes have to be taken into account if the radar observations are to be interpreted adequately and translated into bird behaviour.

CHAPTER FOUR

Radar 'angels' and birds

Radar angels

On the introduction in 1943 of S-band surveillance radars of higher power (500 kW), it was noticed that dot-like echoes appeared on the p.p.i. within the 50-mile range ring much more frequently than had been the case with previous lower-powered radars, and for the first time these clusters of echoes from unknown objects in the airspace began to prove troublesome.

By this time radar operators were well practised in the interpretation of the steady radar echoes produced by fixed ground objects, such as hills or buildings, also of the variable echoes arising from swaying trees. Similarly, the fluctuating reflections from sea waves advancing on a beach – the so-called sea-clutter effect – and the travelling echoes from wind-borne rain clouds or other moving regions of precipitation were well understood. Confusion resulting from the presence of these 'spurious' signals simultaneously with the desired signals from aircraft was frequently serious, but at least the physics underlying the operational difficulties was appreciated, and means for removing the unwanted signals were being actively developed, as described in the last chapter. The randomly distributed dot-like echoes first encountered in significant numbers with the centimetric radar equipments did not receive a ready explanation, and it was at this time that the term 'angels' began to be applied to them.

More precisely, 'angels' was the name given to the discrete radar echoes which were often observed in profusion on the p.p.i. and which could apparently result from reflections from a sensibly clear atmosphere.

Angel theories

It seemed natural at first to look for a meteorological explanation of these angel echoes. A radar echo is received from any volume of the atmosphere if the refractive index of the medium contained within it differs from that of the surrounding air. It was well known that temperature and humidity are far from constant in the inhomogenous atmosphere which normally surrounds us, and remembering the optical effects which are familiarly associated with the turbulent, unmixed heated air rising above the roadman's coke brazier, it seemed reasonable to suppose that similar large-scale eddies could exist in the atmosphere and produce the observed radar echoes. Air pockets of this type are commonly encountered in low-level aircraft flights and contribute to the bumpiness of such flights. This practical experience of their existence tended to make the assumption of a widespread distribution of globules of 'non-standard air' wholly reasonable.

Undoubtedly some radar echoes are produced in this way and recent work performed at the Radio and Space Research Station, Slough, England, and elsewhere, has shown the existence of quite rapid changes of refractive index in the atmosphere – up to ten parts per million over distances of a few centimetres only, both horizontally and vertically (Lane, 1964). This sharp gradient in refractive index can lead to a fairly high reflection coefficient, and so could produce an effective echoing area which would be readily detectable by radar, as is discussed further in Chapter Ten. Vertical looking radars have detected the presence of extended laminar layers in the atmosphere, and have also revealed the passage of wind-borne reflecting pockets of 'non-standard air', i.e. non-standard in respect of temperature, pressure, humidity, and radio refractive index (Saxton et al., 1964).

One of the characteristic features of angel echoes, however, was their dot-like appearance on the p.p.i., from which it was reasonable to conclude that the scattering object producing the echo was of comparatively small spatial extent, certainly less than a radar beam width. This feature was not wholly incompatible with a meteorological explanation of the nature and occurrence of angels, but it certainly rendered such an explanation less likely. More important, it was noticed that angels were not only commonly in motion but that their directions and speeds of movement were frequently different from the speed and direction of the wind at the same locations. This velocity discrepancy strongly suggested that the angels were not wind borne.

It is true that we seldom have accurate knowledge of the wind vector at a particular point in space occupied by angels. It is also true that the wind speed and direction may change fairly quickly with the altitude, but this fact did not provide an explanation of those frequent cases where the direction of angel movement was actually in the opposite direction to the known direction of the ground wind. The conclusion was inevitable – angels were clearly capable of powered flight; indeed, this was why the title 'angel' proved to be such an apt one, although it did not presuppose that angels and birds would ultimately prove to be largely synonymous.

Angels and radar engineers

In the preceding chapters, the main development in microwave radar techniques during the post-war era have been briefly described, and the operational needs which prompted them have been outlined. It was the tremendous improvement in radar performance which resulted from this defence development programme that transformed the occasional angel occurrences associated with the medium powered 10-cm surveillance radars of the Second World War into the ever present and sometimes spectacular angel events characteristic of a modern high-powered 10- or 25-cm radar.

It was the necessity to achieve a full understanding of the angel phenomenon in order to remove the interference effect from operational radars that first prompted the interest of radar engineers and gave the initial impetus to one line of angel research appropriately termed 'angel suppression'. To the engineer it was well known that 'all birds are angels', but it appeared at first an unlikely converse proposition that 'all angels are birds'. It seemed incredible that the massive angel displays which were frequently observed upon the new post-war defence radars could all be attributable to birds. In this connexion, however, it must be remembered that a p.p.i. is an ideal instrument for compressing events taking place over areas of hundreds of square miles into the space of a few tens of square inches only. A consequence of this compression is that a distribution of birds so thinly spread as to correspond to one or two flocks per square mile would still saturate a large region of the p.p.i. Paradoxically, such a fully saturated region would give no indication of angel movement; that angel and bird movements are readily detectable by radar is due to the fact that saturation seldom exists, but is relieved by the thinning effect or open distribution of angels at long range which is discussed later.

Engineers have succeeded in their aim and means now exist for removing angel interference when desired. Fortunately for ornithology, these devices can be readily switched off and so permit the radar to operate at maximum sensitivity for the detection of birds. Engineers have also played their part in subsequent angel study, but it was the interest of meteorologists and ornithologists in seeking to apply the older, low-powered radars which were the legacy of the war, to their appropriate fields of study which led to the growing conviction that a substantial percentage of even the heaviest displays of angels must be attributed to birds. It has been the happy combination of ornithologists, meteorologists, physicists, and radar engineers that has ensured spectacular progress in the unravelling of radar angel phenomena and in the application of radar to ornithological research – a good example of the value of mixing scientific disciplines.

Birds as angels: the basis of radar ornithology

Later chapters of this book are concerned with various aspects of bird behaviour which have become accessible to close and detailed study only because of the radar method of observing bird movement which has now become available. For the results of these later studies to be wholly acceptable to the reader, it seems desirable to review the many investigations which were conducted in England, America, and Switzerland in the decade following the war on the correlation between radar angels and airborne birds 'proceeding on their lawful occasions', i.e. foraging for food or engaged upon migratory flights.

The circumstances under which the angel/bird problem was encountered by these widely separated workers were as different as the equipment which they employed. So also were the geographic environments in which they operated, the bird species involved, and the flight habits of the birds which provided the radar phenomena that were being observed. A review of all this fascinating work which, it must be remembered, was being pursued simultaneously and independently, does not lead to the identification of a single discoverer of the fact that birds give radar echoes. On the contrary, it is clear that this fact was well understood and widely known long before the researches now to be described. The objective was to determine what proportion of the angels observed were attributable to birds and whether the radar results supported and extended the visual observations of ordinary bird watchers. The real result of this phase of research was the unanimous conclusion by all radar workers that military science had placed a valuable new tool at the disposal of the research ornithologist which could be relied upon to supply essential information on bird movements, both by day and by night.

Wartime reports on birds as angels

It was fortunate for ornithology that Dr David Lack, now the Director of the Edward Grey Ornithological Institute, Oxford, should have been selected to work upon the operational problems encountered by the Army in their use of radar for anti-aircraft and coastal defence. This wartime radar experience has been put to good use by Lack during the post-war upsurge of ornithological research by radar methods, in which he has been both a pioneer and one of the most distinguished researchers in the field.

It was as members of the Army Operational Group that Lack and Varley (1945) first received evidence, in 1941, from Dr E. S. Shire, that echoes from birds had been received upon an experimental centimetric radar. Confirmation was obtained by G. C. Varley in September 1941, when he observed radar echoes from Gannets (*Sula bassana*) flying singly off Dover, and correlated the echoes with visual sightings. Although there had been earlier recognition of bird echoes upon the metric radars of the Royal Air Force, as mentioned in Chapter Two, this was the first time in Britain that a radar sighting of birds had been fully recorded by a radar operational specialist who was also an expert in field ornithology. That birds can indeed produce radar echoes was convincingly established by a wartime experiment of Major J. A. Ramsey of the British Coast and Anti-Aircraft Experimental Establishment. He suspended a Herring Gull (*Larus argentatus*) from a captive balloon and observed both balloon and gull with a centimetric radar of very narrow beamwidth. Separate radar echoes were received from both objects (Lack and Varley, 1945).

Subsequent to 1941 there were a number of well authenticated records of birds being detected by military radars both in this country and overseas. Bonham and Blake (1956), in the course of describing some observations on birds at sea, made in 1950 with the aid of a ship's radar, refer to an earlier American Naval Research Laboratory Report of 1939, in which R. M. Page reported the occurrence of a radar echo from a boatswain's bird. This observation was made with an experimental metric radar on board U.S.S. *New York* in Atlantic waters around Puerto Rico; radar and visually observed positions of the bird were found to correlate. Investigations of radar echoes from the lower atmosphere were made by Crawford (1949) with the aid of a vertically looking radar which provided for simultaneous observations at two wavelengths of 3·2 cm and 1·25 cm respectively. He concluded that, 'the chief, and possibly the only, sources of lower atmosphere reflections are flying insects and birds'.

In the first radar ornithological report to appear in the civilian scientific literature, Lack and Varley (1945) comment, 'As yet, the radar results have produced little of ornithological interest except to show how frequently birds fly at night over the sea.' Nevertheless, by 1945 there was a clear and widespread recognition by many who had had access to the secret military radar installations that birds were substantial contributors to angel interference and that large birds and flocks of birds could be tracked for many miles upon the p.p.i. What had not been possible during this first phase of the 'new ornithology' was the systematic application of radar to bird studies – the exigencies of the war prevented the pursuit of pure researches of this type.

Angels and meteorology

At the time of his ornithological investigations Harper (1957) was in charge of the British Meteorological Office Radar Research Station which was situated at East Hill, near Dunstable, in Buckinghamshire. This station was located close to the Chiltern Hills, about 30 miles north-west of London, and occupied a clear site in open country which provided good radar viewing. Wartime S-band equipment was employed and comprised a surveillance set of 500-kW power feeding a linear array. This aerial provided a symmetrical fan beam of radiation of width $1\frac{1}{4}°$ in the horizontal plane, and 6° in the vertical. A similar transmitter/receiver was used for the nodding height finder (Chapter Eleven) but the horizontal beam width in this case was $7\frac{1}{2}°$ in the azimuthal plane and $1\frac{1}{2}°$ in the vertical sweep plane. Both radars employed a two microsecond pulse. The research programme of this radar station was primarily meteorological, but a fuller understanding of angel phenomena was required in order to identify radar echoes arising from non-meteorological causes, and so to prevent such signals from confusing the meteorological phenomena being studied.

Although these radars were much less powerful than modern equipments, nevertheless, Harper was able to observe angel occurrences on most operational days and sometimes the angels were seen to extend to a range of 48 miles. Height measurements showed that the majority of the angels were below 5,000 ft. Recording of the daytime density of angels at this station had been maintained since 1952, so that analysis of these records permitted Harper to show that the periods of most intense angel activity corresponded to the times of spring and autumn bird migration. Perhaps the most convincing evidence adduced by Harper in support of his conclusion that even the densest displays of angels were explicable in terms of the movement of migrating birds across the field of view of the radar was that which related to the directions of movement of the angels. These were derived from photographs of the tube. Harper recorded, on one negative, four to six rotations of the aerial, spaced at about one minute intervals; one shorter interval at the end of the sequence was included in order to define the direction of the movement. This technique was necessary because the p.p.i.'s employed by Harper did not use the long afterglow magnesium fluoride phosphor which is now usual, and which provides the 'tails' to the echoes in many of the pictures in this book.

Harper analysed the directions of movement of the angels during the spring and autumn and compared their directions with that of the wind. Fig. 4.1 shows the mean directions of angel movement as observed on thirty-two days during the spring period, mid-February to mid-April, for the years 1952–7. Wind

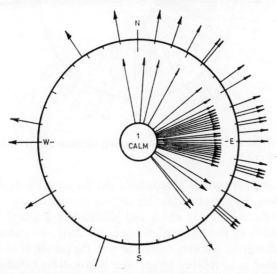

FIG. 4.1. Directions of angel movements during spring over Hertfordshire (after Harper, *Proc. Roy. Soc.*, 1958)

directions are plotted in the outer zone. Similar results are plotted in Fig. 4.2 for 46 days of the autumn period, September to mid-December, for the same years.

It will be seen from Fig. 4.1 that all the spring directions lie within a 150° sector, and that 22 of the 32 directions lie within the easterly sector 065°–105°. Wind directions were derived from the Meteorological Office Records. Although there was a general tendency for the occurrence of major angel movements to be associated with a following or tail wind, analysis of the results for individual days showed a marked divergence between angel track and wind direction, i.e. the majority of the angels were certainly not wind borne.

Fig. 4.2 shows that the general direction of angel movement in the autumn is towards the south-west in this part of England. The wind directions of Fig. 4.2 are more spread than those of Fig. 4.1, but analysis of angel movements and wind directions for the individual days again revealed a cross wind component of velocity in the angel track. A general correlation was noted between angel activity and the presence of roughly following winds which were favourable to the migrants' desired direction of movement.

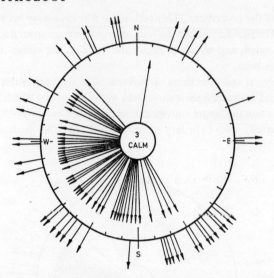

FIG. 4.2. Directions of angel movements during autumn over Hertfordshire (after Harper, *Proc. Roy. Soc.*, 1958)

Harper pointed out that his observations did not accord with any meteorological explanation; he suggested that his easterly movements were caused by the departures of flocks of birds which had wintered in England back to their breeding grounds in north-central Europe. Similarly, he suggested that his autumnal angel movements were consistent with the pattern of bird migration in southern England as established by ordinary bird-watching studies.

Birds seen by missile radars
Direct visual correspondence of a bird flock with an angel seen on a steerable, tracking radar was achieved by Harper in 1957. A wavelength of 10 cm and a power of 250 kW (1 μs pulse) was employed in this radar which provided a symmetrical beam of 6° width from a parabolic reflector of 4-ft aperture. Although designed for following balloon borne reflectors for the purpose of wind speed and direction measurement, this radar was capable of detecting angels out to a range of 5,000 yd and, using the split beam device with which this radar was fitted, it was possible to follow manually such point targets with great accuracy. Range and bearing errors were only ±20 yards and ±0·1° respectively. Short-range angel echoes detected on the p.p.i. of the surveillance radar could be acquired on the wind finding radar and the direction and speed of motion measured. A low-powered telescope was mounted on the aerial of the radar such that its axis was aligned to the electrical and mechanical axes of the array. Directing the aerial of the radar on to a selected p.p.i. target simultaneously aligned the telescope on to the same target; in this way direct correspondence of radar angel and bird flock seen visually through the telescope was achieved on 18 out of 25 angels followed by the wind radar to within 2,000 yd.

Observations of radar echoes from flocks of sea birds by means of a steerable, precision radar were also made by J. S. Stewart (1963) as early as 1952 and under most interesting circumstances. Stewart was concerned with the development of a 3-cm, narrow-beamed, fire-control radar. Testing of the equipment took place at Tantallon, on the Firth of Forth, so that the Bass Rock at $1\frac{1}{2}$ miles was a convenient and readily recognizable permanent echo which was fully delineated by such a high resolution system. It was noted that the echo from the rock was greatly extended to the north-east, particularly during the breeding time of the gulls which congregate on the rock. The prevailing wind in this area during the gulls' breeding time is from the south-west, and since there is a marked tendency for the nesting sites to be located on the north-eastern side of the rock, the result is that the air on the lee-side of the rock is heavily populated with flying gulls. Radar echoes from the soaring gulls produce a noticeable elongation of the permanent echo from the rock itself.

The researches of Sutter in Switzerland

Ernst Sutter was an ornithologist working at the Natural History Museum, Basle, when in 1954, he was invited to view the bird activity as revealed by the p.p.i. of the S-band control radar newly installed at Zürich–Kloten airport. Observations made the previous year with the X-band approach radar had revealed the occasional presence of echoes which could not be associated with aircraft; subsequent investigation by Flying Control and by the Zürich Bird Watching Society had established that birds were in large measure responsible for these mysterious echoes. Sutter's reaction to his first view of the p.p.i. and the dynamic picture of bird movements which it gave is worth quoting:

A form was given here to what was happening invisibly in the night sky and, in a very small picture, one saw the moving stream of migrant birds in a circle of ten miles' radius. It is difficult enough to obtain, in the daytime, a reliable picture of the state of migration over a large region and now I find myself standing in front of a small marvellous mirror which reproduces events, if not in terms of their individual constituents, at least in their entirety and with amazing clarity (Sutter, 1957b).

Sutter immediately perceived that the Kloten radar was an instrument potentially capable of assisting him with the alpine bird migration studies on which he was engaged, but first it was necessary to show that the time variation and spatial distribution of the radar echoes corresponded to the bird migration picture which was presented to the field observer. Such a study was attempted in October 1955 when observations made by a number of bird watchers were compared with the p.p.i. records. Direct correspondence of individual bird or flock sightings proved difficult to achieve, but one identification did prove conspicuously successful. A flock of Grey Geese (*Anser anser*) which were flying over Breitenloo gave precise time and position agreement with a sharply defined radar echo.

Although unambiguous correlation between the radar plots and the bird

67

watcher's records in this first test proved to be impossible, it was noted that the time variation of the total radar activity corresponded closely with the flight frequency as observed visually. It was concluded that the radar provided a reliable insight into the general course of the migration. Sutter recognized that one unanswered question which might limit the usefulness of his radar as an instrument for collecting data on the progress of a migration was whether the radar was recording the presence of the flocks of small birds (finches, larks, thrushes) which formed the greater proportion of the migrant streams whose passage he was studying. At least the results of the 1955 observations were sufficiently encouraging to justify the mounting of a much more detailed investigation, and in undertaking this work in 1956, Sutter was also greatly encouraged by Weitnauer's (1956) delightful study of the night flight of the swift (Chapter Ten).

In this more detailed study of October 1956, use was again made of the Kloten surveillance radar. This was a 10-cm equipment of 450-kW peak power, which provided a performance diagram of the fan beam, $cosec^2$ type discussed in Chapter One. The horizontal beam width was $1°$ and cover in elevation extended from $0.5°$ to $30°$. An aerial rotation speed of 10 r.p.m. was employed, so that a pulse recurrence frequency of 850/s resulted in 14 strikes on the target. The p.p.i. was adjusted to cover a radius of 10 miles only and photographs were taken every 5 min, the shutter being left open for durations of 1–3 min. In this way a good overall picture was obtained of the flight directions, flight densities and velocities for correlation with the records of the field observers. These bird-watchers were placed at five locations around the Kloten district and made their observations on five days during October 1956.

Frequency of occurrence curves of the radar echoes were prepared from the p.p.i. films and compared with the histograms of the bird flights compiled by the bird watchers in the field. The measure of agreement between the two sets of results was good, provided that the circumstances under which the observations were made did not tend to favour too heavily either of the two techniques of viewing. Thus good agreement was obtained in fine, clear weather and when the altitudes of the migratory flights were neither too low to be missed by the radar nor too high to escape visual detection by the bird watchers. Under conditions of poor visibility or in the presence of low, layered cloud the agreement was not so good.

Sutter concluded from this work that radar and visual methods of bird watching tend to be complementary. If the birds fly at a great height, and if the presence of cloud hides the birds from the watcher's eyes, then radar is the only source of information about the progress of a migration. He recognized that radar provides a better overall view of the entire course of a flight, but he considered that his results did not make it certain whether trust could be put in the absolute magnitude of the flight frequency derived from the radar. Sutter perceived that at least the radar estimates of the frequency of flight were not inferior to those of the field observer even in clear weather; under conditions of poor visibility the radar results were vastly superior, because of its ability to detect what Sutter figuratively described as 'concealed flights'. It is true that radar, as Sutter used it, could not provide evidence on the species of birds involved, but he decided that his study justified the acceptance of radar as a method of observing bird migration and proceeded to investigate the night movements of birds in the vicinity of Kloten (Sutter, 1957a).

Birds as angels on high-power radars

It will be appreciated that a subject such as 'radar angels', interwoven as it is with the history of the development of military radar equipment, has been hedged around with the restrictions imposed by the need for preserving military security. During the war the security was absolute, but even after the war the disclosure of facts relating to the 'angel seeing' capability of a new radar was not possible until years after the observations had been made and the radar made obsolete, since the performance of the radar was clearly implicit in the scope of the bird observations. More powerful microwave radars were in course of development in Britain from 1949 onwards, and the angel activity observed upon the p.p.i.'s of these equipments was very great indeed.

Investigations into angel phenomena were made by radar engineers of the Royal Radar Establishment, Malvern, who were operating with S-band equipment and, also, by the Marconi Research Laboratory which was developing an L-band radar. The spectacular displays of angels which were encountered will be appreciated from Plate 9, where dense angels extend to 100 miles, and the question was whether all these angels could be ascribed to birds. Angels of this density greatly exceeded previous experience in the Royal Air Force; the activity was also substantially greater than that covered by Harper's investigation and enormously greater than the 10 mile p.p.i. coverage of Sutter.

Observations up to 1956 at an experimental station in Norfolk by the Royal Radar Establishment revealed no correlation between angel occurrences and any specific meteorological factors, which until then had been considered to be one of the likely causative agents of the heavy angel displays. It was noted, however, in the further prosecution of angel research at this station by Tedd and Lack (1958) that there was a marked connexion between heavy angel occurrences and the general weather situation. Dense displays of angels tended to be associated with anticyclonic weather and with light winds. The presence of rain, bad visibility, or strong winds, on the other hand, seemed to ensure the absence of angels. A study of the monthly variation in angel activity revealed marked peaks at the two periods in the year which correspond respectively to the spring exodus of winter visitors from the British Isles and to their return in the autumn. The big eastward departures from the coastal region of Norfolk take place from mid-February until mid-April, the species involved being mainly chaffinches, blackbirds, starlings, and redwings. These same species are involved in the reverse flow of the autumn, the movements taking place during October and November. It was the general conclusion of Tedd and Lack that even the dense

F

displays of angels observed on high powered radar sets in Britain were mainly produced by birds, with passerine birds on migration as the chief contributors.

Observations were also made during this time by the Royal Radar Establishment at Gt Malvern, using an experimental S-band stacked beam radar. Results from this work were reported by Houghton and Coultas (1958) and included measurements on air speeds of angels, altitudes, and target-echoing areas. It was shown that a bird explanation of these springtime angel displays was in accordance with the known pattern of bird migration in this region of England. As in the case of Harper's work (Harper, 1957), the most significant single reason for identifying angels with birds was the wide disparity between the tracks of the angels and the known direction of the wind, i.e. the angels were making good their tracks by powered flight. Other reasons given for the bird identity of angels included the following:

(1) The air speeds of the angels were found to extend over the range 15–53 knots, i.e. roughly the same range of speeds as birds.

(2) Masses of discrete angel echoes were moving on the same heading.

(3) Although the air speeds and altitudes of different targets were dissimilar, each target maintained its own air speed and altitude roughly constant.

As noted above, the initial purpose of British radar engineers was to understand the causes of heavy angel displays in order that electronic units could be included in the radar to eliminate the angels. It was noted by the Marconi workers that while the velocity-corrected Doppler devices described in the last chapter could be employed successfully to eliminate echoes from wind-borne rain clouds, the same method did not work so well with angels, indicating that the angels possessed velocity vectors differing both from that of the wind and from each other, i.e. the angels were performing powered flights.

Similar experiments with the same general objectives were also in progress in the United States during these same years, i.e. 1952–8. Perhaps the American experimental programme most directly comparable with the angel elimination work of the Royal Radar Establishment and Marconi workers was that reported by Richardson and his collaborators at the Massachusetts Institute of Technology (Richardson et al., 1957 and 1958). This research programme was commenced at Cape Cod in 1956 with the aid of a high-powered L-band radar. Discrete angels were observed on the p.p.i., and were known to arise from comparatively low altitude targets, since the echoes were produced only by the lower beam of the double beamed radar that was at first employed. Careful analysis of the echo pulses from these targets showed them to be identical in length with that of the transmitted pulse, i.e. every echo arose from essentially a point target. Doppler measurement of speed of the angels showed that it was always less than 60 knots. The diurnal and seasonal variations of these particular Cape Cod angels were next studied, and it was found that there were more angels in the summer months than during the winter, and usually more targets during daylight hours than during the night. Attempts were first made to correlate the angel echoes with sea clutter and with weather effects, but a bird explanation of their origin ultimately proved to be the most feasible. Professor Charles Blake, former Professor of Comparative Anatomy at Massachusetts Institute of Technology and an experienced bird watcher, assisted in the identification of the angel echoes with a mixed population of sea gulls and sea ducks which frequent this area. Films of the p.p.i. taken by the time-compression method permitted the angel movements to be correlated with the known feeding operations of these species. Similarly, the north eastward flow of angels seen on the p.p.i. in the late evening during spring was shown to correspond to the migration habits of certain land birds. The southward flow of the same species observed on nights during the autumn continued until dawn, which also corresponded to the fact that these migrating birds reached their resting and feeding grounds at this time.

The general conclusion on the equivalence of birds and angels to be drawn from the varied researches described in this chapter may be conveniently summed up by a quotation from the report by Richardson and his co-workers:

It is evident from the observations made in the course of this experiment that a high-power radar, coupled with occasional airborne identification as to type of birds, would become a very strong tool in the hands of an ornithologist.

It is hoped that the later chapters of this book will show that this was indeed a true assessment of the contribution that radar could make to ornithology.

Radar measurements of the speed of bird flight

Radar methods of velocity measurement applicable to aircraft and angels have been described in Chapter Two. With the equivalence of angels and birds established by the investigations reviewed in the present chapter, it will be useful to summarize the radar speed results that have been obtained on birds, since speed can provide a useful clue to the species responsible for a particular angel. Although much experimental work has yet to be done before a comprehensive and accurate library of bird speeds can be compiled for the use of radar ornithologists, many useful measurements have already been made by a number of investigators in the course of other studies. Probably the first report of such a radar speed measurement was that of Lack and Varley (1945) on the Pink-Footed Goose (*Anser brachyrhynchus*) by a Royal Air Force radar station in East Anglia. The birds were observed visually by a Royal Observer Corps post and were tracked by radar for 79 miles, which they covered in 139 min, corresponding to an average speed of 34 m.p.h. (28 knots). On taking out the wind the resulting air speed was 21·2 knots, the altitude being 5,000 ft.

A particularly interesting speed measurement was made by H. Hofmann in January 1956, and which was reported by Sutter (1956). Hofmann was the Radar Controller at Kloten, which is the airport of Zurich. The day of the incident was one of poor visibility with complete cloud cover, and full Air Safety Procedures were in operation. It was for this reason that close attention was paid to a target which suddenly appeared at 15.30 hours some 30 km to the north-east of the station, moving at the very slow aircraft speed of 32 knots. Radio attempts to contact the 'rogue' aircraft failed and so a light aircraft, manned by the Air Safety Department, took off to investigate. The mystery was solved when the pilot, vectored on to the target by radar control and having achieved radar coincidence with it, observed a flock of lapwings some 120 strong, flying at an altitude of about 7,000 ft above sea level and nearly 1,000 ft above the upper surface of the lowest cloud layer. This observation was important from many points of view, for it not only established visually that birds were responsible for the slow-moving radar echo, but it also supplied valuable information on speed, altitude, and the number of birds in this particular flock. Actual disappearance of the plover into the cloud was also witnessed by the pilot. A total radar track of 90 km was plotted on this echo and yielded an average speed of 29·5 knots, the wind correction being practically zero. This same Zurich radar was employed by Sutter (1957) to measure the speed of flight of the Grey Goose (*Anser anser*). Fifty-two birds were seen by his field observers to be flying in a V-formation, and gave precise time and position agreement with a sharply defined echo on the p.p.i. Four minutes of tracking on the radar was obtained and a distance of 3·5 km was covered, corresponding to a ground speed of 29·1 knots but no wind data was given to permit a still air speed to be derived.

Measurements on passerine spring migration over England were made by Harper (1957) and still air speeds in the range 19–47 knots were obtained, with a maximum concentration at 27·5 knots. It is interesting to compare this figure with the radar-measured average ground speed for small passerines in North America which, according to Drury and Keith (1962), is 25 knots. A still air speed range of 18–26 knots was measured by Drury and his co-workers in Massachusetts for small birds of the warbler type, but high accuracy could not be achieved in this work since it was not possible to follow for sufficiently long the feeble, fluctuating echoes which these birds give (Drury *et al.*, 1961).

Lapwing flights over the sea were observed in June 1959 by Bourne and gave air speeds of 35 knots (Lack, 1962a). The most obvious migrating movements into Norfolk from Scandinavia during late August and early September consist of masses of small echoes which Lack has identified with chats, warblers, and flycatchers. Speed measurements on these echoes were made on days of light wind in anticyclonic weather, in order that errors due to uncertain wind state at the altitude of the birds should be kept small. In fact, the wind speed on the five measurement days ranged between 8–15 knots, and the extracted air speeds spread from 17–24 knots, the average being 20·0 knots. Other early morning measurements on similar passerine movements over the sea off Norfolk and directed S.S.E. gave average air speeds of 19·3 knots. Lack concluded that these birds were small night migrants that had left Scotland the previous evening, and that the species involved were almost certainly warblers and chats (Lack, 1963a). A very accurate determination of the air speed of the Sand Martin was given by Lack in the final paper of this series. Strong echoes were seen to form from a known sand martin roost at Welney in Cambridgeshire, and the birds, after climbing to an altitude of 7,000 ft, flew the 61 miles to Felixstowe, Suffolk, in

80 min. After allowing for the wind, which varied little with height on this occasion, an air speed of 28 knots was obtained. Good tracking was also obtained on echoes typical of waders during April 1961 when birds of this species were known to be leaving Norfolk in a north-easterly direction. Air speeds ranged from 37–41 knots.

Speeds of passerine movements over the sea off the coast of Norfolk were made throughout the year by Tedd and Lack (1958), and the results were analysed to determine whether there was any evidence for a seasonal change in the air speed. These results are given below:

Estimated air speed of radar echoes

	Number of events	
Speed in knots	Spring (Feb.–Apr.)	Autumn (Sept.–Nov.)
0–9	0	0
10–19	22	8
20–29	25	11
30–39	15	1
40–49	11	1
50–59	0	1
Average speed	27 knots	23 knots

The spring or emigrant speed is clearly higher than that possessed by the immigrants in autumn. It is true that the bird populations involved in these major movements of the year were far from identical and so the results can only be suggestive, nevertheless it is interesting to compare them with the starling figures quoted later.

Estimation of the air speeds of echoes observed from a Norfolk radar station were also made by Lack and Parslow (1962), during a study of the falls of night migrants on the east coast of England during the autumns of 1960 and 1961. The following classification was given for morning echoes observed over the sea:

Echo	Air speed (knots)	Occurrence	Presumed species
Very small and closely packed	20	September	Chats, warblers and flycatchers
Larger and more spaced	30	Late September and October	Thrushes
Large and well spaced travelling west	30	September and October	Lapwing
Well spaced but smaller than lapwing echoes	30–40	September	Arctic waders

Further useful additions to this table of bird air speeds were made on a radar in the Isle of Lewis in the Hebrides by Lee (1963). Wheatears were shown to return an air speed of approximately 20 knots on the sea crossing from Iceland while redwings achieved an air speed in the range 30–35 knots. Greylag Geese (*Anser anser*) gave much higher speeds and from two mornings of observation during April 1962, when direct visual association of flocks of these birds with radar echoes was made, the measured air speeds were 53 and 55 knots respectively.

Similar observation of passage migration by means of a radar conveniently located on an island in the path of the birds were made by Adams (1962) from Cyprus during the autumn of 1958 and the spring of 1959. Masses of fine echoes typical of warblers were observed moving southwards from the island at dusk and it was possible to estimate the speed only from the ill-defined movement of the leading edge of a haze of unresolved echoes. Air speeds in the order of 20–30 knots were obtained. A springtime observation was also made on some large bird echoes flying in a westerly direction and which were attributed to Cranes (*Balearicidae*). Radar tracking on these flocks was possible over a distance of 40 miles and the air speed ranged over 46–66 knots, but the wind could only be estimated roughly at the altitude of 13,000 ft at which the flights took place.

Bergman and Donner (1964) showed that the still-air speed of the Common Scoter and Long-tailed Duck were 45 and 40 knots respectively, which occurred for low altitude flights over the sea in the Gulf of Finland. Over land the altitude is increased to about 3,000 ft and the speed is then about 10 per cent higher. It

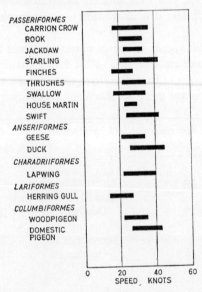

FIG. 4.3. Some radar measurements of the flight speeds of birds (after Houghton. Crown Copyright. Reproduced with the permission of The Controller, H.M.S.O.)

was considered by Bergman and Donner that this increased speed was probably due to the lower density of the air at the higher altitude.

The problem of gathering information on the flight speeds of birds sufficient to establish speed criteria for species identification of echoes on the p.p.i. has been discussed by Houghton (1963-4). He points out that it is not enough to make a few unco-ordinated speed determinations; it is necessary to produce speed distributions and variances for a species from a large number of measurements made under known flight conditions. Fig. 4.3 shows a chart of a number of bird speeds which were reported by Houghton. This chart is based on results secured with an accurate position-measuring radar, used in association with an optical telescope, for the dual purpose of bird identification and guidance of the radar aerial. The speeds are approximately true air speeds, since in no case were the measurements made with a wind of greater than 5 knots, but the chart does not embody enough results to permit the most probable speed for a species to be indicated.

Flight speed of starlings dispersing from the roost

When starlings fly out from their roosts in the morning they produce an expanding ring pattern on the p.p.i., as shown in Plate 14. These expanding rings, when observed by the time compression method, provide a convenient means of measuring the speed of the starling. Moreover, since estimates of distance travelled can be made along a number of radial paths from the roost it is possible to determine the wind speed and direction accurately and so to arrive at a good value for the still air speed of the birds. Unfortunately, complete rings on the p.p.i. only occur with light winds of less than 6 knots; with stronger winds the birds moving upwind fly low and are missed by the radar, so that a partial ring only is seen on the p.p.i., with its axis in the downwind direction. Speed estimation under these circumstances is not so accurate, since the local wind data is not known precisely.

Measurements of starling speed using the film method were made by Eastwood et al. (1962), on a number of dispersals taken over two complete years. The mean air speed was found to be 37 knots. Curiously, the speed was higher in winter than in summer, the respective mean figures being 40 and 32 knots. The difference between the two sets of results for the periods November to March and June to August respectively, were statistically significant at the 1 per cent level. Inevitably, these winter and summer values refer mainly to different roosts, indeed to different populations, but the speed difference remains as a curious fact which it is tempting to associate with the spring/autumn effect for passerines noted by Tedd and Lack above. Does the flight performance of a bird change with the season? Is there possibly a change in its metabolic processes? Much more experimental work will be necessary before these interesting questions can be answered.

Measurements on two starling arcs from a roost in Hertfordshire by Harper (1959) gave air speeds of 29·5 and 33·5 knots respectively. That these values of the starling air speeds were lower than the visual estimates of 35–41 knots given by Meinertzhagen (1955) was considered by Harper to be due to the fact that the starlings were climbing steadily from the roost at the rate of 60 ft/min. When starlings leave their temporary roosts to join the migrant stream in spring the dispersals commence as arcs but these soon straighten out into long lines of birds which advance eastwards. Harper estimated the migration speed as 37 knots. Lack (1960b) made radar speed measurements on such line echoes as they were moving out to sea off the coast of East Anglia and was able to maintain continuity of tracks for periods of half an hour. Observations on 18 flocks on 7 different mornings gave mean air speeds between 29 and 44 knots. The wide spread of speed was attributed by Lack to the error introduced by assuming that the wind speed and direction at the altitude of the birds was that of the wind taken at Hemsby. When the results of all the 18 mornings were averaged the mean speed was 37 knots.

From these various radar observations on the mass movements of starlings it seems fair to conclude that the most probable value for the still-air speed of this bird is 37 knots, and no significant speed difference seems to arise from over-land or over-sea flights. A seasonal difference is suspected but has yet to be fully established.

Radar is capable of measuring bird speeds at all altitudes with high accuracy. It is also able to track birds for long distances and so can arrive at speeds which are a true measure of the average performance of a bird over a substantial length of time, as compared to the old method of short, visible flights timed by stop-watch. Nevertheless, much detailed work has yet to be done before radar echo speed can be used as a fully reliable method of species identification. In addition, simultaneous determination of altitude and wind state will also be necessary if the derived bird speeds are to be truly significant. Radar has yet far to go before it can rival the species coverage, accuracy of identification and the mass of detail on speed estimates which were presented by Meinertzhagen (1955). But the value of the radar contribution to this difficult subject of bird velocity determination will steadily and inevitably increase.

CHAPTER FIVE

The time variation of angel echoes

The pattern of the angel display upon the p.p.i. of a radar station is always changing; this may be appreciated by reference to the sequence of photographs shown on Plate 9. The appearance of the p.p.i. at Bushy Hill on a fine spring morning may be as in Plate 6 (*b*), where angels are seen to extend to a range of 100 miles. In sharp contrast is the light angel display characteristic of a June evening as in Plate 20. Sometimes the p.p.i. may be clear of echoes which indicates almost total grounding of all birds within the cover of the radar. An intermediate state is illustrated in Plate 12 with medium angel density present out to sea off the Kent coast, but with little activity over land.

These pictures demonstrate that angel activity is dependent upon both the time of the day and the season of the year, and so a complete unravelling of the various factors which can influence the density of an angel display requires the systematic collecting of records over a considerable period of time. The changing appearance of angel formations upon the p.p.i. is, of course, indicative of the fluctuating level of bird flight activity, and remembering how many and varied these bird missions may be, it will be seen that the problem of angel interpretation is a formidable one. During the day many birds will be making short, low-altitude foraging flights, but such flights do not occur during the night, and so will not contribute to the nocturnal angels. Other birds will be performing transfer flights of greater duration but at altitudes usually less than 1,000 ft. Some birds of prey at slightly higher altitudes may be present during the day, while, at the appropriate seasons of the year, heavy concentrations of migrating birds will contribute to the general angel activity. Such migratory movements occur both by day and by night, and the flights may be executed at heights of many thousands of feet.

All these birds, no matter the purpose of the flight on which they are engaged, may provide echoes on the p.p.i., for the radar 'sees' all the birds which happen to come within its range. How helpful it would be if the radar could also distinguish between the various kinds of flight; better still, if it could identify the bird species involved. It is true that some of the angel movements possess special features which are readily recognizable, for example the dispersal of starlings from their roosts at sunrise, or the vesper flights of swifts on summer evenings. But the contribution of special flights of this type to the sum total of angel activity is usually small, so that the only method of study available to the radar ornithologist is to collect all possible data on the occurrence of angels and then to attempt patiently the task of interpretation and correlation, complicated though it is.

P.p.i. appearance of a uniform distribution of simple targets

In order to explain how the problem of the interpretation of angel distributions may be tackled, it will be helpful to consider first a very simple example. Let us examine what the appearance of the p.p.i. would be if the Bushy Hill radar were scanning a uniform distribution of identical, spherical targets. We will assume that the spheres possess an echoing area of 50 cm², and are all located at a common altitude of 4,000 ft. Now the limiting range at which such a target would be seen may be calculated from the Radar Equation, and turns out to be 53·5

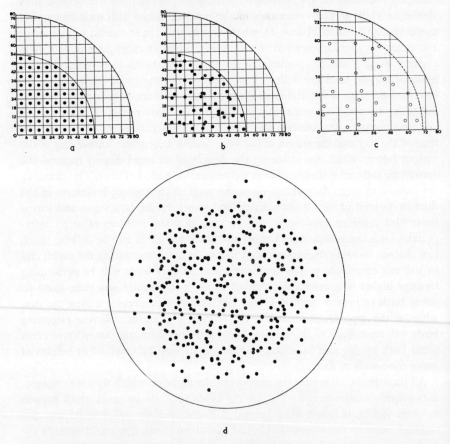

FIG. 5.1. Model of an angel distribution on the p.p.i.

(*a*) Appearance on the p.p.i. of a lattice distribution of identical, spherical targets each of 50-cm² echoing area

(*b*) Appearance on the p.p.i. of a random distribution of 50-cm² targets (limiting range 53·3 miles)

(*c*) Appearance on the p.p.i. of a random distribution of 300-cm² targets (limiting range 70 miles)

(*d*) Appearance on the p.p.i. of a mixed distribution of 50- and 300-cm² targets miles. Fig. 5.1 (*a*) shows a very simple distribution with the spheres symmetrically disposed at the centres of the squares composing the grid; it follows that all the spheres lying within the circle of visibility, which is of radius 53·5 miles, would paint echoes on the p.p.i. No targets outside this circle would be seen.

A slightly more realistic distribution is shown in Fig. 5.1 (*b*), in which the same number of targets are plotted as in Fig. 5.1 (*a*) but the position of an individual sphere within its 6 mile × 6 mile square has been fixed at random. Such a distribution is easily realized by the simple method of throwing two dice and plotting the two numbers obtained as the (*xy*) coordinates of the sphere within its box. According to this simple model all targets within the 53·3-mile circle would again be seen by the radar and would be recorded upon the p.p.i.; it is clear that there would be no apparent reduction in density of the angels as the range increases until the sharp cut-off imposed by the circle of limiting range.

To make the problem a little closer to reality, we will now suppose that a second quasi-random distribution of targets co-exists with the first family.The second set of targets is composed of spheres each having an echoing area of 300 cm², the same altitude of 4,000 ft is maintained but the density of the distribution is such that one sphere is randomly situated within every 12 mile square. This lower density distribution of the larger targets corresponds to the fact that angels of large echoing area occur less frequently than those with smaller echoing areas. The limiting range of visibility for the larger targets calculated from the Radar Equation is 70 miles, and a circle of this radius is shown on Fig. 5.1 (*c*). All the targets of the second family which lie within this circle are seen by the radar; these visible targets are indicated by open circles.

The appearance of the p.p.i. with the two combined distributions is shown in Fig. 5.1 (*d*), and begins to have the familiar look of an actual p.p.i. carrying an angel display. In particular, the 'thinning effect' or fall off in density of targets with range which characterizes a real display of angels is now apparent. Clearly, a still closer approximation to reality would be obtained by considering a complex distribution made up of a larger number of families of targets according to the scheme:

Family	Cross-section (cm²)	Density (angels/m²)	Limiting range of visibility (miles)
1st	A_1	d_1	r_1
2nd	A_2	d_2	r_2
3rd etc.	A_3	d_3	r_3

Such a distribution would show a very smooth thinning effect, even though there would still exist a succession of sharp cut-offs, each characteristic of one family of targets.

Factors influencing angel density

The above model illustrates the point that a single distribution of identical and non-directional scatterers would show a sharp cut-off in range, whereas a complex assembly of scatterers made up of a superposition of simple distributions would lead to the fall off in angel density with range which is observed with actual angel displays. In view of this correspondence it will be useful to inquire how birds in flight can provide the families of targets postulated in the model and which would interact with the Radar Equation to produce the angel distributions observed. This analysis will help us to arrive at an estimate of the numbers of birds contained in a particular movement from a count of the angels on the p.p.i., but the transfer function from angels to birds is not a simple one.

It will be convenient to list the various factors which contribute to variations in angel density, and then to consider their relevance to bird studies. A suitable method of classification of these factors is to consider them either as derivative of certain properties of the targets themselves, or as arising from the engineering characteristics of the radar equipment employed.

Properties of the target　　　Density of birds
　　　　　　　　　　　　　　　Size and aspect of birds
　　　　　　　　　　　　　　　Grouping of birds
　　　　　　　　　　　　　　　Flight altitude

Equipment characteristics　　Vertical performance diagram of the radar
　　　　　　　　　　　　　　　Horizontal beam width of the aerial
　　　　　　　　　　　　　　　Extent of the pulse volume
　　　　　　　　　　　　　　　Equipment sensitivity
　　　　　　　　　　　　　　　Display limitations

Density of birds

The number of birds airborne directly influences the density of angel distribution. In general, such distributions are far from uniform, since the birds obviously tend to be more densely grouped in regions close to migratory highways. Throughout the year, the southern North Sea is crossed and recrossed by birds virtually 'commuting' between the continent and the south-east of England. In contrast, the moving bird population off the east coast of Scotland is comparatively small, being more remote from a frequented bird highway.

Size and aspect of birds

Birds of different species differ in size and so present different echoing areas to the radar waves. Chapter Three has examined the relationship between the mass of a bird and its target cross-section. It was shown that this quantity, for a given size of bird, can depend upon the wavelength of the radiation employed, and also upon the aspect of the bird with respect to the radar. A mixed distribution of birds might contain small warblers with echoing areas of only 2 cm^2 up to birds

80

the size of a goose with a cross-section of 1,000 cm^2 – and all these targets might show variation in their effective echoing areas due to changing aspect.

Grouping of birds

Equally important with the total number of birds under surveillance as a factor determining the angel density is the manner of their distribution, i.e. whether the birds occur singly or in groups. The number of birds which combine to yield a single angel is particularly significant, and the degree of grouping may vary, not only with the species, but also as between night and day flights performed by birds of the same species. This important subject is considered in detail when the counting of birds by radar is discussed in Chapter Twelve.

Flight altitude

Birds fly at a wide range of altitudes, and the manner of their distribution in altitude can interact with the Vertical Performance Diagram of the radar to affect the density and extent of the angel display seen upon the p.p.i.

Vertical performance diagram

Even if the birds all flew in the same horizontal plane, the shape of the radar beam in the vertical plane would still affect the form of the angel display. A rotating pencil beam radar would only 'see' a narrow annular ring of birds, while a fan beam would see a substantially greater number if the elevation of the nose of the pattern shown in Fig. 1.8 were set at the appropriate angle. It is, of course, possible for birds to fly so low that they pass beneath the lower edge of the beam. In the case of Bushy Hill the effective height of the aerial is 250 ft; it is surrounded by flat, low-lying country so that with the lower edge of the beam grazing the earth's surface very few targets are missed beneath the beam. With such a low elevation beam, trouble with permanent echoes can be experienced, but this is prevented in this particular equipment by the use of the M.T.I. device. Nevertheless, due to the curvature of the earth, a radio horizon must exist for every ground radar; the effect of this is discussed further in Chapter Eleven.

Horizontal beam width

The use of various forms of reflectors to focus the radio energy into a narrow beam has been described. Such focusing is usually far from perfect and results in a divergent beam whose angular spread is dependent upon the ratio of the aperture of the aerial to the radio wavelength. In addition, a number of subsidiary beams are also produced, called 'sidelobes', which are very small compared to the main beam, but these can give 'spurious' p.p.i. paints from large targets at short range; a substantial increase in back scatter from the ground can be caused in this way.

The result of having a divergent beam is that the tangential resolving power of the radar diminishes with the range, and two aircraft separated by half a mile, which show on the p.p.i. as two distinct echoes at a range of 30 miles, give only one combined echo when the range is 100 miles. Bushy Hill has a horizontal beam width of 0·8°, so that, for complete resolution, the minimum separations of two targets at various distances are roughly as follows:

Range (miles)	10	20	30	40	60	80	100
Separation	260 yd	520 yd	780 yd	0·6 m	0·9 m	1·2 m	1·5 m

This means that a uniform distribution of identical targets would still show a thinning effect within the limiting range circle, due to the fall-off of azimuthal resolving power with range; targets separated by less than a beam width tangentially would be combined into one if their ranges were approximately the same.

Pulse volume

Most surveillance radars usually operate with a pulse duration time which is measured in microseconds, Bushy Hill for example has a pulse width of 5 μs. Range resolution is therefore limited as well as angular resolution, and targets which possess a radial range difference less than $\frac{1}{2}c\tau$ (0·46 miles at Bushy Hill) cannot be seen as separate echoes upon the p.p.i. but are combined into a composite target.

Resolution in the vertical plane is obviously zero in the case of a fan beam radar since there is no directional discrimination in this plane. The combination of these three resolution limits in range, azimuth, and elevation means that all targets which are contained within a so-called 'pulse volume' will form a single echo upon the p.p.i. It will be seen that if a distribution of birds were imagined which was uniform vertically as well as horizontally, this limitation of spatial resolving power would impose a drastic thinning upon the angels since the magnitude of the pulse volume increases as the square of the range. In practice the effect is not quite so marked due to the fact that the majority of birds fly below 8,000 ft (Chapter Eleven), so that the pulse volume for birds does not vary as the square of the range but increases to a maximum in a roughly linear manner and then falls to zero at the radio horizon.

Equipment sensitivity

The equipment parameters which govern the 'seeing power' of a radar were summarized in the Radar Equation. Although changes in transmitter output, receiver noise figure, or display perception factor can affect the performance of the radar, modern equipment should not suffer from these troubles, so complete have electronic monitoring systems now become. It is of interest to use the Radar Equation to calculate the limiting range of visibility at Bushy Hill for all birds having echoing areas greater than 2 cm², i.e. for birds larger in size than the chiff-chaff. The figure turns out to be 32 miles. This means that all birds or angels of greater echoing area than this and lying within a range of 32 miles would be seen by the radar. A blind range less than this of course exists for angles of elevation greater than 30° since no radiation at all passes into this 'cone of silence'.

The Bushy Hill vertical performance diagram for a target of echoing area 2 cm^2 is shown in Fig. 1.8.

Display limitations

Limitation of both range and azimuth resolutions can also occur due to the finite size of the echo paint upon the phosphor screen of the cathode ray tube. The spot is usually about $\frac{1}{4}$ mm in diameter, which means a range of 0·13 miles in the case of a tube having a face diameter of 30 cm and displaying a range of 80 miles. If the same tube has its time base switched to display 240 miles to the radius then the spot itself covers a linear range of 0·4 miles. In this case the diameter of the spot is approximately equal to the range resolution caused by the finite pulse length and no degradation of resolution results. But spot size can be a limitation in the case of a radar whose pulse length is only 1 μs and which possesses a range resolution of 0·1 miles. Normally such a short pulse radar is operated on a magnified display with a time base corresponding to a few miles only, such as the p.p.i. of a marine radar, and then the finite spot size presents no difficulty. Radar displays are measuring instruments, and so it is necessary always to study the limitation on accuracy which might be imposed by the characteristics of the particular form of display employed.

Target signal fluctuation: signature analysis

The illustration of a mixed target distribution discussed above possessed the great advantage that the individual scatterers of the various families were all spheres, and, as we have seen, a sphere presents a non-varying echoing area to the radio wave. In consequence, the signal from one sphere would be constant, and its amplitude would depend only upon the size and location of the sphere. If a small number of spheres were contained within the pulse volume, so that the resultant signal were the sum of contributions from the separate spheres, taking account of both the amplitudes and the phases of every contributory signal, then this resultant would be constant in time for a fixed configuration of the targets. A small change in this configuration, however, would greatly affect the amplitude of the resultant signal, due to the phase differences that would be introduced. For example, if only two identical spheres were involved, each producing a signal of amplitude a, then the amplitude of the combined signals would be $2a$ or zero, according as the waves scattered from the two spheres arrived at the radar aerial in phase or out of phase respectively.

For a radar wavelength of 23 cm this change to the out of phase condition from the state of reinforcement would be produced by moving one of the spheres radially through one quarter of a wavelength. In this way the 'go and return' path difference for the waves scattered from the displaced sphere would be half a wavelength, i.e. this wavetrain would be 180° out of phase with that scattered from the fixed sphere and so the two wavetrains would cancel completely. If a large number of spheres were contained within the pulse volume, as happens in the case of raindrops, the percentage change in resultant signal due to random

83

movements of the drops is practically zero. It was shown in Chapter Three that the resultant signal can then only be calculated from the sum of the powers contributed by the individual scatterers.

Changing spheres into birds means that a single target no longer presents a constant echoing area, but one which changes with the aspect of the bird. In addition, angels containing a few birds will give fluctuating signals, due to the wave-interference effect described above. Photographic recording of the amplitudes of successive pulses from an angel as displayed by an A-scope can give very valuable information on the change of echoing area of the target, which, in turn, permits multiple bird targets to be distinguished from single birds. This type of study is termed 'Signature Analysis'.

Signatures of targets on the L-band radar

Signatures of targets observed on the L-band tracker at Bushy Hill were recorded with the aid of an A-scope and a motor-driven 35-mm camera. By arranging for the travel of the film to be parallel to the trace of the A-scope a pulse-by-pulse recording of the signal from a selected target could conveniently be made. In this method it is necessary to arrange that the A-scope displays only a limited range interval, otherwise, superposition of the pulses from an assembly of targets hopelessly confuses the picture. With the radar first operating in the scanning mode a p.p.i. picture of the general aircraft or angel activity is built up. From this picture targets of interest can be selected for signature analysis and the aerial steered on to them for film records to be made.

Plate 8 (a) shows the signature of a strong, isolated permanent echo provided by the steel television tower at Mendlesham in Suffolk; this target is situated 42 miles to the north-east of Bushy Hill. Since the pulse repetition frequency of the L-band radar is 250 pulses per second, the time between successive pulses on this record is $1/250$ s. It will be seen that the pulse amplitude was remarkably constant, as would be expected of a permanent echo of calibration quality.

Plate 8 (b) is the signature of an aircraft receding from the station at a speed of 300 knots. This is a good example of a complex target, in that a number of active reflection points on the aircraft are involved which are separated from each other by a large number of wavelengths, but which are locked rigidly together – apart from the inevitable vibrations of the aircraft structure. It will be seen that the reflected pulse train pattern does not show any sign of rapid fluctuation or fading, nor was this apparent over film shots lasting many seconds.

Plate 8 (c) refers to a night-time angel observed over the sea at a distance of 42 miles. This signature is seen to exhibit rapid fluctuation and the time taken to pass from minimum to minimum on the portion of film shown is $1/17$ s.

Angel fading patterns

The angel signature patterns of Plate 8 are typical of the signal variations from a complex target made up of a number of independent scattering centres. Rayleigh was the first to study the distribution of the successive amplitudes assumed by a

(a)

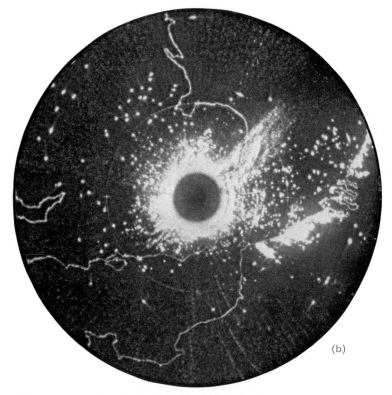

(b)

I (a). The radar aerials at Bushy Hill, Essex. On the left is steerable tracker of 30-ft diameter, and on the right a surveillance radar with 'electric fire' type of reflector, 75 ft × 25 ft

I (b). Long-range p.p.i. picture from Bushy Hill showing aircraft, angels, clouds, and video map; also ground echoes due to anomalous propagation
(Range = 160 miles, 25 June 1964, 14.45 h)

(a)

(b)

2 (*a*). Radar Operations Room at Bushy Hill showing p.p.i. consoles and photographic recording equipment

2 (*b*). A nodding-beam, radar height-finder operating on a wavelength of 10 cm (after Eastwood and Rider, *British Birds*, 1965)

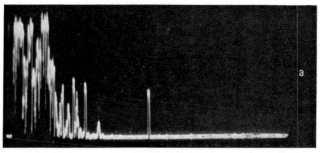

ground echoes   aircraft

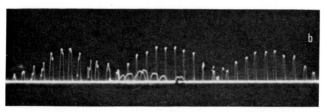

angel   aircraft   aircraft
            angel

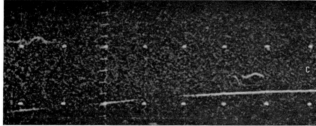

meteor   100 miles

rocket   50 miles

6-second markers

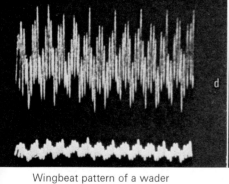
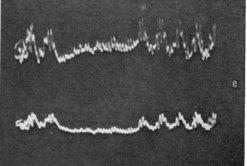

Wingbeat pattern of a wader   Wingbeats of a Redwing in
                                                'leaping' type flight

3 (a). Aircraft echo on an A-scope for the measurement of range
3 (b). Successive echo pulses from a group of aircraft and angels during passage of
the radar beam over them
3 (c). Z-scan traces of a rocket and meteors passing through a radar beam
3 (d) and (e). Signatures of single birds observed on an S-band target-tracking
radar (after Schaefer, 1966)

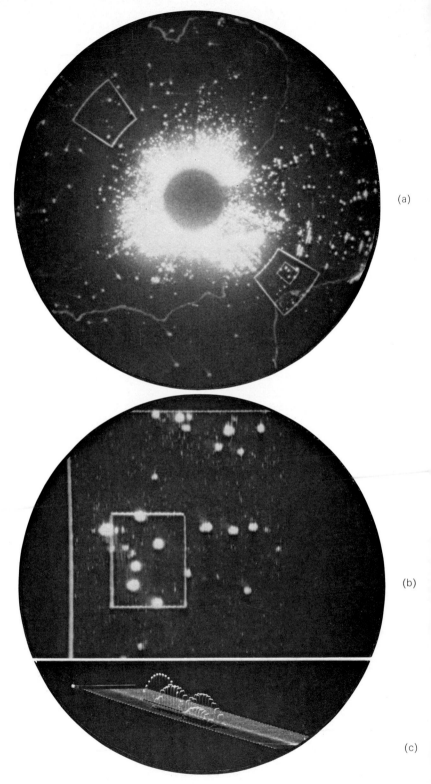

4 (a). P.p.i. with 'bucket' over the Straits of Dover
4 (b). Radar microscope (B-scope) picture of bird flocks contained in the bucket
4 (c). Magic Carpet display of the signal amplitude patterns given by a close group of angels shown on the B-scope

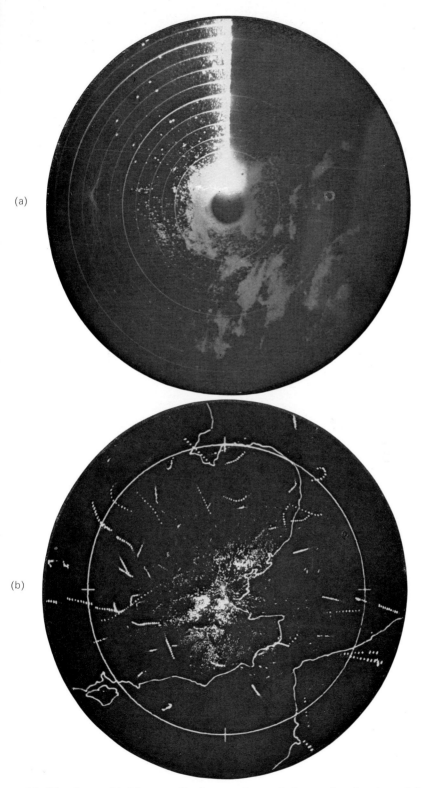

(a)

(b)

5 (*a*). The decay of brightness of paints on the p.p.i. due to the afterglow of the phosphor

5 (*b*). P.p.i. picture obtained by leaving the shutter of the camera open for ten successive revolutions of the aerial. The curved aircraft tracks will be noted

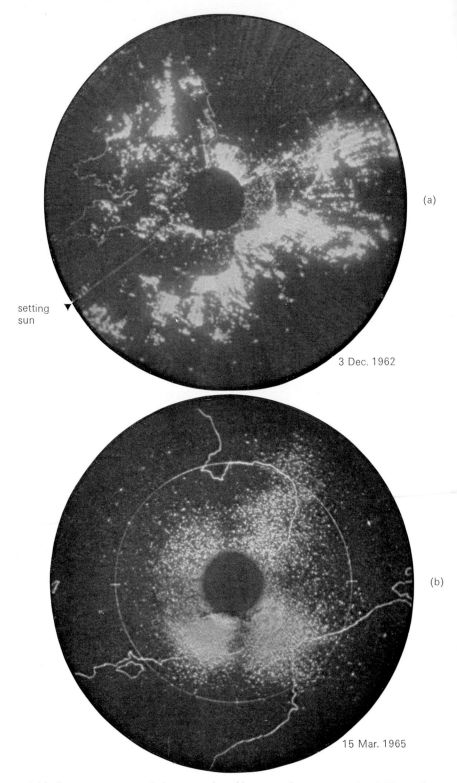

setting
sun

3 Dec. 1962

(a)

(b)

15 Mar. 1965

6 (a). Long-range ground clutter produced by anomalous propagation (3 December 1962, 15.35 h, Range = 240 miles)
6 (b). M.T.I. wedges recorded at Bushy Hill on spring migrants flying in an easterly direction; the wedges extend roughly north and south indicating slight track changes in the upper and lower parts of the region (10.00 h, 15 March 1965)

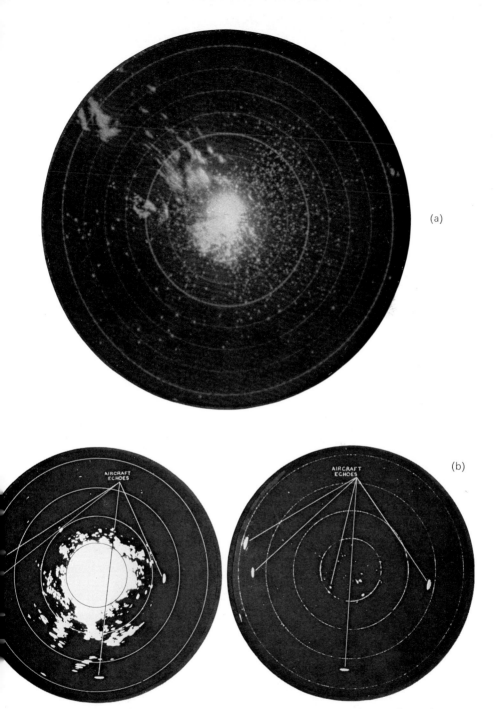

(a)

(b)

7 (*a*). The p.p.i. of an S-band surveillance radar showing aircraft, angels, and clouds

7 (*b*). The p.p.i. of a 50-cm radar showing suppression of permanent echoes by the use of a Moving Target Indicator unit

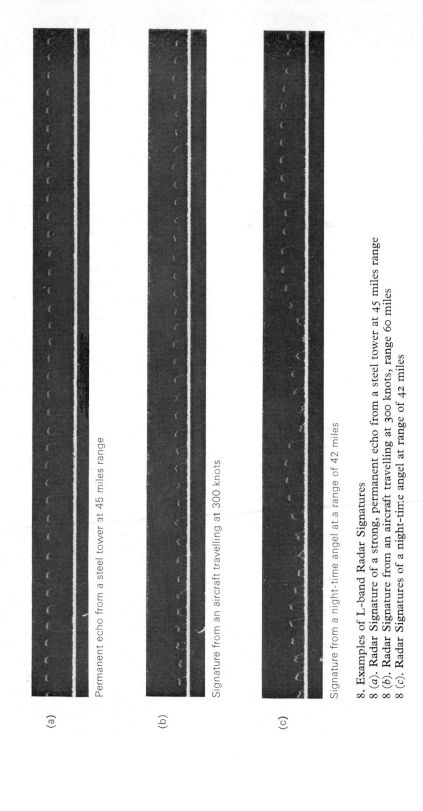

(a)

Permanent echo from a steel tower at 45 miles range

(b)

Signature from an aircraft travelling at 300 knots

(c)

Signature from a night-time angel at a range of 42 miles

8. Examples of L-band Radar Signatures

8 (a). Radar Signature of a strong, permanent echo from a steel tower at 45 miles range
8 (b). Radar Signature from an aircraft travelling at 300 knots, range 60 miles
8 (c). Radar Signatures of a night-time angel at range of 42 miles

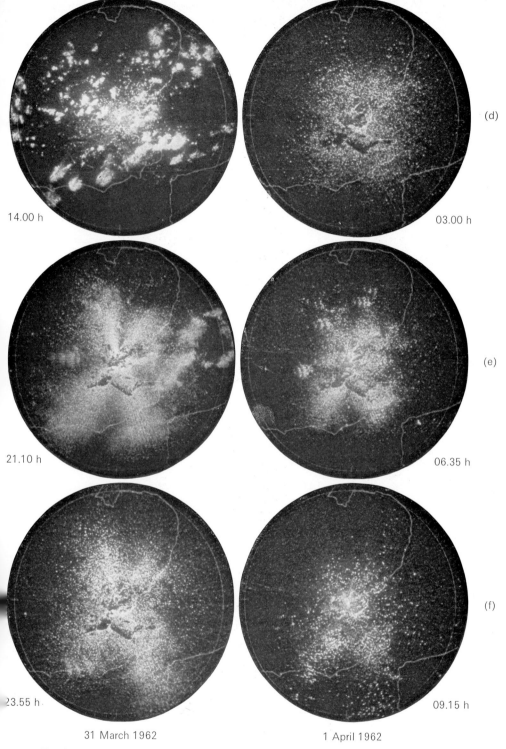

14.00 h

03.00 h   (d)

21.10 h

06.35 h   (e)

23.55 h

09.15 h   (f)

31 March 1962   1 April 1962

9. P.p.i. records of the angel state on 31 March–1 April 1962, as observed at Bushy Hill

(a) 14.00 h   (d) 03.00 h
(b) 21.10 h   (e) 06.35 h
(c) 23.55 h   (f) 09.15 h

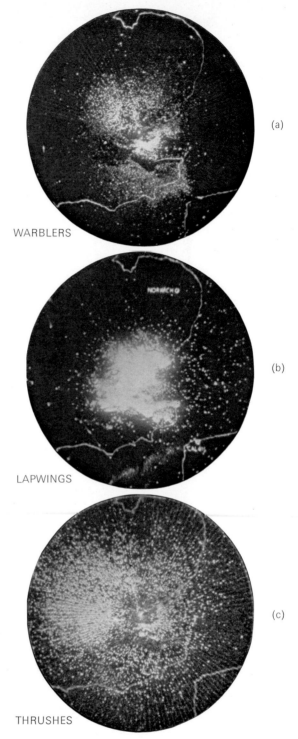

WARBLERS (a)

LAPWINGS (b)

THRUSHES (c)

10 (a). Nocturnal southward departure of summer residents in August – mainly warblers (24 August 1959, 21.00 h. See Fig. 8.2, after Lack and Eastwood, *British Birds*, 1962)

10 (b). Echoes from lapwings moving west (12.25 h, 23 December 1958. See Fig. 8.1)

10 (c). Easterly nocturnal movement of thrush-like echoes and southerly movement of smaller passerines (24 November 1959. See Fig. 8.3)

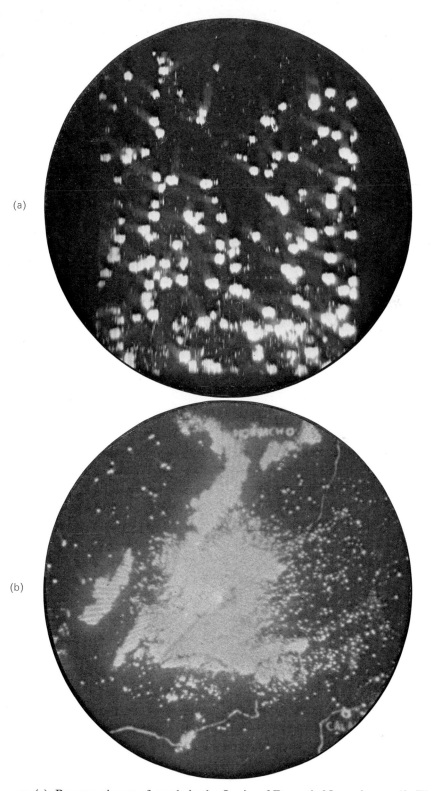

(a)

(b)

11 (*a*). B-scope picture of angels in the Straits of Dover (7 November 1958). The bright trails indicate direction of movement
11 (*b*). Migrating birds leaving the N. and S. Forelands on a March morning in the presence of a strong S.S.W. wind. (See Fig. 8.4)

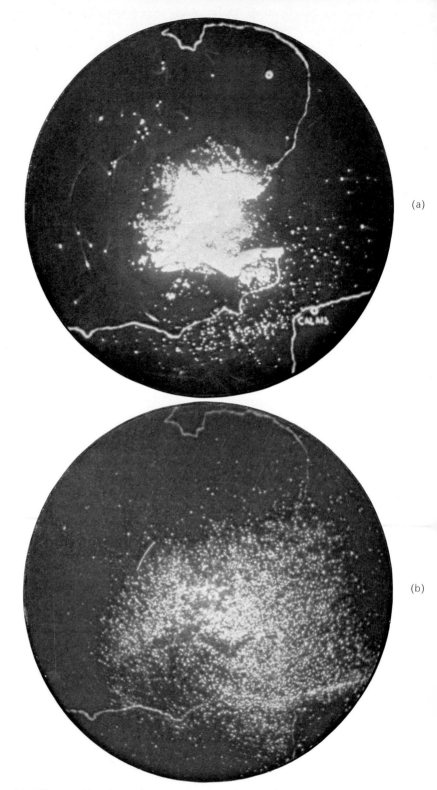

(a)

(b)

12 (*a*). Westward hard weather movement, especially from Cap Gris Nez, on the 3 February 1959. (See Fig. 8.7, after Lack and Eastwood, *British Birds*, 1962)
12 (*b*). Diurnal arrival of chaffinches on 6 October 1959, with coasting movement to Cap Gris Nez and on to Kent. (See Fig. 8.8. After Lack and Eastwood, *British Birds*, 1962)

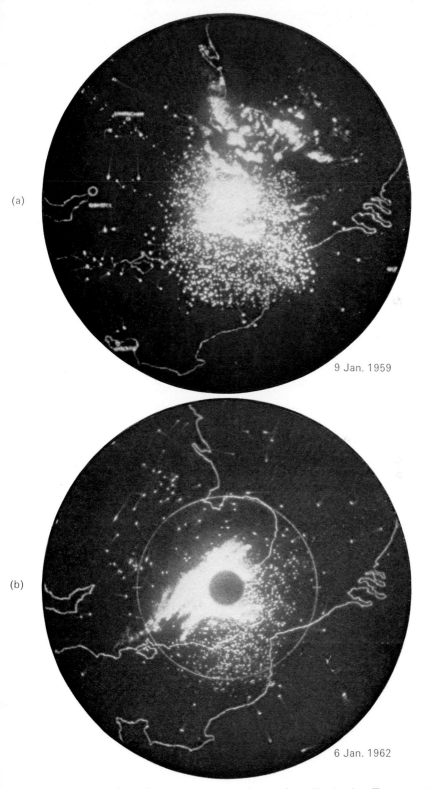

(a)

9 Jan. 1959

(b)

6 Jan. 1962

13 (a). Diurnal hard weather movement, southward from England to France, with snow clouds to the North. (9 January 1959. See Fig. 8.10, after Lack and Eastwood, *British Birds*, 1962)

13 (b). Completion of a hard weather movement; lapwings following a warm front and returning from France to England (6 January 1962. See Fig. 8.11, after Eastwood and Rider, *British Birds*, 1965)

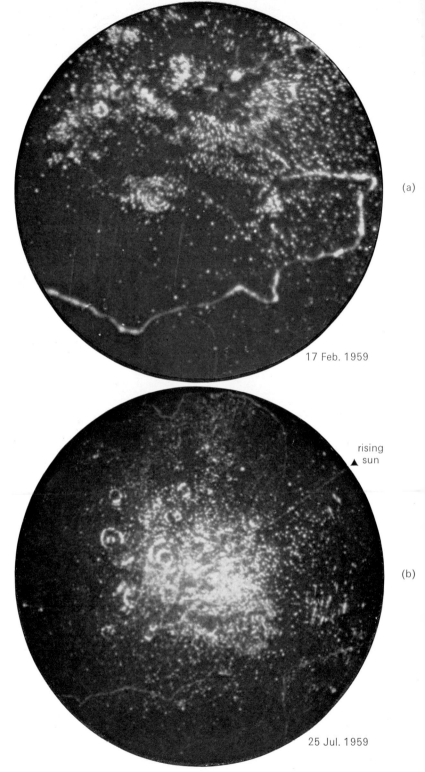

(a)

17 Feb. 1959

rising
▲ sun

(b)

25 Jul. 1959

14 (a). A ring angel at Mereworth (17 February 1959. After Eastwood, Bell, and Phelp, *Nature*, 1959)
14 (b). Ring angels on 25 July 1959, occurring simultaneously with the noise trace from the rising sun (after Eastwood, Isted, and Rider, *Proc. Roy. Soc.*, 1962)

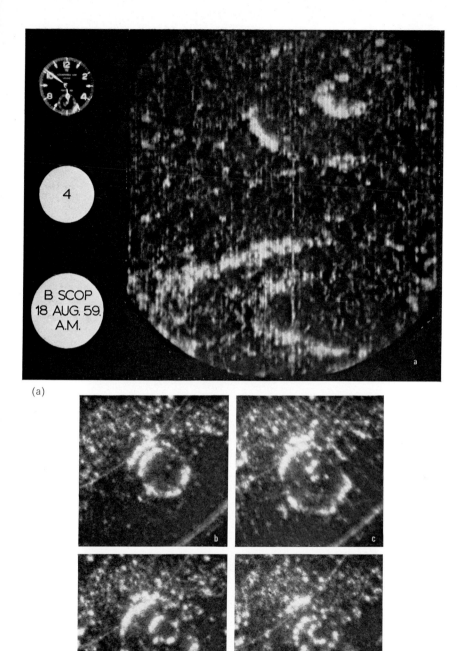

(a)

(b)

15 (*a*). B-scope display of rings from the Frating and Ipswich roosts (18 August 1959). The overlapping of rings from these adjacent roosts is shown, also the radio signal identifying the fourth wave of birds from Frating (after Eastwood, Isted, and Rider, *Proc. Roy. Soc.*, 1962)

15 (*b*). Portions of p.p.i. at one minute intervals showing displacement of rings downwind. (Canterbury roost – 1 September 1959. After Eastwood, Isted, and Rider, *Proc. Roy. Soc.*, 1962)

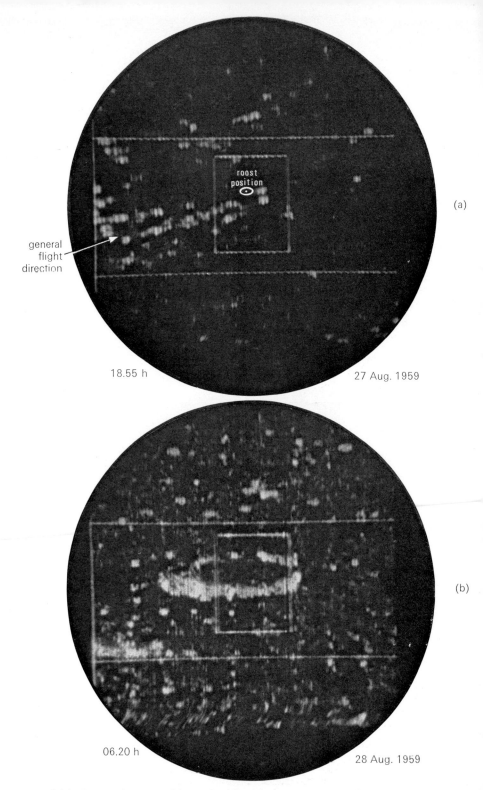

16 (*a*). An evening assembly at the Matching roost seen on the radar microscope (p.m. 27 August 1959)

16 (*b*). The dispersal on the following morning (a.m. 28 August 1959. After Eastwood, Isted, and Rider, *Proc. Roy. Soc.*, 1962)

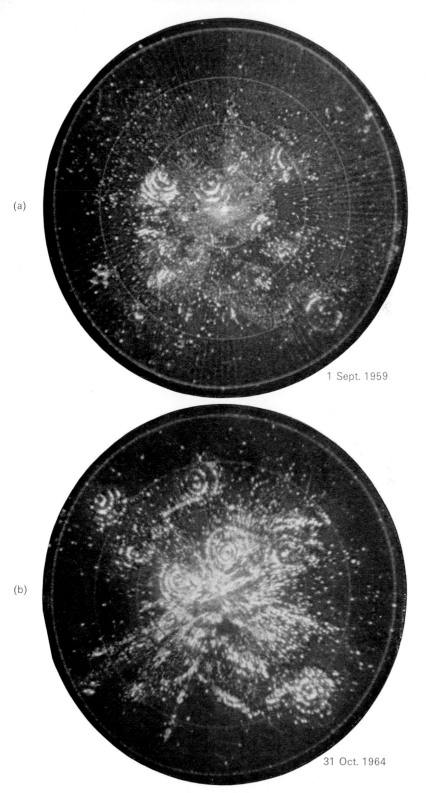

(a)

1 Sept. 1959

(b)

31 Oct. 1964

17 (a). The starling dispersals on the morning of 1 September 1959, showing some dispersals in sector form caused by the local wind (after Eastwood, Isted, and Rider, *Proc. Roy. Soc.*, 1962)
17 (b). The starling dispersals on the morning of 31 October 1964

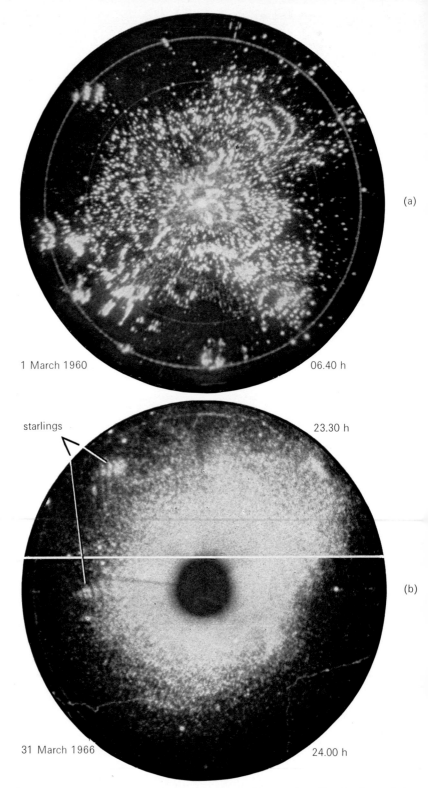

(a)

1 March 1960   06.40 h

starlings   23.30 h

(b)

31 March 1966   24.00 h

18 (a). Eastward migration of starlings in the early morning directly from their roosts (1 March 1960). Thick range ring 40 n.m. radius (after Eastwood, Isted, and Rider, *Proc. Roy. Soc.*, 1962)
18 (b). Sector dispersal and eastward migration of starlings at 23.30 and at *midnight* (31 March 1966)

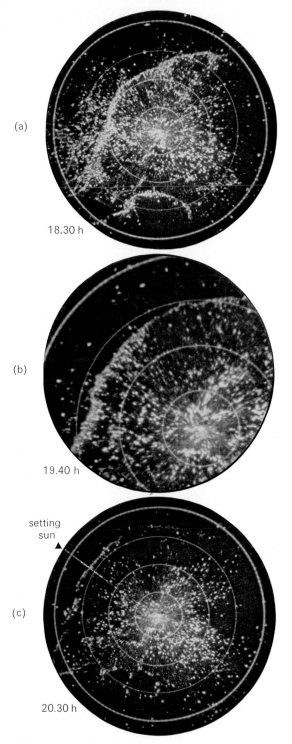

19. Progress of a sea-breeze front on 20 June 1960, as recorded by Bushy Hill radar:
(a). Situation at 18.30 h
(b). Section of the northern front at 19.40 h
(c). Appearance of the front just before sunset

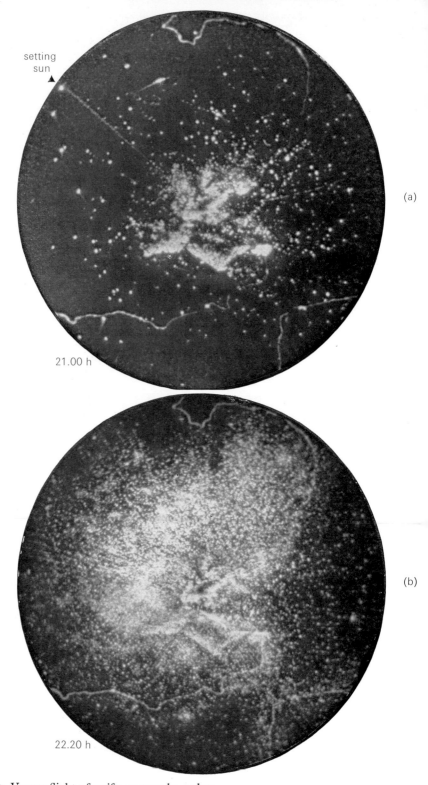

20. Vesper flight of swifts as seen by radar:
(*a*). Quiet tube at 21.00 h (22 June 1959)
(*b*). Echoes from night ascended swifts at 22.20 h (22 June 1959. After Eastwood,
Proc. XIIIth Int. Ornith. Congress, 1963)

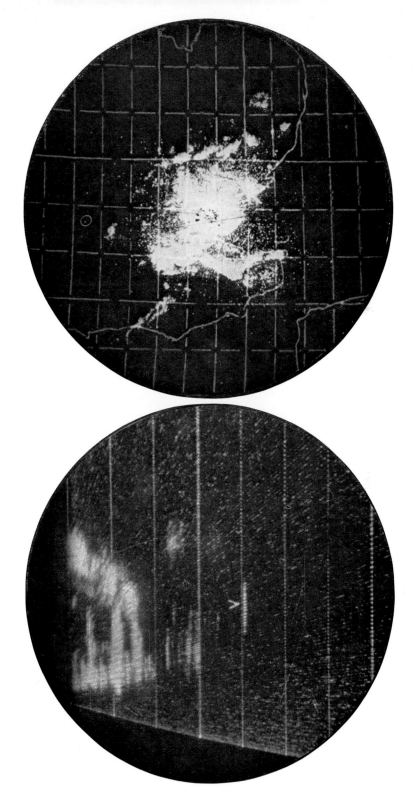

21. *Above*, plan position display and, *below*, associated range–height display for 02.00 h on 22 August 1958. The target, ringed above and arrowed below, is at a range of 51 miles and a height of 10,000 ft (after Eastwood and Rider, *British Birds*, 1965)

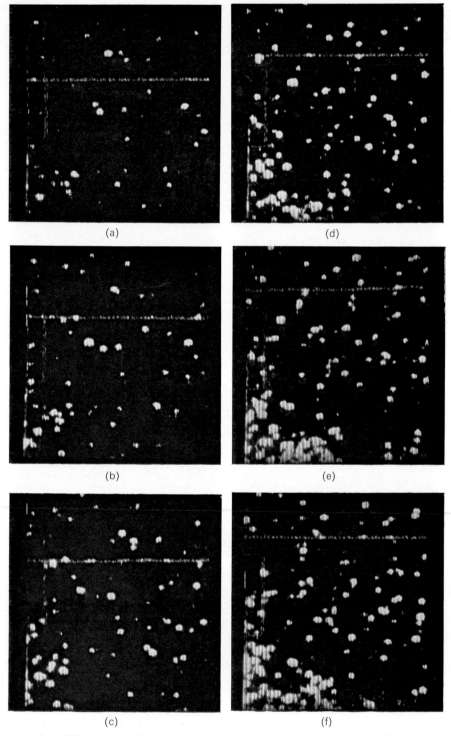

22. Angel Fluctuations. B-scope photographs for successive revolutions of the aerial at power levels of:

(a) $\frac{1}{4}$ MW
(b) $\frac{1}{2}$ MW
(c) 1 MW

(d) 2 MW
(e) 3 MW
(f) 4 MW

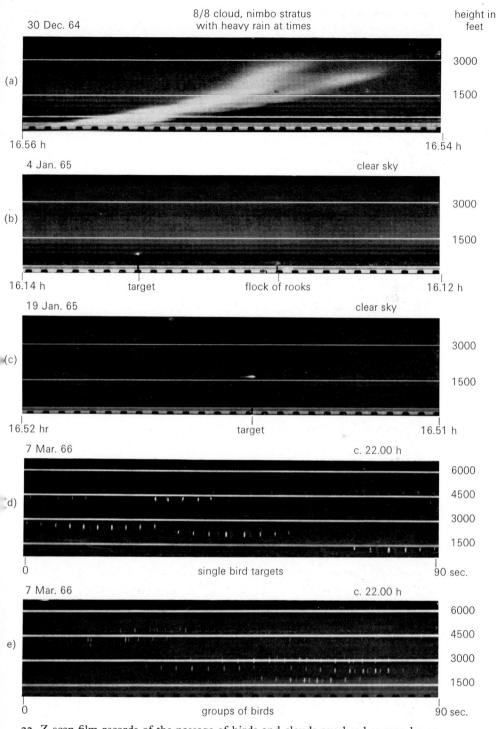

23. Z-scan film records of the passage of birds and clouds overhead as seen by an X-band radar

   (i) Fixed aerial, vertical beam   (*a*) showing clouds (16.54 h on 30 December 1964) (*b*) showing a flock of rooks (16.12 h on 4 January 1965) (*c*) showing a single bird (16.51 h on 19 January 1965)

  (ii) Scanning beam about the vertical   (*d*) separate bird targets showing change in range as the birds pass overhead (22.00 h on 7 March 1966) (*e*) group of birds (22.00 h on 7 March 1966)

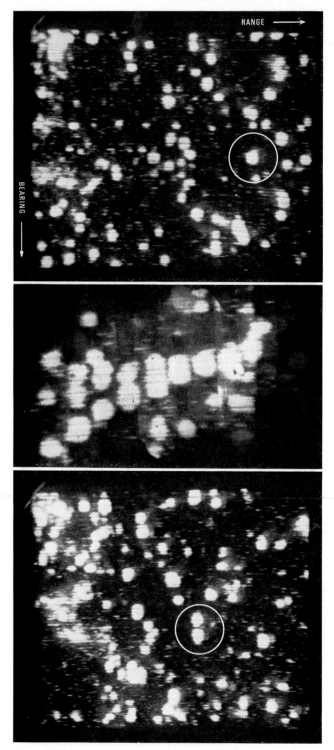

24. The fission of angels as seen on the radar microscope or B-scope. A region 20 miles by 20° on the p.p.i. is displayed with rectangular co-ordinates in the two outside photographs which are separated by nine minutes; the intervening positions of the ringed echo are extracted in the middle to show the splitting of the bird flock (after Eastwood and Rider, *British Birds*, 1964)

signal which is the resultant of a number of signals of varying amplitudes and phases. If the amplitudes and phases of the component signals vary randomly, then the solution to the phase-amplitude polygon is similar to the 'drunken-walk' problem and the amplitudes of the resultant signal follow a Rayleigh distribution. Departure from this distribution occurs in the case of a small number of component signals, and Norton *et al.* (1955) have shown how a rough estimate can be made of their number from the form of the distribution established experimentally.

Eastwood and Rider (1966) applied this method to the frequency distribution of echo signals from an angel and showed that a typical L-band angel signal was contributed by five or more identical scattering centres, moving independently with respect to each other. In other words, according to this method of analysis a typical L-band angel, observed at a range of $\sim$ 40 miles, is composed of about five or more birds.

Signatures of bird targets at X-band
For the purpose of securing the signatures of single bird targets passing over Bushy Hill, Eastwood and Rider (1966) employed an X-band radar whose beam was directed vertically upwards. A Height-Azimuth Indicator, as described in Chapter Eleven, displayed the signals and every bird which flew into the beam produced on the display a closed circle whose radius corresponded to the altitude. In this way, suitable signals could be selected for signature analysis using the A-scope and motorized camera technique described above. The pulse repetition frequency was 1250 and the signals were recorded during the few seconds required for the bird to fly through the beam.

It was found that the pulse amplitudes were approximately constant and showed none of the rapid irregular fluctuations of the L-band angel echoes. The conclusion drawn from this work was that the X-band radar was usually seeing single bird echoes as opposed to the multi-bird angels seen and recorded by the L-band equipments. Further evidence in support of this conclusion was provided by the fact that the X-band echoes showed none of the pulse stretching which was usually present on the L-band angel echoes. The result is of great importance for the altitude and bird counting studies described later. It was to be expected that the X-band radar would see only single birds by reason of the short pulse length, short range and consequent small pulse volume which were employed – but it was valuable to have direct confirmation of the fact by means of signature analysis.

Signatures of bird targets at S-band
The signatures of single birds in flight have also been studied by Schaefer (1966) using an S-band fire control equipment as described in Chapter Eleven. This radar could be operated in a scanning mode to allow targets of interest to be detected and acquired. Thereafter, the aerial could be locked on to a selected

G

target and the auto-follow device caused the aerial to track the target. The changes in the amplitudes of successive pulses could then be observed upon a cathode ray oscilloscope and recorded photographically. This equipment had a pulse length of half a microsecond and a working range from 3,000 ft, to a maximum of 7,500 ft for small birds, and 12,000 ft for a bird the size of a duck. In consequence, the pulse-volume was small and single birds were usually observed and subjected to signature analysis. A pulse repetition frequency of 1,500/s was employed which, in association with appropriate electrical filtering circuits, permitted rapid changes in the signal reflected from a bird to be detected and measured. Provision was also made for the output of the radar receiver to be monitored by headphones so that the change in signal amplitude could be detected aurally.

It was found by Schaefer that periodic changes in the reflected pulse amplitude did indeed occur. Plate 3 (d) shows the A-scope pictures of the pulse patterns which were obtained from a single bird target. The upper trace corresponds to the a.c. input to the oscilloscope while the lower trace corresponds to the d.c. input. This record clearly shows that the amplitudes of successive pulses from the bird were varying in a rhythmic fashion at the rate of about $13\frac{1}{2}$ c/s. The duration of the trace on this picture corresponds to one second only. The form of the time variation of the echo signal varied from target to target, and so the effect was not attributable to the nature of the electrical circuits employed, but was indicative rather of a cyclic variation in the echoing area of the bird due to its flight action.

When a bird is executing a level flight, its wingbeat pattern may be described by a number of parameters, such as the number of beats per second, or the relative duration of the beating phase of the flight as compared to that of the pause. This is illustrated in Plate 3 (e) which clearly shows the occurrence of a number of wing beats followed by a period of quiescence which is characteristic of the 'leaping' bird type of flight. There are also differences between the times taken for the downstroke of the wing as compared to the upstroke, a ratio which is different as between passerines and waders. Similarly, the duration of the gliding phase varies for different birds. It will be clear that if these typical flight patterns were known for various species of birds, then it would be possible to achieve unambiguous identification of birds seen on the radar from the wingbeat pattern observed on the A-scope.

Schaefer is seeking to compile a library of bird flight patterns by means of slow-motion telephotography, the birds being observed through the telescope attached to the radar, and the results obtained so far would suggest that the bird responsible for Plate 3 (e) was most probably a redwing, certainly a bird of the thrush type or smaller. It was also considered that Plate 3 (d) was probably produced by a small wader. Unfortunately, this method of identifying the species of bird responsible for a radar echo can only apply to a target observed at short range, since only one bird must be allowed to contribute to the pulse amplitude fluctuation. Nevertheless, this technique of identification may well assist in building up a better library of identifiable echo types for angels seen on a surveillance radar.

Signal measurements suggest that the change in amplitude of the echo signal due to the wingbeat effect may be as much as 25 per cent of the average value of the signal. It follows from the radar equation that the corresponding change in the echoing area of the bird could be as much as 50 per cent, which is surprisingly large.

In the case of Plate 3 (e) the fluctuation in echoing area of the bird took place at the rate of 11 c/s. Schaefer interpreted this variation in terms of the rhythmic expansion and contraction of the pectoral muscle consequent upon flapping of the wings. Work performed by Edwards and Houghton (1959) has shown that the outstretched wings of a bird in flight do not contribute significantly to the echoing area so that the change which Schaefer detected must have been attributable to a change in the size of the bird's body, in particular to an extension of the body dimension parallel to the electric field in the incident wave.

It will be noted that the wave forms of Plate 3 (d, e) show the presence of a high-frequency signal in addition to the periodic variation due to the wingbeat. This arises from the polarization effect associated with this type of radar equipment. The 'split' beam which is used for auto-following and for accurate measurement of angles, is achieved by spinning the dipole feeding the aerial at the rate of 33 c/s. In consequence, the polarization of the radio wave emitted from this aerial is changing from vertical to horizontal at the rate of 66 c/s. The instantaneous echo received from the bird measures, in effect, the extension of the body dimension parallel to the direction of the electric field in the incident wave, and so the fluctuation of the signal due to the polarization effect can be used to measure the changes in the shape of the bird during flight, also the change in aspect.

Signature analysis of radar echoes from birds is likely, in the future, to contribute significantly to the understanding of bird flight phenomena.

Bird interpretation of angel densities

The above discussion will have shown that when a radar is recording angel movements it is, in fact, viewing a complex distribution of birds, in which bird sizes, ranges, altitudes, aspects, and manner of association are all simultaneously changing. In consequence, the radar signals which these targets produce are far from constant, but are subject to rapid growth and fading. The combination of all these effects is to produce an angel pattern on the p.p.i. whose density falls off with range, and which also varies with time. When application of radar to the counting of migrant birds is considered in Chapter Twelve it will be necessary to try to quantify these various angel effects; for the moment we are concerned with the qualitative aspects of angel phenomena. In view of the number of variables involved it is hardly to be expected that the time variation of angel density will prove to be simple; the amazing fact is that it has proved to be meaningful in terms of bird behaviour.

Daily variation in angel activity over Zürich (Switzerland)

Sutter used the Zürich airport radar to investigate the change in flight frequency during the progress of an October night from 18.00 h to 06.00 h. With true scientific caution, and in spite of his daytime observations, Sutter insisted that his night-time results on flight activity should be taken as suggestive only, since 'the matter of whether the frequency diagrams deduced from the radar picture represent a true state of the behaviour cannot be considered as proved' (Sutter 1957a). Radar studies made by a number of observers both prior and subsequent to this work have left little room for doubt that birds and angels may be substantially equated even in quantitative studies.

Sutter employed a method of photographic recording of the p.p.i. which permitted him to extract bird track direction as well as frequency of flight; a

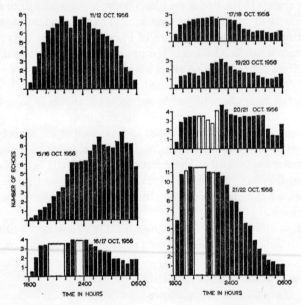

FIG. 5.2. The night-time variation of angel activity at Zürich, October, 1956
Ordinate – number of echoes in hundreds crossing a flight front of two nautical miles in each half hour
Abscissa – time in hours from 18.00 to 06.00
The white rectangles show estimated minimum values during the interval
(after Sutter, *Rev. Suisse de Zool.*, 1957a)

comparatively short range of 10 miles was employed. In order to measure the activity, use was made of the circumstance that the predominant track direction of these particular migrants was from north-east to south-west. The angel density was estimated by counts within two squares of 2 miles × 2 miles, located at ranges of 5 miles in the north-east and south-west sectors respectively, and the average taken. This operation was repeated on an average of four frames per

88

half hour. The calculation of the frequency of angel transit across a 2-mile front was finally made by taking these densities in association with an assumed average speed of the birds of 24 knots.

Clearly such a method of estimating flight activity can only be approximate, but it is sufficiently accurate to indicate the changes in activity which occurred during the hours of observation. Fig. 5.2 shows the frequency diagrams which were obtained from the night-time pictures; the marked variation which occurred from night to night will be noted. In spite of the absence of a constant pattern certain general similarities are present. Thus there is a rapid increase in activity during the first part of the night to a maximum, which was usually achieved slightly before midnight, followed by a pronounced fall-off in activity during the early hours of the morning. Sutter tended to regard the diagram for the night of 11/12 October as probably the standard pattern of variation of bird activity during the night, and suggested that deviations from it were probably the result of adverse meteorological conditions. In support of this interpretation he pointed out that his diagram for this night was similar to the bird activity curve obtained by Lowery with the moon-watching method (Lowery, 1951). It has to be remembered, however, that both Sutter and Lowery were observing the comparatively local variation in activity; knowledge of the activity over a large area can modify greatly the interpretation of changes taking place within a small region.

Fig. 5.3 is a representation of the time variation in angel activity which was measured by Sutter for 21 October 1956, during the daytime hours 06.00–18.00 h. The same method of echo counting was employed as described above, and the

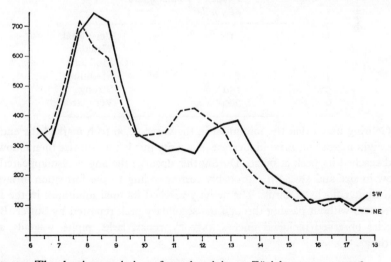

FIG. 5.3. The daytime variation of angel activity at Zürich, autumn, 1956
Ordinate – number of echoes
Abscissa – time in hours
(after Sutter, *Orn. Beob.*, 1957b)

two curves correspond to the activities derived from the counts in the north-west and south-east sectors respectively. The remarkable similarity between these two curves emphasizes the parallel flow lines which the migrating birds were pursuing, since the density counts 5 miles up-stream, i.e. to the north-east, agree closely with the count taken 5 miles to the south-west. Although Sutter found it convenient and significant to present his measured activities in terms of the number of birds crossing a 2-mile front, it should be noted that his basic method of activity estimation was simply to make echo counts within a 2-mile square. Number of echoes per 2 miles front per half hour means that for an assumed speed of 24 knots the ordinates on these curves correspond to the number of angels in an area of 24 sq miles, so that the activity was varying from 1 or 2 angels per sq mile to about 30 or 40 per sq mile; the counts being made at a range of 5 miles from the radar.

Fig. 5.3 suggests the presence of two peaks of activity, one in mid-morning at 09.00 h and a second one in the early afternoon. Again, this pattern was not repeated on all the observational days, but a pronounced minimum in the late afternoon about 16.00 h was present on all the curves.

Further studies of the diurnal angel activity in the vicinity of Zurich were made by Gehring (1963) who also employed the Kloten airport radar. The daily activity curve which he considered to be typical for the autumn flow of migrants is shown in Fig. 5.4. Angel densities are plotted as ordinates on this diagram according to the scale:

Density scale	Number of angels in a 2 mile × 2 mile square at 5 miles	Designation
1	10	Very weak
2	20	Weak
3	50	Moderate
4	100	Medium
5	150	Strong
6	200+	Very strong

Gehring noted that the minimum in the curve at 06.10 h marked the end of the night migration. A rapid increase in activity just before sunrise then followed and reached its peak at 06.20. During this upsurge the angels also appeared to grow in size and strength – probably corresponding to the formation of larger and tighter flocks of birds. The activity reached its final minimum in the late afternoon without passing through the secondary peak reported by Sutter. Bird species observed included finches, pigeons, rooks, larks, pipits, wagtails, and starlings.

Daily variation in angel activity over Hertfordshire (England)
The time variation of angel activity was also studied by Harper (1958), who classified the densities of his angel displays on the basis of the maximum number

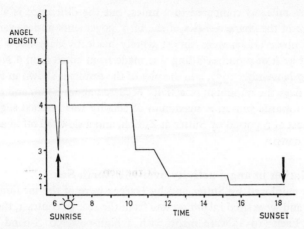

FIG. 5.4. The daily activity of autumnal migration at Zürich, autumn, 1957 (after Gehring, *Orn. Beob.*, 1963)

of well-defined angels contained within the 10 and 15-mile range rings in any 20° azimuth sector of the display. 'Light activity' corresponded to an angel content of up to 5 in the sample area of 25 sq miles; 'heavy activity' on the other hand, was the designation applied to a density of about 40 angels in this same area. It will be seen that these figures correspond to absolute densities of 1/5 angel per sq mile and 8/5 angels per sq mile, the sample area being located at a distance of 12½ miles from the radar station. These density figures are much smaller than Sutter's values quoted above, which is in part attributable to the

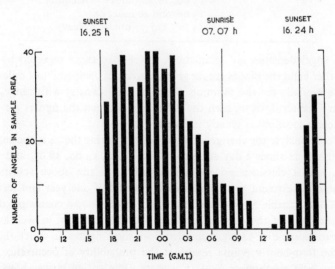

FIG. 5.5. Hourly variation of angel activity over Hertfordshire, autumn, 1957 (after Harper, *Proc. Roy. Soc.*, 1958)

range of 12½ miles as compared to 5 miles, but the difference is also partly a consequence of the characteristics of the bird movements under examination.

Harper's observations were almost wholly made by day, but a continuous sequence of 33 h of p.p.i. recording was made from 09.00 h on 6 November to 18.00 h on 7 November 1957, and the plot of the results is shown in Fig. 5.5. On both these days the minimum of activity occurred about noon, and commenced to increase towards sunset. A maximum of activity was reached slightly before midnight, just as reported by Sutter at Zürich, and a slow fall off in activity took place until dawn.

Daily variation in angel activity over the North Sea
The radars employed by Sutter and by Harper were of the medium power S-band type, and were sited inland remote from the sea. In contrast, the studies of Tedd and Lack (1958) were made with a high-powered S-band equipment located near the sea. In this work, angel activity was assessed in terms of the spatial extension of the angel echoes. Four levels of activity were employed which were roughly defined by their echo densities at certain ranges. Echo densities were measured by counts of echoes contained in an area of 1 cm^2 of the p.p.i. tube face. On the range scales employed, this area of tube corresponded to a geographical region of about 40 sq miles.

Density scale	Angels/40 sq miles	Designation
0	—	None
1	>5	Light
	15 at 40 miles or	
2	5–15 out to 50 miles	Medium
	>15 beyond 40 miles or	
3	5–15 beyond 50 miles	Heavy

These angel densities are again much lower than those reported by Sutter. On the other hand the ranges are far greater, 40 miles compared to 5 miles. When allowance is made for the thinning effect of angel density with range, as discussed in Chapter Twelve, then the difference between the figures for the two very different locations is greatly reduced.

In order to analyse the changes of angel activity during the 24 h, the angel state was observed six times a day at 02.00, 06.00, 10.00, 14.00, 18.00, and 22.00 h G.M.T., and a classification applied according to the above scheme. This technique of assessment was applied over a period of one year and resulted in 1,362 out of a possible 2,190 observations, i.e. 365 days × 6 counts per day, and formed the basis of the seasonal analysis considered below, as well as of the diurnal variations. Fig. 5.6 was compiled from these figures, in which the ordinates at the four-hourly points represent the probability of occurrence at that hour of at least medium or Scale 2 activity. The spring curve shows a pronounced afternoon minimum, followed by a growth in activity culminating in a maximum at 22.00 h with a long period of falling activity thereafter until the afternoon minimum is once more reached. In later studies, this spring curve was found to possess a subsidiary peak at 06.00 h, although frequently masked by the heavy night migrant activity. Analysis of the autumn results again showed the presence of an afternoon minimum in the curve of activity, and a maximum at 22.00 h, but in contrast to the spring curve the secondary maximum occurred later in the mid-morning at about 09.00–10.00 h.

Meteorological conditions were carefully recorded during the progress of this work, and so it was possible for Tedd and Lack to conclude that there was a close correlation between the occurrence of medium and dense angel displays and the general weather situation. It was noted that the heaviest displays took place in the presence of light winds accompanying anticyclonic weather. Angel displays in the 'medium' or 'light' categories seemed to be less exacting in their weather requirements which, in fact, were very varied, but the significant observation was made that rain, bad visibility or strong winds all seemed to be prejudicial to the presence of angels. All these facts were in accordance with the bird interpretation

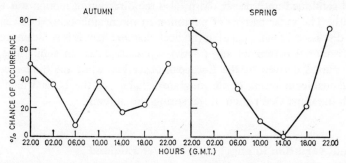

FIG. 5.6. Hourly variation of angel activity over the North Sea (after Tedd and Lack, *Proc. Roy. Soc.*, 1958)

of radar angels, and also threw light upon certain differences between the spring and autumn daily activity curves of Fig. 5.6. Thus the spring curve relates in the main to the mass departures of the winter visitors from East Anglia towards Denmark, Holland, and Belgium, and the radar was observing these departures at their point of commencement. In the autumn, on the other hand, the radar was recording the arrivals of the immigrant wintering birds after making a sea crossing of 100 to 500 miles depending upon the point of the continental coast line from which the birds had made their departure. The occurrence of the morning maximum in the autumn is probably explicable in terms of the ocean crossing time of 2–10 h, depending upon the path followed by the birds, and the wind state. Since the departure time from the continental coast will probably be in accordance with the various activity curves reproduced in this chapter, it will take place at some time on the rising part of the curve between late afternoon and the maximum just before midnight, and so a morning arrival off the coast of Britain seemed reasonable.

Daily variation in angel activity over New England (U.S.A.)

Studies of the time variation of angel activity off Cape Cod, Massachusetts, were made by Richardson and his collaborators in 1956 (Richardson *et al.*, 1958), but no systematic counting of angel densities was undertaken. It was noted that there were usually more targets during daylight hours than during the night, and the phenomenon which received closest scrutiny was the outward rush of angels from the Cape just about sunrise during the spring; this was interpreted as the movement of gulls out to sea to their feeding grounds. A more leisurely return to the Cape in the evening was also noted, and corresponded to the known return of the gulls to the shore, particularly of the breeding birds. After the cessation of the local bird activity in the evening, the p.p.i. became overspread with true migratory activity, the angels approaching from the south in the spring and heading to the north-east. This type of angel activity reached a peak just before midnight, and then proceeded to fall off in the early morning. In the autumn, the pattern was somewhat different, since the activity commenced later in the evening and continued until nearly dawn; also the direction of motion was towards the south. The radar pattern of migration in the neighbourhood of Cape Cod will be discussed in more detail in the next chapter; here it is sufficient to notice that the diurnal pattern of angel activity possessed certain similarities to the activity curves derived by the European observers, while the differences were understandable in terms of the migratory habits of the birds which passed through the Cape Cod region in the spring and autumn.

Seasonal variation in angel activity over England

Using the numbers of angels in his sample areas situated between 10 and 15 miles range, Harper defined a set of five activity states which he used to analyse the angel activity observed on 188 days during the period 1952–7. These observations have been grouped by half months in Fig. 5.7 which gives the number of days on which 'very light', 'light', 'moderate', 'heavy', or 'very heavy' activity was observed.

Fig. 5.7 shows clearly the presence of peaks of activity during the spring and the autumn, and the complete absence of assessable activity during the months of June and July. This radar record applied only to the daytime activity during the hours 09.00–17.30 h. It was not possible, in general, to operate the equipment at night, and it was for this reason that the heavy night time activity which was known to be present from the one set of night activity figures discussed above was unable to influence the general analysis. Nevertheless, the main features of the seasonal activity in this region of England were clear enough from this diagram, and could readily be related to the known pattern of bird migration, i.e. the movements of birds which breed in Britain into the country in spring and out in the autumn, the arrivals and departures of birds from north-central Europe which winter in England and in Ireland and return to their continental

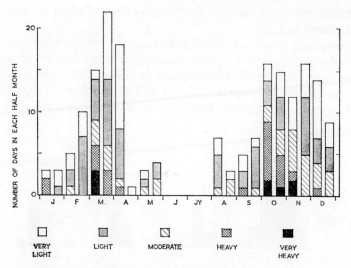

FIG. 5.7. Seasonal variation in angel activity over Hertfordshire, 1952–7 (after Harper, *Proc. Roy. Soc.*, 1958)

breeding grounds in spring, and finally, the movements of passage migrants through the British Isles during the spring and autumn.

The Norfolk observations of Tedd and Lack (1958), permitted an analysis to be made of seasonal variation in angel activity over the southern North Sea and off the Norfolk coast. In Fig. 5.8 the probability of occurrence of heavy angel displays is plotted against the month of the year, and separate curves are shown for the daytime and night-time observations. Heavy angel displays by day are seen to be most likely in March, October, and November, and this result is in substantial agreement with the conclusions to be drawn from Harper's curves of Fig. 5.7. Night-time occurrence of heavy angel activity is seen to be most probable in the months of March, April, and November.

Monthly variations in activity were also analysed by Lack (1959), from observations taken over 1956–8 at the Norfolk station. Activity was assessed according to the scale already quoted, and the activity index for the month was derived by taking the percentage of days in each month on which migration occurred. These figures have been plotted in Fig. 5.9 as the ordinates against the corresponding month as abscissae; night and day patterns are shown separately,

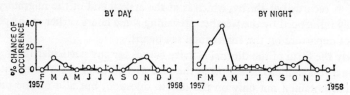

FIG. 5.8. Monthly variation in angel activity over the North Sea, 1957–8 (after Tedd and Lack, *Proc. Roy. Soc.*, 1958)

95

and the black rectangles show the percentage of days on which the activity was heavy, i.e. scale 2 or 3.

Tedd and Lack concluded that all the dense and most of the medium angel displays observed on their equipment could be explained in terms of migrating passerine birds 'since no other British birds (including shorebirds) are common enough, and passerine species are common only on migration' (Tedd and Lack, 1958). In a later series of papers which are considered in the next chapter, Lack

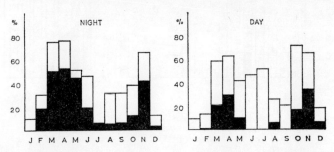

FIG. 5.9. Seasonal variation in angel activity over the North Sea, 1956–8 (after Lack, *Ibis*, 1959a)

(1958 *et seq.*), proceeded to apply the Norfolk radar to a detailed analysis of the migratory movements across the southern North Sea. He has succeeded in throwing much light on what might be termed the fine structure of the time variation in angel activity which it has been the purpose of the present chapter to present in broad outline only.

The diurnal cycle as observed at Bushy Hill and its fluctuation during the year

The changing pattern of angel activity during the twenty-four hours is well illustrated by Plate 9 which presents the angel state at four-hourly intervals as observed on the 31 March–1 April 1962, at Bushy Hill. This particular spring day was well suited to the west–east movement of the birds, in that the wind was light and westerly, and the weather was fine and clear, i.e. visibility was good and there was a total absence of rain. With a different selection of the prevailing weather factors the pictures of the activity could have been wholly different. The activity pattern for an autumn day would also differ from the spring picture of Plate 9 since, in the case of the main east–west movement of the autumn, the activity as recorded at Bushy, which is at the arrival end of the migratory flow, is heavily influenced by the weather prevailing some hours earlier at the possible points of departure on the continental sea board.

Clearly the form of the diurnal activity curves for any particular radar station must be a function of the season of the year as well as of the weather situation which has obtained not only on the day in question, but also on the previous group of days. In this connexion it is interesting to note the point made by Drury and Keith (1962), that the migration of songbirds down the New England coast

is accomplished in a few days only, the birds having waited until favourable
weather conditions were offered to them; in view of this fact it would be futile to
expect a constant daily pattern of angel activity in this or any other region.

In order to emphasize that a single curve of angel activity cannot be used to
describe the daily variation at Bushy Hill throughout the year, Fig. 5.10 compares

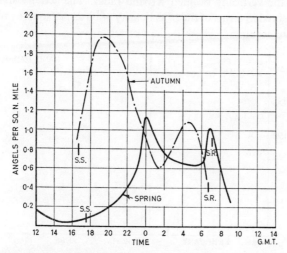

FIG. 5.10. Comparison of daily activity curves for the spring (1960) and autumn
(1964) as measured at Bushy Hill

the daily variation observed on a favourable spring day with an equally favourable day selected from the autumn migration period. These curves show the
density of angels per square nautical mile, measured at a point 20 miles north-east
of Bushy Hill and its variation during the twenty-four hours. Sunset and sunrise
times are indicated on the diagram. The differences between the two curves are
apparent, and show that a daily activity curve must be related to the season of the
year, the direction of bird flow and the interaction between this flow and the
geography of the region. Certain common features are also traceable between
these curves and the curves of other workers discussed above, and presumably
arise from similar bird reactions to a common stimulus, for example, the growth
in activity after sunset would appear to be related to the stimulus provided by
the absence of light.

During his interesting study of trans-Mediterranean migration, Casement
(1966) noticed that when his ship-borne radar was within range of the land the
main movement of passerines from the coast could be observed to commence
about three-quarters of an hour after sunset. This increase in activity was quite
rapid and unmistakable. When the ship was in the path of the migrant stream,
but standing well out to sea, the growth in angel activity was less rapid, also
the peak was of lower intensity and occurred later. Casement considered that this
change in form of the activity curve was caused by the different speeds of the

various species involved in the movement. He suggested that the time of the peak in the curve could be used to measure the distance travelled by the migrants and so suggest the probable position of their point of departure.

That marked variations in the nocturnal flight activity of migrant birds may occur from night to night, was observed during the spring of 1966 at Bushy Hill by means of the vertically beamed X-band radar. The activity shown on Fig. 5.11 was measured in terms of the peak density of birds per square mile, observed during the late evening.

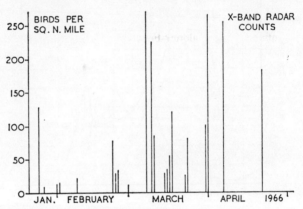

FIG. 5.11. Changes in density of migrant birds over Bushy Hill as observed by night on a vertically beamed X-Band radar (spring, 1966)

The rapidity of the change in bird flight activity which took place during the course of one evening, is well illustrated by the figures for 24 February 1966; the densities estimated from bird transits during consecutive quarter-hour intervals were as follows:

Nocturnal activity of birds, 24 February 1966

Time	18.00	18.15	18.30	18.45	19.00	19.15	19.30	19.45	20.00	20.15	20.30
Birds per sq. mile	3	5	18	5	32	9	15	12	20	4	16

Nocturnal flight activity is very variable and is closely linked with local weather conditions. The heaviest activity at the Essex coast has been observed on warm, spring nights with a light westerly wind, not exceeding 5 knots, combined with clear skies and the moon near full. Birds, like man, choose their weather with care for their survival depends upon it.

CHAPTER SIX

Radar patterns of bird migration in Europe

Why do birds migrate, and how is such an involved control operation learnt and executed? For that matter, why do many creatures migrate, for migration is by no means confined to birds alone? Feeding and breeding would appear to be the obvious reply to these questions rather than a complete answer. Mobility is, perhaps, that characteristic of living creatures which most sharply distinguishes them from the plants, and which permits them to forage for food over a much greater area than is available even to the most extended root system of a sedentary plant. But it is the purposeful journeyings of certain creatures over vast distances, in order to arrive at regions of the earth peculiarly suited to their breeding requirements, which is the essential and distinguishing feature of migration. Mobility for feeding, or to avoid the extremes of hot and cold, is understandable, but the journeyings of salmon, whales, eels, and especially birds for the purpose of reproduction are not so readily comprehensible. It is for this reason that the study of bird migration is interesting and exciting, and why the advent of radar is so timely, for it can supply information on the migratory flights of birds that is not obtainable in any other way.

Why use radar?

Before radar became available as a bird-watching instrument, the only method for tracing the migrations of birds was by visual observations in the daytime, some precision to the movements being given by bird ringing exercises. Such observations are as necessary as ever, but we now know that the progress of even a daytime movement can be misinterpreted by ground level observations only, since many day migrations are by no means confined to the first 1,000 ft of altitude accessible to binocular-assisted vision. At night-time the information on bird flight was practically non-existent until the moon-watching experiments of Lowery (1951) or by use of the acoustic method of logging the night calls of birds passing overhead; clearly, only low-altitude flights could be detected by these means. It was usually necessary to infer the nature and density of the night activity by seeing on the ground the following morning migrants that had not been present on the previous day. Such an examination can only be local, and depends moreover upon the assumption that the new arrivals represent a fair sample of the species participating in the nocturnal migration; also it is presumed that the number of falls is roughly indicative of the density of the previous night's movement.

These assumptions can be far removed from the facts. Plate 21 illustrates the

99

FIG. 6.1. Bird movements over eastern England near midnight on 21 August 1958. Somewhat disturbed weather with light S.E. wind in southern North Sea. Three small movements of waders and/or gulls. One S.S.W. from Wash had almost ceased by 23.00, another S.W. over straits of Dover and Pas de Calais still continued, the third came in west over Norfolk and gradually changed direction from W. to S.W. and eventually S. The frontal cloud *A.B.* moved slowly N.W. during the night

position as 'seen' from Bushy Hill on 22 August 1958, and a diagrammatic key of the events in progress is given in Fig. 6.1, as derived from time compression films. It was a fine summer's evening with a light southerly wind which was advancing the frontal cloud formation *AB* northwards. A number of dispersed wader-like echoes were moving southwards from the Wash; at the same time a steady stream of similar echoes was crossing the coast of East Anglia and was sweeping west and south-west in a deep penetration of the country without alighting at the coast. Visual observation or searching for falls of night migrants would both have been unavailing, and without radar such a movement would inevitably have gone undetected and unrecorded.

No claim is made here that radar is infallible and detects all bird movements; this is not so, and Chapter Three has shown how information can be lost due to obscuration by rain and cloud. Similarly, the discussion of the radiation pattern explained how very low-flying birds may sometimes be missed because they are below the radar beam. Close study of the bird migration patterns detected by modern surveillance radars has been possible only at those locations where such equipments have been made available for ornithological research as a part-time activity, since the radars were primarily sited for the prosecution of radar research or to meet the air cover needs of defence or Civil Air Traffic Control. Nevertheless, the availability of such radars to ornithological workers is likely to increase in the future, and so it will be useful to have available the radar picture of migration as far as it has been drawn to date. We shall find that radar provides a comprehensive picture of broad-front migration; it also supplies detailed information on the influence of such factors as wind state, temperature, cloud cover, or rain, and so makes a contribution to the study of the navigation problem. These special aspects are treated in a later chapter. Although radar has not, and probably cannot, provide a solution to the question of 'how do birds navigate', it is providing some fairly precise boundary conditions that an acceptable theory must satisfy.

Collecting radar information on North Sea migrations

Probably the region where bird movements have been more intensively investigated by radar than anywhere else in the world is that of the southern North Sea. The S-band station at Bard Hill in Norfolk used by Lack and his collaborators, together with the Marconi Station at Bushy Hill in Essex, have provided comprehensive radar cover over this region for a number of years. A mass of data has been accumulated for this region, whose analysis has led to a remarkably detailed picture of the migratory movements both by day and by night. Of importance also is the fact that the south-eastern corner of England and the seas adjoining form a very busy international cross-roads from the bird-migration point of view. A further reason why special interest attached to bird movements in this region is the location of England on the edge of the continental land mass, at the meeting point of the eastward-streaming Atlantic air with air over the Continent. The vagaries of England's weather stem from this 'confrontation of airs'; we shall find that radar reveals that birds, too, are sensitive to the meteorological instability inherent in this situation.

Lack's comprehensive study of trans-North Sea migration occupied a period of five years 1958–63 (Lack, 1959–63). In this investigation use was also made of radar data for 1955–8 recorded by Royal Air Force operators (Tedd and Lack 1958) at the same Norfolk Radar station. The migration picture compiled from the records of Bard Hill has been complemented by studies based on the Bushy Hill records 1958–62, whose radar cover is south of that provided by Bard Hill, the degree of overlap being sufficient to provide continuity over the whole southern part of the North Sea, through the Straits of Dover and into the English Channel.

The important radar facts to be extracted from the p.p.i. films are:

Time (season, month, day, hour).
Density of the angels and their distribution.
Type of angel.
Direction and speed of the angels.
Altitudes (not always available).
Presence of cloud or rain formations, location and movement.

H

General information on the weather situation and, in particular, figures on temperature, wind speed and direction, also base and ceiling heights of clouds, are necessary for the understanding of the radar results, and can be conveniently obtained from the Meteorological Office Records. It is true that instrument readings usually refer to specific locations which may not coincide with the region of interest on a particular radar film. Obviously, this is the case when movements take place over the sea, but the synoptic charts prepared by the Meteorological Office usually give the necessary information.

Attention has already been drawn to the fact that the major shortcoming of radar is the lack of positive identification of the species of bird which may be under observation. Assistance to identification may be drawn from the appearance of the radar echo, also from the altitude and speed of motion, but the interpretation of the radar picture of bird movements rests upon a judicious association of the radar results with the known behaviour pattern of the various species of birds which frequent or visit this North European region. In spite of the precision of the radar observations, their interpretation in terms of birds is inferential, nevertheless, the sum total of the facts which contribute to the migration pattern detailed below invests the result with a probability which borders on certainty.

The seasonal pattern of North Sea bird movements

Lack (1963b) summarized the monthly state of bird movements across the southern North Sea as in Table 6.1 which sets forth the percentage of the movements observed in each month, that exceed Scale 1 in activity; bearings are indicated at the heads of the columns.

In this table the activity figures for the successive months under the bearing of the movement in question are comparable with each other, but the percentages for the different bearings in the same month are not comparable. This is because some movements can be assessed more easily than others, in particular, departures tended to be recorded as of higher density than arrivals according to the Tedd–Lack system of assessing, since the density is measured as the maximum area covered by the movement. Birds at departure tend to leave within a much shorter period of time than that observed for the arrivals, and so an arrival movement is less concentrated. Sometimes two or more movements overlap with each other; this also makes assessment difficult, and this is why the south-south-west activity figure for September is omitted, since it was difficult to estimate in the presence of the much heavier movement to the south-south-east.

An alternative mode of presenting the monthly activity figures of Table 6.1 would have been to show the average density of each movement in each month, but the form of the seasonal variation would have been effectively the same. In fact, this method of presentation is used in Table 6.2, taken from Lack and Eastwood (1962), which gives the combined night and day activities as observed at Bushy Hill, roughly 80 miles to the south of Bard Hill.

TABLE 6.1 *Frequency of migratory movements throughout the year as recorded at Bard Hill, Norfolk*

	E.	W.	N.N.E.	S.S.W.	N.N.W.	S.S.E.
At night						
January	31	8	2	16	0	7
February	56	2	12	0	10	5
March	70	10	4	2	2	4
April	76	3	26	2	18	3
May	12	16	35	0	26	2
June	17	33	5	2	0	0
July	7	21	0	8	5	10
August	(51)	20	2	4	0	(86)
September	36	32	0	(?)	1	66
October	20	38	1	39	3	35
November	9	52	2	21	4	16
December	16	23	3	6	0	10
By day						
January	11	9	4	18	2	5
February	33	5	13	0	7	0
March	56	9	4	3	3	7
April	55	3	16	6	24	12
May	10	2	34	2	17	3
June	19	28	2	2	5	0
July	13	27	0	18	3	11
August	5	19	0	18	0	23
September	0	32	0	47	0	49
October	0	43	0	55	2	28
November	7	32	0	44	0	4
December	17	20	3	17	3	20

NOTE: The percentages of E. and S.S.E. movements at night in August may have been inflated by ascended Swifts which were not on migration. The percentage of S.S.W. movements at night in September could not be assessed owing to their being obscured by the larger S.S.E. movements. The percentage of N.N.W. movements is certainly too low at night (from *Ibis, 105,* p. 485, 1963)

Examination of these tables shows that three main movements may be distinguished:

Spring	Autumn
(1) From West to East →	← From East to West
(2) N.N.W. ↖	↘ S.S.E.
(3) N.N.E. ↗	↙ S.S.W.

Movement No. 1

This spring movement and its autumn reciprocal is presumed to consist of the winter visitors to the British Isles, i.e. species which spend the winter in England

TABLE 6.2 *Frequency of migratory movements throughout the year as recorded at Bushy Hill, Essex*

The density of migration is expressed on the same arbitrary scale of 0–3 as in Tedd and Lack (1958) and Lack (1959, 1960); x indicates that some migration was recorded, but that the average density was less than 0·05, and a dash means no migration. Since the averages are based on 2½ times as many morning as evening figures, and since more migration occurs by night than day, they are lower than they would have been if they had referred to an equal number of nights and days.

Month	Number of observations	Mean density of migration per observation					
		E.	W.	N.N.E.	S.S.W.	N.N.W.	S.S.E.
January	46	0·4	0·2	0·3	0·5	0·1	0·1
February*	35	0·6	0·2	0·1	x	0·1	—
March*	50	1·7	0·1	0·3	0·1	0·2	0·2
April	20	1·7	0·2	0·5	0·1	0·6	0·1
May	18	0·3	0·2	1·1	0·1	0·7	x
June	13	0·7	0·7	0·2	x	0·1	—
July	11	0·3	0·9	—	0·3	—	0·5
August	12	0·4	0·6	—	0·4	—	1·4
September	11	0·9	0·9	—	0·5	0·1	0·9
October	30	0·2	0·4	0·1	0·6	x	0·5
November	13	0·2	0·5	—	0·7	x	0·2
December	20	0·1	0·9	0·1	0·6	x	0·2

* February covers the 1st–23rd only; the 24th–29th are included with March because this was done earlier (Lack, 1960) and because big eastward departures often begin then (from *British Birds*, 55, 390, 1962)

and breed on the Continent. The species involved are probably the chaffinch, starling, blackbird, song thrush, and lapwing.

Emigration of all these species is largest between the end of February and mid-April; post-breeding immigrant movements commence with the lapwing at the end of May but the heavy passerine movements do not begin until the end of September. Heavy angel displays are produced by these movements both by night and day.

Movement No. 2
This movement is much larger by night than by day, and occurs substantially overland in England, being much more conspicuous on the south coast than on the east coast of England, although some birds travel between East Anglia and Belgium. It is presumed that British passerine summer residents are the species chiefly involved in this movement which is most dense in late August–September in the emigrant post-breeding phase, and again, in late April–May during the arrival or immigrant period.

Movement No. 3
This movement mainly takes place over south-eastern England, the Straits of Dover, and the Pas de Calais. It is a smaller movement than the two above, and is

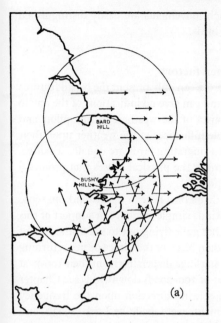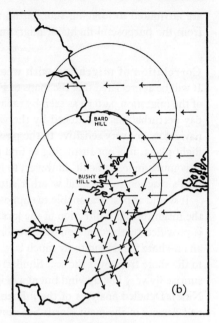

FIG. 6.2. Pattern of the main bird migration across the North Sea as seen by radar. The radar stations at Bard Hill and Bushy Hill are shown; the circles are 80 n.m. radius
(a) Spring
(b) Autumn

considered to be formed by species travelling between Scandinavia and Spain. Both passerines and waders are involved, as is indicated by the form of the echoes, and this migration takes place chiefly at night.

Fig. 6.2 illustrates the general locations and directions of these movements for the spring and autumn periods respectively. But the Tables show that migration is far from being confined to these two seasons and that some movements occur in every month of the year, including the middle of winter and the middle of summer. One of the results achieved by radar is the recognition that so-called reversed migration is a much more common occurrence than had been supposed. This is discussed more fully in Chapter Eight in connexion with 'hard weather movements'.

Although Bushy Hill overlooks the estuaries of the Crouch, Blackwater, and Colne rivers and the salt marshes adjoining, it has not so far proved possible to identify any major movements associated with waterfowl or seabirds. This has also been the experience at Bard Hill, although in this case it was possible for Lack (1960) to detect the departure of shore birds towards the north-east in spring, and the arrival of gulls on a south-westerly track in the autumn. Irregular movements of angels over the estuaries have been observed from Bushy Hill and

105

are attributed to foraging shorebirds; such movements are easily distinguished from the purposeful flights of migrating birds.

Correlation of migration with weather factors

It will be appreciated that the maps of Fig. 6.2 can only present the broad features of the migration pattern as seen by radar and can give no indications of the day to day perturbations introduced by the vagaries of the weather. Airline pilots and navigators are very sensitive to the possible influences of the weather upon their flight plans; it is not surprising to find that migrating birds are equally sensitive. It is much more difficult, however, to identify the physical causes that prompt a bird's reaction to the local weather situation.

It would appear reasonable to suppose that a bird near to the ground can sense the magnitude and direction of the local wind; simple evidence in support of this is provided by the common observation that gulls flying out to sea in the face of an on-shore wind tend to fly much lower than birds of the same species returning to the shore from over the sea. Similarly, starlings dispersing from their roosts at sunrise fly very low upwind but at a height of 100–200 ft downwind (see Chapter Nine). Detailed analyses of the influence of wind direction upon the frequency and density of the main North Sea movements were made by Lack (1963b) and by Lack and Eastwood (1962). This work shows that more migration occurs with following than with opposed winds. This effect is most marked during the winter period when very few movements of birds take place other than with a following wind, that is, a wind lying within 45° of the heading of the birds. During the autumn scarcely any movements take place in the presence of a head wind, but some movements do occur with cross winds provided that these are very light. In the spring, on the other hand, although the denser movements apparently require following winds for their stimulation, substantial movements also take place in the presence of cross winds and even in the face of head winds.

Among the weather factors which might exert a possible influence upon a bird's tendency to migrate is the temperature. The degree of cloud cover can also have an effect, for birds are remarkably sensitive to light, as is shown by the behaviour of birds during the onset of a total eclipse of the sun; the ordinary behaviour of birds at dawn and sunset is too well known to require comment. Even the general weather situation was included by Lack in a statistical search for correlation between the average density of migration and the various meteorological variables that might influence migration. The form of relation assumed was:

$$m = at + bw + pc + kd + ng + z$$

In this expression the density of migration m is expressed as a function of temperature in °F (t), wind speed in knots (w), wind direction (d – having value 4 for W. winds, 3 for N.W. and S.W., 2 for N. and S., 1 for N.E. and S.E., and 0 for E. winds), cloud-cover in eighths (c), the general weather situation

(g – having values of 2 for anticyclonic, 1 for transitional and 0 for disturbed weather) and z is an arbitrary constant.

The various weather factors, however, are not independent and so it is necessary to perform a multiple-regression type of analysis, which, in this instance, was executed by the Biometry Unit of Oxford University. It has to be admitted that this type of analysis, when applied to the correlation of variables such as density of migration, whose numerical expression can hardly be precise, might be considered to have doubtful validity. Nevertheless, the resulting equations for night and day migration in the spring, even if regarded as suggestive only, are still extremely interesting as indicating which weather factors have a statistically significant effect:

Spring night $m = 0.06\ t - 0.02\ w - 0.10\ c + 0.40\ d + 0.12\ g - 0.59$
Spring day $\quad m = 0.03\ t - 0.02\ w - 0.08\ c + 0.31\ d + 0.05\ g + 0.16$

In the case of night migration it was found that the figures for temperature, cloud-cover, speed, and direction of the wind were all statistically significant at the 1,000:1 level, but the general weather situation did not have any significant effect. Wind direction and cloud cover were again statistically significant at the 1,000:1 level for the day-migration results, with wind speed at 100:1 and temperature at 20:1, which are surprisingly different from the night-time result. The influence of the general weather situation on the day-migration density was again not detectable.

A different set of equations described the autumn migration, which showed that temperature had then no significant influence and that the factor of chief importance at this season was the wind direction. The main difference between the spring and autumn was the influence of temperature on the night migration in the spring but not in the autumn.

Birds as weather prophets

These reactions of the birds to the various weather factors must not be regarded as the result of any special sensory devices with which they are endowed; they must be viewed rather as adaptions which these species have acquired in order to fit them for migratory operations in a particular geographical environment. The birds are concerned with the utilization of the British Isles either as a breeding region or as a wintering 'resort'. They find this island separated from the Continent by a comparatively short sea crossing, but movements within the whole of this area have to take place in a weather environment which is highly variable. The only 'regularities' in this weather pattern are a consequence of the general easterly movement of high and low pressure centres across the Atlantic to impinge on the continental air mass. Prevailing winds in the region are westerly and so are favourable to the mass emigrations of the birds from the British Isles towards the east in the spring. In the autumn, on the other hand, the flow of birds takes place to the west and so is not helped by this general wind pattern. Autumn westerly movements, therefore, have to take place during the interruptions to the easterly air stream and the birds have to be more opportunist at this season.

It seems clear that the migratory behaviour of a bird at any moment is a resultant response to two classes of stimuli; the first being internal, i.e. a consequence of the physiological state of the bird and its preparedness for reproduction. The second stimulus is external and is a function of the local weather situation. Temperature, wind-speed, wind-direction, and cloud cover can all be directly appreciated but the general weather situation cannot; consistent with this view of the bird's total reaction is its behaviour in mid-winter, when the radar records of bird movements across the North Sea show that the influence of the wind direction is paramount. Almost without exception, movements then take place with a generally following wind. Lack's interpretation of this observation is that at this time the bird's internal urges are nicely balanced between the autumn and spring extremes. The bird is ready to move to the west or east impartially and so moves wholly in accordance with the stimulus provided by the weather situation, i.e. movements to and fro across the sea take place in accordance only with the wind direction. Thus radar shows that in mid-winter there is a succession of movements across the southern North Sea, westerly movements taking place with cold easterly winds and easterly movements in the presence of warm westerlies. Such 'commuting' flights possess advantage from the feeding point of view, since to leave a frost-bound Continent and to return when it has thawed has obvious advantages. The species which behave in this way are probably thrushes, starlings, and lapwings. Alternating 'frost-flights' of this type are discussed more fully in Chapter Eight.

Springtime movements of night-migrants in the English Channel

The south coast of England provides a major gateway for the entrance of migrants into the country from the Continent and the general course, constitution, and timing of such movements have long been inferred from the sightings of bird watchers. Radar observations on the subsequent penetration of migrants into the country after crossing the coast were made by Harper (1958) and by Houghton and Coultas (1958). Houghton's radar sightings at Malvern showed that the migrants east of the station during March/April moved in a direction east-north-east; observation towards the west was not possible because of the screening effect of the Malvern Hills. Migrants' tracks measured by Harper at Dunstable were in a general easterly direction during February–April, and towards the south-west in the autumn (September–December) as discussed in Chapter Three. Radar p.p.i. photographs of birds crossing the Channel taken from Bushy Hill are shown in Plate 13 and discussed in Chapter Eight, but bird altitude effects combined with screening from the South Downs limited such records to the eastern portion of the Channel, i.e. east of Worthing in Sussex.

Detailed study of the passage of night-migrants from France into southern England during the spring of 1962 were made by Parslow (1962) from a Royal Air Force S-band radar station situated in Hampshire. Parslow's objective in this series of observations was not so much to establish accurate radar tracks on the paths of the birds as to measure the degree of correlation between the density and position of the radar migration on the one hand, with the species and number of birds seen at two observatories on the other. The bird observatories were located at Hengistbury Head and Portland Bill respectively.

The major movements during April/May in this region mostly take place at night and are made up of large assemblies of small echoes which provide a luminous haze on the p.p.i. characteristic of masses of small passerines such as warblers. Parslow considered that warblers, goldcrests, flycatchers, and chats were the probable species involved. This movement was directed west of north usually north-north-west, as in Fig. 6.3, although occasional movements towards

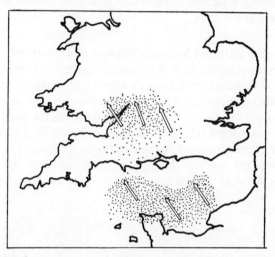

FIG. 6.3. Nocturnal movements of small passerines from France to Southern England, 22 April 1962 (after Parslow, *Bird Migration*, 1962)

the north-north-east or north-east were also observed. It was noted that the track of the movement varied from night to night according to the wind state, but no endeavour was made to refine the directional measurements in order to detect the presence or otherwise of drift correction by the birds since this was not the purpose of the research. Fig. 6.3 also shows the onward passage of migrants inland from the south coast, with an average track that was also directed north-north-west, but which showed much more variation than the track of the birds over the sea.

Fig. 6.3 represents the appearance of the p.p.i. at 21.50 h on 22 April 1962, when the density of migration was at its peak. Commencement of the movement usually took place about 40 min after sunset and the time of maximum density over the Channel occurred some 2 h later. On this occasion, which was one of the largest immigrations of the spring, very few birds were seen at the bird observatories on the following morning, which suggested that most of the birds had not alighted at the coast, but had continued their flight inland. By dawn, the density of the radar immigration had decreased greatly and few echoes were visible thereafter. The crossing was made in fine, anticyclonic weather and was assisted by light southerly to south-east winds, so that the crossing from Cherbourg was made in about 3 h.

It was noted that the migration was greatly deterred by the presence of unfavourable winds, particularly when these were strong. If a light migration took place under these unfavourable conditions, the occurrence of falls of migrants at the English coast was relatively greater than when a heavy migration under favourable wind state took place; presumably this was because the transit time and fatigue effects were greater in the former case so that the birds immediately alighted on making a landfall – this effect was most marked when the birds encountered rain at the coast.

Radar migration patterns between Norway and Scotland

Valuable information on the form of the autumn migration between Scandinavia and the north of Scotland was gained by Myres (1964), during his study of the dawn ascent and reorientation of Scandinavian thrushes. His observations were made in 1960 from an S-band radar station situated in the Shetland Isles and the pattern of movement in the autumn was as indicated by the black arrows on Fig. 6.4. This migratory movement was of the broad-front type which passed over or a little to the south of the Shetlands between 22.00 and 02.00 h. The movement was directed towards south-west to west, and from its speed of ad-

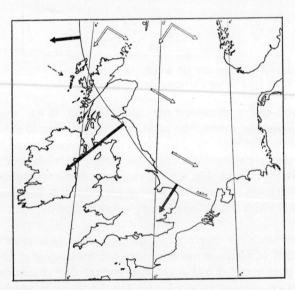

FIG. 6.4. Nocturnal movement of thrushes in the autumn from Norway towards the British Isles, and re-oriented directions after dawn as observed by radar (after Myres, *Ibis*, 1964)

vance it was estimated that the birds had begun their journey from the coast of Norway about sunset.

The birds involved in this movement were redwing, blackbird, and fieldfare; their tracks appeared to spread out radially from southern Norway, where the broad front movement observed from the Shetlands is shown as continuous with that observed from Norfolk. The continuous black line marks the position of the leading birds about dawn in September–October (06.00 h).

It was noticed by Myres that the radar density of this autumn passage migration, as observed from the Shetlands, greatly decreased as the night advanced. Just before dawn a rapid increase of angel density occurred which Myres named the 'Dawn Ascent'. The fall-off in angel density was attributed by Myres to the birds flying at such a low altitude that they passed beneath the radar beam and were no longer detected. The restoration of angel density at dawn took place so rapidly that Myres concluded that it could not be due to new birds entering the area but must be ascribed to birds already in the area gaining altitude and re-entering the radar cover.

This dawn ascent behaviour is so remarkable that it is very desirable that confirmation of the effect should be obtained by use of a height-finder radar. It is not obvious why birds over the sea should deliberately lose altitude at night. Indeed, measurements on night migrants over the North Sea by Eastwood and Rider (1965) show that the average altitude at night is higher than during the day. It might be that the bird's 'altimeter', perhaps its vestibular organ, lost accuracy as the night advanced, so causing the birds to lose height; the slowly sinking birds, gaining sight of the sea at first light, reacted by climbing to a higher and safer level. It is also possible that air currents were responsible for the altitude change. On the other hand, perhaps the dawn ascent, as Myres suggested, is related to the remarkable reorientational behaviour which frequently follows.

Fig. 6.4 shows that the track of the movement would have caused many of the birds to fly on over the Atlantic and so they would not have reached the coast of Scotland at all if they had not made a drastic change of course. In fact, such a change in track was observed on the radar and took place at dawn. Myres (1964) has shown that the subsequent direction of the movement is as indicated by the 'white' arrows, and apparently holds over all the sea area indicated, North Sea included. It has been pointed out by Myres that this fascinating piece of bird navigation which radar has uncovered would be a highly valuable adaptation in the behaviour pattern of birds frequenting the Atlantic seaboard; it would help to prevent serious losses of birds penetrating too deeply over the Atlantic due to overflying various parts of the British Isles.

The progress of the autumn migration in eastern Scotland (Aberdeenshire) during 1962 was also studied by Wilcock (1965) using both radar and visual watching in the field. The general form of the movements he observed is shown in Fig. 6.5.

The movement directed S.W./S.S.W. occurred in late autumn and was composed of clearly defined though smallish echoes typical of thrushes. Since the movement arrived at the coast of Scotland in the early morning, it was certain that the flocks of thrushes had left Scandinavia at about sunset, and so the movement can be regarded as part of that reported by Myres (1964) from his radar in the Shetlands. Overland movements, mainly towards the south-west and west, also occurred in the late autumn and were ascribed to the dispersal of winter visitors already arrived in Scotland. The other major nocturnal movement during the first part of the autumn took place overland and was directed S.E./S.S.E. Being composed of finely dispersed, low intensity echoes, it seemed

FIG. 6.5. Radar pattern of autumn migration in eastern Scotland

certain that these angels could be ascribed to departing passerine summer visitors such as the willow warbler and wheatear. A few departures in the same general S.E./S.S.E. direction were also seen in the early morning after dawn. The echoes associated with this diurnal movement were coarser than those of the nocturnal departures and were ascribed with some certainty to swallows and meadow pipits.

Wilcock noted that although the total number of movements into Aberdeen-shire was not greatly dissimilar to that observed in Norfolk for the same autumn period during the previous year (Wilcock, 1964), the migration densities were much lower. It appears probable from these observations, and remembering that similar radars were involved in the two areas, that the total autumnal influx of winter visitors into north-east Scotland is much less than that into East Anglia. In the course of these studies Wilcock also observed the dawn ascent and re-orientation phenomena over the North Sea of Scandinavian migrants, as reported by Myres.

Radar observations in the Outer Hebrides

Radar observations of bird movements off the north-west coast of Scotland were made by Lee (1963) a member of Lack's group at the Edward Grey Institute, during the autumn of 1961 and the spring of 1962. As in the case of the East Anglian work described above, this Hebridean research programme was rendered possible by the presence of a Royal Air Force S-band radar station on the Isle of Lewis, which was made available by the kindness of the Commanding Officer. This station is ideally located for the observation of migration between the mainland of Scotland and the summer breeding grounds in Iceland and Greenland of birds such as wheatears and redwings; also thrushes from Scandinavia en route for Ireland.

The autumn observations extended from late August until early November 1961, and provide a comprehensive record of the movements which took place, although detailed statistical study and correlation with weather effects was not possible; the absence of p.p.i. films was also a disadvantage to the analysis. Springtime study extended only from late March until 21 April 1962, when the work was abruptly terminated by the death of Stephen Lee under tragic circumstances. While watching sea-birds he fell from the cliffs of the island and was killed.

The principal autumn radar movements in the vicinity of Lewis are shown in

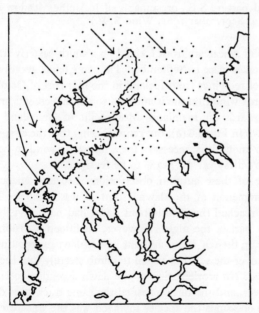

FIG. 6.6. P.p.i. patterns of migration around the Isle of Lewis (after Lee, *Ibis*, 1963)

(*a*) Typical broad front arrival S.E., presumably of Wheatears from Iceland (10.30 h, 5 September 1961, Wind W.N.W.)

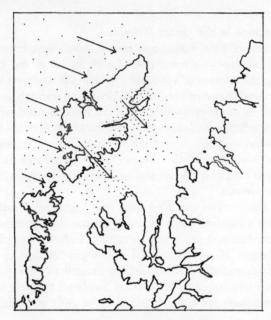

(b) (i) Typical broad front arrival heading E.S.E. continuing from previous evening, presumably of Wheatears from Greenland

(ii) Morning departure S.E., presumably of Icelandic Meadow Pipits (05.45 h, 20 September 1961, Wind S.W.)

Fig. 6.6. Arrival of wheatears from Iceland on a south-easterly track is shown in Fig. 6.6 (a) and takes place in September. The same figure serves also to describe the movements of redwings from Iceland in the first part of October. Practically none of these birds winter on the island and so the movements are continued on a broad front towards the mainland. Movements of Greenland wheatears also occurred as shown in Fig. 6.6 (b), but remembering that the airspeed of this bird is only about 20 knots, it is necessary for a following wind to be present if the journey of 1,200 miles over the sea is to be feasible.

In the course of these autumn observations Lee also encountered Myres' interesting phenomenon of the dawn ascent. It was noted by Lee that night migrants which reached the island about dawn had been invisible to the radar during the later part of the night. However, on fifteen occasions these targets began to appear 'in the sea' about an hour before dawn, suggesting that they had been flying low over the sea, but began to climb steadily into the radar cover as dawn approached. No reorientation of the dawn ascended Icelandic birds was observed, however, and the birds pursued the same track after dawn as before. On three of the occasions the species involved was the wheatear, which is thus the only bird other than the thrush in which the dawn ascent behaviour has been observed.

A third movement characteristic of the autumn was the arrival of Scan-

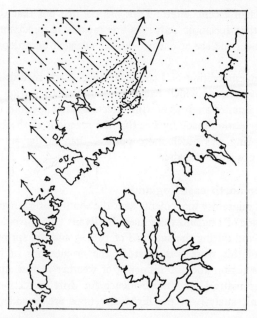

(c) Departures of limicoline birds (larger, well-spaced echoes) starting 2 h before dark, and of passerine birds (smaller, denser echoes) at nightfall, chiefly N.W. for Iceland (Golden Plover, Redwing) with some N.N.E., for the Faeroes or North Norway (20·40 h, 14 April 1962, wind S)

dinavian thrushes and drift migrants from Norway in the presence of easterly winds. Although evidence was gained for reorientation after the dawn ascent of such drifted birds, the volume and accuracy of the track data did not permit an analysis for any drift-correction effects. One interesting weather correlation, however, was Lee's suggestion that the birds were evidently much less intimidated by adverse winds than appeared to be the case in the North Sea studies of Lack. If this should prove to be the case then, as Lee suggested, it is probably because the risk of waiting for favourable winds in this stormy region is too great for the birds to accept and so they are adapted to be less wind critical.

Radar data on the spring movements in the Hebrides is incomplete but the main features shown in Fig. 6.6 (c) had been established by Lee before his untimely death. This shows the departure of wader-type echoes towards the north-west commencing about two hours before nightfall, which Lee attributed to golden plover, or possibly gulls. The main departures to the north-west took place at nightfall, however, and were composed of a dense mass of passerine-type echoes spread over a broad front and were not confined to Hebridean departures only but included the mainland of Scotland also. Since many redwings were visible on Lewis at this time, but no Icelandic wheatears, Lee concluded that redwings emigrating to Iceland were mainly responsible for these displays of angels. On one of these occasions (12/13 April) Lee also observed the 'dawn ascent' effect; Lack has pointed out that this observation would suggest that Icelandic redwings are capable of practising the habit of gaining height over the sea at dawn, whether engaged on a departure flight or an arrival flight.

In the subsequent editing of Lee's field notes Lack included some general spring angel-observations which had been compiled by station staff in earlier years. Although detailed analysis of wind effects was not possible, there was much support for a suggestion made by Lee that the reactions of the birds to adverse winds in the spring was much more positive than in the autumn and more nearly like that observed elsewhere.

Migration over north-east England

Observations of migratory movements over the south-eastern region of Scotland and the north-east of England were made by Evans (1966) from a radar station in Northumberland during the autumns of 1961–3 and the spring of 1963. The main purpose of this work was to study the orientations of passerine night migrants in this region and the influence of weather factors upon their flight behaviour; these matters, and the evidence for drift correction which Evans deduced from his analysis of the flight directions are considered in Chapter Eight.

Nocturnal departures from this region during August and September consisted mainly of small passerines such as warblers, chats and flycatchers. Some of these birds had bred in northern England or southern Scotland, but included also passage migrants from Iceland and Greenland. The tracks of the migrants as measured by the radar varied from night to night but always lay between east and south. These directions indicate different areas of departure of the birds. Thus birds leaving south-eastern Scotland flying on tracks between south-south-east and south-east approached Northumberland via a sea crossing; similarly for birds which arrived in Northumberland from Scotland on a southward directed track. Birds which travelled towards this region on tracks directed between south-east and east originated from inland areas. Evans found that the most frequent tracks in August were oriented between south-east and south-south-east while those in September lay between south-south-east and south-east by south.

During October and November the nocturnal departures also took place along directions east of south, mainly between south-south-east and south-east by south. In Northumberland the migrants mainly involved during early October were wheatears from Iceland or Greenland, but these were joined by Icelandic redwings in late October and November. British robins and song thrushes were probably also present.

During the course of one night the track direction tended to be maintained in spite of wind changes, but the directions were not the same on different nights, a fact which Evans attributed to changes in the participating species. It appeared that some of the movements took place in the presence of cross winds, although the heaviest movements were prompted by favourable winds. Migration occurred most frequently on those nights when the wind was light and following, while strong opposed winds tended to be accompanied by little or no migration. Temperature appeared to have little effect on migratory activity during August or September, but during October and November the onset of migration seemed to be stimulated by a fall in temperature, and this effect appeared to be unrelated to the direction of the wind. Cloud cover reduced the density of migration.

Migration in Switzerland

The autumn movements of bird migrants through the Swiss valleys were observed by Sutter over a number of years, following his demonstration in 1956 that the study of night migrants by radar was feasible (Sutter, 1957b).

The main direction of bird flow was from the north-east to the south-west and was remarkably constant, both from night to night as well as from autumn to autumn. A vivid demonstration of this constancy of direction on a particular night is provided by the wedge-like obscuration of echoes which occurs on some of Sutter's p.p.i. picture along an axis 160°–340°. This wedge-like shadow arises from the cancellation of echoes moving tangentially to the radar beam, due to the Moving Target Indicator device with which this radar was fitted, and serves as an accurate method of measuring the flight direction of masses of birds, provided that they are moving along parallel tracks; this was obviously the case for Sutter's birds.

Autumn migration towards the south-west in this region fits in with movements of migrants towards certain of the Alpine passes, which is one feature of the migration pattern in south-western Switzerland. The movement of migrants from the Val d'Illiez across the Col de Bretolet has been studied by Vuilleumier (1963) and shown to be a consequence of both weather factors and topography. An actual bird passage over the pass was vividly described by Gerster (1960) and included thrushes, ring-ousels, and robins by night and hedge sparrows, pied wagtails, yellow wagtails, and tree pipits by day. This is not to suggest that the passes provide regular migration corridors across the high Alps, on the contrary, the migration is usually on a broad front but certain wind states, particularly the 'foehn wind' of this region, can produce a concentration of birds at the passes, due to the obstacle of the high Bernese Alps. This results in the spectacular crossings which not infrequently occur at the Col de Bretolet; 30 September 1958 must have been a near record, for on that day 300,000 hirundines passed over the Bretolet. Such a concentration does not take place in the spring, and flights are spread over the whole region. Change of wind can produce a sudden and marked change in the direction of migration, as was noted by Sutter on the night of 11/12 October 1956 when the flight tracks on his radar changed from the usual north east – south west to east – west, consequent upon a wind change from south-south-east to west-south-west. No results have yet been published of radar directions of migration in the spring as observed at Kloten. It will be interesting to learn whether the spring paths are reciprocals of the autumn tracks or whether the more diffuse movements of the spring in this region do not permit specific preferred tracks to be assigned.

Radar migration studies in Sweden and Finland

Some interesting radar observations upon bird migrations taking place in mid-Sweden were made by Mascher, Stolt, and Wallin (1962). Advantage was taken of the new S-band Air Traffic Control Radar which had been installed at the Arlanda civil airport, 35 km north-north-west of Stockholm, to make a comparison between the density and frequency of radar angels as recorded from the p.p.i., with the frequencies and directions of bird flights observed visually at four field stations located 5–10 miles from the station.

Springtime migratory movements in this part of Sweden are usually directed towards the north-east, dependent upon the wind state, and involve thrushes, finches, buntings, crows, ducks, and lapwings. Records of the angel state on the

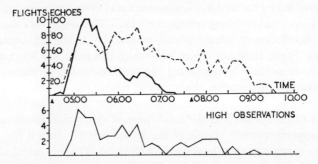

FIG. 6.7. Morning migration at Arlanda, Sweden, on 13 April 1960. The upper curve shows the frequencies of radar echoes (solid line) compared with the frequencies of observed bird flights (not individual birds) as the mean of four observation points (broken line). The triangles indicate the start and end of radar recording. The curve for 'high observations' is of parties of birds flying high and, therefore, more likely to be displayed on the radar screen (after Mascher, Stolt, and Wallin, *Ibis*, 1962)

p.p.i. and counts of the number of angels per 100 sq. miles were made on four mornings, 13–16 April 1960, between the hours of 04.30 to 10.00, i.e. from dawn to late morning. During these hours details of passing birds were simultaneously observed visually by the field parties. Bird species, directions of flight, and number of flocks were all recorded. A rough distinction was also made between low flights and 'high flights', i.e., flights occurring above 500 ft.

Although the hours of radar observation were rather limited, the operational period spanned the morning peak of migration. Results for the morning of 13 April are shown in Fig. 6.7. Some general correlation between the visual and radar curves on this figure is apparent, particularly between the visual and radar 'high flights', but there are also some notable discrepancies. Thus the radar indicates a virtual cessation of activity at 07.20 although the field activity continued until 09.30 and still included a good percentage of 'high flights'. In addition, the radar peak of migration occurred one hour earlier than the visual peak.

It was concluded by Mascher and his co-workers that the absence of detailed correlation between the radar and visual results must mean that the radar echoes related to birds migrating at heights outside the visual range. Similarly, the visible migration which was estimated to take place at altitudes below 650 ft was thought to be too low to be seen by the radar. Support for those conclusions was found in the fact that low altitude reversed migration was observed to be present on all days, but little signs of it were to be seen on the radar. Mascher also suggested that their measurements of the still-air speed of the radar echoes, which gave 35–43 m.p.h. as the probable speeds, was a speed range appropriate for waders and ducks, but not for the passerines observed visually.

That major discrepancies can exist between visual and radar estimates of diurnal migration has been pointed out by Lack (1960); these differences emphasize the need for complementary radar and visual observations when seeking to understand the factors which influence migration. This aspect of the matter was noted by Sutter (1957) and was re-emphasized by Wilcock (1964) in his comparison of radar and visual records of coasting movements in Norfolk. Wilcock showed that migrants with following winds tend to fly well above visual range whereas with strongly opposed winds they fly below the radar cover.

A detailed study of migration over the Gulf of Finland was made by Bergman and Donner (1964) with the aid of military and air traffic control radars sited along the south coast of Finland. The investigation was confined to the period 10–28 May during the years 1960–2, since this is the time of year when the concentrated spring migration takes place of the common scoter and the long-tailed duck. Identification by radar of the species of birds taking part in a major migratory movement is very difficult, but this research is noteworthy for the unusual feature that the larger portion of the echoes seen on the radar during the later half of May, and which were following north-easterly tracks, were provided by ducks of these two species. Another very interesting feature of the investigation was the high correlation which the authors established between the radar estimates of migration activity and that recorded in the field. The reason for this agreement is, perhaps, to be found in the altitudes flown and also in the fact that these ducks tend to move in flocks of about 150. The birds were readily identifiable in the field, both visually and by means of their characteristic calls.

During the spring long-tailed ducks and common scoters cross the Gulf of Finland en route to their arctic breeding places. The general direction of progress is towards the north-east, but there are marked differences in the flight patterns, which Bergman and Donner attributed to the viewing conditions experienced by the birds. On clear days the pattern of movement is as shown in Fig. 6.8. The birds, advancing from the south-west, tend to take a more easterly course as the coast is approached. Nearer to the coast the deflexion is increased, with the result that a great channel of birds is often formed which is parallel to the coast and

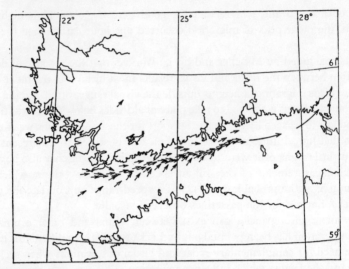

FIG. 6.8. Migration of the Common Scoter and Long-tailed Duck across the Gulf of Finland. General pattern in daylight with high or medium visibility. Note general absence of migrants over land, except a few flocks in the lake region (after Bergman and Donner, *Acta. Zool. Fenn.*, 1964)

lies just outside the outer archipelago. At night, or during the day when the visibility is poor at the coast, no deflexion of the flight paths occur, and the birds cross the coast on the same heading as shown in Fig. 6.9. They continue the migration without alighting until suitable resting lakes are reached in the interior of the country.

The autumn migration of the long-tailed duck follows roughly a reciprocal course, except that the concentration of migrants, then moving in a south-westerly direction, takes place along the northern coast of Estonia. A great many of the flocks appear to make the flight from the White Sea to the Gulf of Finland in one stage and probably the same long flight is made in spring in the reverse direction.

Weather influences the progress of this duck migration in a manner similar to that reported by Lack for passerines over the North Sea. Thus the density of migration was highest in the presence of light tailwinds and Bergmann and Donner obtained a significant correlation between migration density and the speed increase or decrease produced by the wind. No evidence was found for correction of the drift produced by the wind and the birds flew on a constant heading. This inability to correct for drift would not react unfavourably on the birds since, in the presence of complete overcast, no migratory flights took place. Temperature appeared to play no part in the progress of the migration.

Radar patterns over the Mediterranean
Movements of migrating birds across the Mediterranean Sea during the spring-time exodus from Africa, northward into Europe, and the reverse journey of

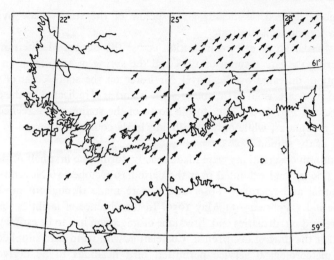

FIG. 6.9. General course of the migration of the Common Scoter and Long-tailed Duck across southern Finland during the night (after Bergman and Donner, *Acta. Zool. Fenn.*, 1964)

the autumn, have long excited the interest of ornithologists; such interest existed even in biblical times! It is true that many species avoid the hazards of a direct north–south crossing of this sea barrier by making detours through the Iberian Peninsular or down through Italy and Sicily, but birds have been observed on a large variety of sea crossing routes whose lengths range from 100 to 700 miles (Moreau, 1961). There is little reason to doubt that every part of the Mediterranean is crossed by numbers of birds.

South of the Mediterranean lies the equally difficult hazard of the Sahara desert, which involves a minimum crossing distance of 900 miles over inhospitable terrain on which it would be dangerous for birds to alight, even for a rest, and certainly with no hope of finding sustenance. A narrow coastal strip separates the sea from the desert on this north–south migratory route followed by vast numbers of insectivorous birds that breed in Europe and winter in Africa, south of the Sahara. Evidence for this migration pathway is drawn from sightings of birds in flight made in the coastal region, from ships in the Mediterranean and from falls of migrants upon the northern coast of Africa.

The review and analysis of migration in this region, which was made by Moreau (1961), makes exciting reading, particularly his demonstration that many birds must make the crossing non-stop from Europe to central Africa – a distance of some 1,500 miles, and that the birds possess the fuel capacity needed for such a flight. The detective work involved in this study is all the more remarkable when the scantiness of much of the evidence is taken into account, and final assessment of some of Moreau's conclusions must await the accumulation of more precise data on bird movements. Radar is capable of supplying much of the information required, as details given below of the study made by Adams (1962) in Cyprus will illustrate.

Adams' radar study of bird migration across the eastern Mediterranean was made during the late autumn of 1958 and the spring of 1959 from an S-band radar station, operated by the Royal Air Force on the south coast of Cyprus. Good radar cover existed to the south of the island as is indicated by the 60-mile-range circle of Fig. 6.10. Cover to the north of the station was screened by the Troodos mountains, while only high-flying birds could be observed to the east and west of the station.

The autumn observations were made mostly during the first half of the night, (18.00–24.00 h), and extended over the period 19 October–16 November 1958. Both diurnal and nocturnal observations were made throughout most of the spring period 5 February–31 May 1959. In the absence of facilities for photographic recording, densities and directions of migration had to be estimated from the p.p.i. at the time of occurrence. Correlation with wind data supplied by the island's meteorological service permitted bird headings to be derived from the measured directions of the tracks.

Fig. 6.10 shows the directions of the main migratory movements observed in the autumn. Observations made on three occasions only suggested a daytime broad-front passage of scattered echoes in a direction south to south-east. The more extended night-time records showed that a distribution of small angels, in the form of a fine haze of light, built up along the south coast of the island in the early evening and moved out to sea in a southerly direction. This type of

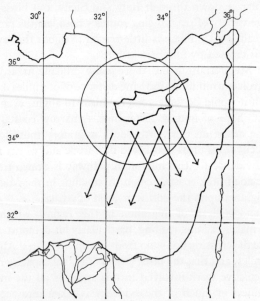

FIG. 6.10. Average directions of migration from Cyprus in autumn observed by radar (after Adams, *Ibis*, 1962)

radar echo formation is typical of that given by masses of small birds such as warblers and agrees with Bourne's finding that most small night migrants seen in autumn on the island are warblers (Bourne, 1959, 1960). The density of this movement was maintained for about two hours and fell off sharply thereafter, probably corresponding to the total departure of all the migrants in the island. During October, the average direction of this regular early evening movement lay between south-east and south-south-east by south, corresponding to headings between east-south-east by east and south-south-east. This movement also continued during November but was then accompanied by a separate and distinct movement directed towards the south-west; this latter movement was

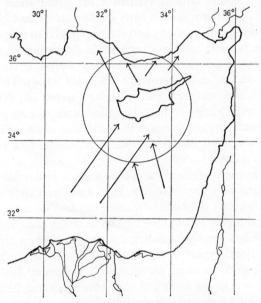

FIG. 6.11. Average directions of migration in the eastern Mediterranean in spring as observed by radar from Cyprus (after Adams, *Ibis*, 1962)

coarser in structure than the former and seemed to be produced by species other than warblers and corresponded more to thrush-type echoes.

The average directions of migration observed by radar in spring are as shown in Fig. 6.11, and are seen to be substantially the reciprocal of those flown in the autumn. Although two main directions are shown on this figure, the populations associated with them were very dissimilar, that directed to the north-west amounted to only one ninth of the north-easterly movement, for which the average track lay between 030°–035°. An analysis of all the track directions measured in the spring and of the bird headings derived from them, by making appropriate allowance for the wind speed and direction, suggested that there was an average easterly drift of 10°–15°. That the birds were possibly aware of this drift, or at least made some correction for it, was suggested by the fact that

123

the spread of headings was greater than the spread of tracks (see Appendix). Since the radar was monitoring only a comparatively small portion of the eastern Mediterranean it seems reasonable to assume that these movements reported by Adams were taking place over a front very much broader than the east–west extension of Cyprus itself, and that the island was in no way acting as a focal point or intermediate station for the migration. The most favoured direction of flow was 030°–035°, and the tendency to correct to this track would then have relevance to the migratory movement as a whole, and would not relate to any need of the birds to make a landfall on Cyprus after departure from the region of the Nile delta.

In the spring the first birds arrived over the island about midnight; the density of angels thereafter remained fairly steady until 05.00–08.00, after which the flow fell off during the morning and early afternoon to a deep minimum at dusk. It was not possible to identify species in the spring by the appearance of the echoes on the p.p.i. since most of the birds arrived at the island in large flocks which masked the characteristics of individual echoes. The distance from Egypt to Cyprus is roughly 200 miles; Adams pointed out that these arrival times of angels over Cyprus, on the assumption of an average ground speed of 35 knots, suggested strong departures from the Nile coast commencing about dusk and continuing until midnight; reduced departures took place after midnight and ceased at dawn.

Weather in the eastern Mediterranean is, in general, favourable to the migrants and provides them with good visibility, light winds and comparative freedom from cloud and overcast. Favourable weather can lead to 'non-standard' movement of birds and also to propagation conditions which cause radar detection of movements at ranges greatly exceeding the normal. Thus a radar view of the coast of Egypt from Cyprus is by no means infrequent during the summer months. On one such occasion, the night of 9 November 1958, a heavy bird movement was observed on a track of 225° from Syria and Lebanon to Egypt. Again, on 10 April a heavy movement from Israel and Lebanon was observed at 22.00 h and surged towards the island, the depth of the wave of birds being at least 70 miles; this was the densest radar display seen by Adams during the whole period.

Confirmation of the broad front nature of the migration pattern across the Mediterranean as a whole has recently been provided by Casement (1966). Although many years are likely to pass before the inevitable spread of powerful Air Traffic Control radars around the Mediterranean provides the comprehensive radar cover needed to establish the detailed movements of bird migrants in this region, Casement has been able to build up a valuable mosaic of the likely migration pattern by means of observations made with the aid of the surveillance radar of an aircraft carrier. The observations were made at various points in the Mediterranean, and at irregular intervals as permitted by the Service operations of the carrier, but covered the springs of 1961, 1962, and 1963 and the autumn of 1962. Visual sightings of birds were also made to complement the p.p.i. records.

The 10-cm radar employed provided useful bird cover to a range of about 15 miles. This region of radar surveillance was carried along with the speed of the ship, so that to determine the directions of the bird tracks seen on the p.p.i. it was necessary to perform a Triangle of Velocities calculation. A further calculation was required to 'take out the wind' in order to derive the birds' heading from the track. Casement found that the variation of these headings for certain of his sets of observations was significantly greater than the variation in the tracks from which they were derived. This circumstance suggested to him that in these cases at least the birds involved had made some adjustment of their headings to correct for drift by the wind (see Appendix).

Three main types of radar echo were distinguished by Casement:

(1) *Large and fast (by night)* – These targets moved with a speed between 30 and 50 knots, and were attributed to ducks and waders with a proportion of turtle doves also present.

(2) *Large and slow (by day)* – Targets in this class had an air speed between 20 and 25 knots and showed courses which were often erratic. They were attributed to single large raptors, or groups of herons or other large birds.

(3) *Small (by night)* – The most frequent echoes were of this type and occurred by night usually in the speed range 20–30 knots. In the past, dense displays of echoes of this kind were commonly attributed to sea clutter, i.e. back scatter from sea waves, but Casement pointed out that the heaviest displays occurred at night in the presence of a flat, calm sea; also a height-finder radar showed that the 'echoes' were airborne, and plotting showed the targets to be in motion. These echoes were attributed to passerine night migrants.

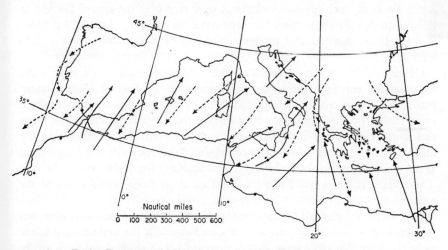

FIG. 6.12. Radar Patterns of Migration across the Mediterranean
Spring ——————> Autumn — — — — —>
(after Casement, *Ibis*, 1966)

The broad pattern of passerine migration which Casement was able to build up from his various observations is summarized in Fig. 6.12. During the spring, movements take place across the whole of the North African coast commencing quite early in the year and continuing as late as mid-May. In the western Mediterranean the movements are directed towards the north-east, but this direction changes to north-north-west in the eastern Mediterranean. The autumn migration is in progress, certainly by mid-August and continues until late October at least. In the autumn the courses flown are roughly the reciprocals of those of the spring. Casement found no evidence to suggest that the various islands in the region formed stepping stones for the progress of the nocturnal migrants, neither were there migratory highways across the Straits of Gibraltar or the Sicilian narrows. The night migrants appeared to be distributed across the broad front with roughly uniform density, except in the region of the Ionian Sea where the density was much reduced in the autumn – as though corresponding to a divide of the great south-westerly stream of birds round the two sides of the Adriatic.

We have already seen how visual estimation of migratory activity across the North Sea can often fail to take account of the vast movements of passerine night migrants which are detected by radar. Casement similarly concluded that the main passage of migrants across the Mediterranean takes place at night. His many visual sightings of birds in the daytime, combined with alightings on the deck of the carrier, permitted him to establish the probable species involved in many of the movements. In the western part of the region these included robins, chaffinches, nightingales, swallows, pipits and larks.

Sightings in the central part of the Mediterranean included firecrest, redstart, robin, chaffinch, nightingale, wheatear, greenfinch, *flava* wagtail and warblers. A few flocks of duck (probably Mallard) were seen over the Ionian Sea and in this region sightings were made on turtle dove, nightingale, reed warbler, sedge warbler, house martin, sand martin, white wagtail, willow warbler, and *flava* wagtail.

Of special interest was Casement's deduction from the time of the peak in the daily activity curve for the spring migration over the Eastern Mediterranean that the birds had not commenced their sea crossing after a rest at the northern coastal strip, but had commenced their flight from regions much farther south and had overflown the coastal region. In the western Mediterranean, on the other hand, the same kind of evidence suggested that the birds had congregated at the coast of Algeria and had commenced their northerly sea crossing from it. These birds had not overflown the coast en route from points south of the Sahara.

The Mediterranean is a fascinating area for the student of bird migration, but the work of Adams in Cyprus and of Casement with his mobile, ship borne radar, indicate that more radar data is needed from this region before it can be claimed that the pattern of migration has been fully recorded and understood.

CHAPTER SEVEN

Radar patterns of bird migration in North America

The studies of bird migration off the coasts of Britain described in the last chapter stemmed from the fortunate circumstance that various high-powered surveillance radars sited round the coast were made available for such work on a part-time basis by the enlightened authorities which controlled them. The eastern seaboard of the New England States is another region of great interest to the ornithologist that has been similarly probed and surveyed by the radar method, and for the same reason, viz., the presence of equipments set up for radar research, defence, and the control of air traffic.

How the migration information was gathered

The Institute of Technology at Boston, Massachusetts, was one of the main U.S.A. centres of radar research during the Second World War. After the war this work was continued by an offshoot of the M.I.T. known as the Lincoln Laboratory. Field work is essential to radar research and the South Truro station was set up by the Lincoln Laboratory to fulfil this need, just as Bard Hill in Norfolk was operated by the Royal Radar Establishment and Bushy Hill by the Marconi Company. Radar films and observations made during 1959–60 at South Truro were placed at the disposal of Drury and Keith (1962) and formed the basis of the detailed study which they made of songbird migration in coastal New England. This programme of research contributed substantially to the understanding of bird migration events which take place every year along the eastern coast of New England, just as the studies of Lack and his collaborators have similarly helped towards a better understanding of migration phenomena over the east coast of (Old) England.

To supplement the radar information derived from South Truro, Drury and Keith also had available radar data obtained at the offshore Texas Tower installations II, III, and IV of the U.S. Air Force Reporting Network. The location of these various stations is shown in Fig. 7.1. To help in the interpretation of the radar observations, and particularly to try to overcome the lack of positive identification of the bird species, use was made of a well-organized group of amateur field observers who reported on their bird sightings during the whole of the radar survey.

The radar pattern of migration in spring

The broad features of the migration pattern derived by Drury and Keith (1962) from the South Truro radar films of the 1959/60 spring and autumn periods are

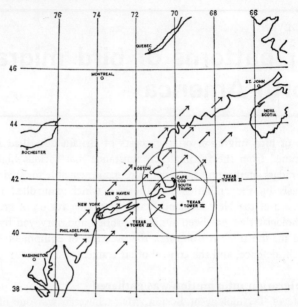

FIG. 7.1. General pattern of the migration movements of the spring off the New England coast (the South Truro and Texas Tower radar installations are indicated)

summarized in Fig. 7.1. Since the performance indices of this radar and that of the associated equipment on Texas Tower III do not differ significantly from the corresponding indices for Bard Hill and Bushy Hill in England, it will help to fix the scale of events if Fig. 7.1 is related to Fig. 6.2 by including the 80-mile range circles for the two American stations. First-class radar data was obtainable within these circles.

It will be apparent from comparison of Fig. 7.1 with Fig. 6.2 that whereas the two English stations were surveying substantially the whole of the bird pathway between south-eastern England and the Continent, the American stations could only observe a section of the massive bird stream which flows twice per year between the southerly wintering grounds and the breeding sites in northern New England, eastern Canada, Newfoundland, and Labrador. The general characteristics of this migration have been inferred from the devoted labours of many decades of bird watchers. The American flights are long and made with an inhospitable ocean lying along the whole of the eastern flank; in contrast, the North Sea flights between Britain and the continent of Europe are short and errors in navigation are not so disastrous.

In spring, the general flight directions of the American migrants may be broadly described as north-eastward. Although these movements to the breeding grounds in the north commence during the unstable weather which characterizes the March/April period in this region, only small-scale movements are at first usually involved. True departure of winter visitors from New England and large scale movements from the south-west to the north-east, whether completely overflying the region or accompanied by falls of spring migrants recognized by ground observers, usually occur in the late spring which, in the main, extends throughout the month of May, but with a variable onset time. At this time of the year the eastern seaboard of the U.S.A. has associated with it the establishment of a well recognized pattern of air flow in which tropical maritime air flows up the Atlantic coast and thrusts back the cold polar air masses.

Clearly, the establishment of this warm air stream towards the north-east during late spring is favourable to the movement of migrants from the south, but stable though these major air-flows may be, perturbations frequently occur and so the progress of the birds to their breeding grounds is by no means a steady flow at uniform density. On the contrary, the greater part of the bird movements takes place in a number of major surges whose occurrences are conditioned by the incidence of air mass movements specially favourable to the north-eastward flight paths the birds wish to pursue. It was shown from radar studies of songbird nocturnal migration that some 60 per cent of a season's total bird passage is accomplished in about twelve nights. In 1959, for example, there was one super-night out of 33 nights of activity recorded by radar in spring; the autumn figure was 14 out of 65. Comparative figures for 1960 were 4 out of 63 in the spring and 8 out of 82 for the autumn. Careful and detailed analysis of the weather states which accompanied these mass movements of birds was made by Drury and Keith in their search for a comprehensive account of all the possible stimuli which, when taken together, could explain the spring pattern of migration in New England. Some interesting conclusions may be drawn from a comparison between these studies and corresponding work in Europe.

The radar pattern of migration in autumn

Spring migration in the New England region is completed by the first few days of June and few migratory movements are observed from this time until about the middle of August. This absence of bird activity corresponds to the 'balance of power' between the warmer air-masses which have moved up from the south and the fully withdrawn polar air-mass, withdrawn because this is the time of maximum irradiation by the sun.

The first phase of the autumn migration as observed by radar commences in early August when the gradual extension and progress of the polar air front towards the south is accompanied by the movement towards the south-west of both adult and immature warblers retracing the path of their spring migration. This movement of warblers continues through August and into early September, when they are joined by towhees and catbirds. By mid-September thrushes have become numerous and the peak of the migration of immature warblers is achieved at this time. Buntings join in the rush to the south about the beginning of October and by the middle of the month have become the chief migrants, but in the first part of October thrushes, blackpoll warblers, myrtle warblers, and yellowthroats make up the major part of the movements then occurring. The peak of the wader migration occurs in early August, while most fresh-water ducks are

129

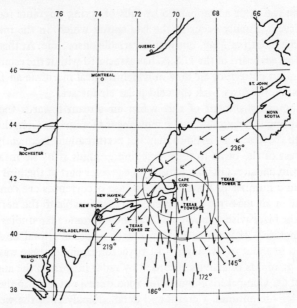

FIG. 7.2. General pattern of the migration movements of the autumn off the New England coast

moving during the period September–November, with movements of sea ducks taking place in late October, as was discussed in Chapter Three in connexion with the pioneer work of Richardson and his collaborators (Richardson *et al.*, 1958). The general directions of these autumn migrations are shown in Fig. 7.2. By mid-November, climatic winter is established over the whole Atlantic seaboard and only local sporadic movements of birds then take place.

TABLE 7.1 *Offshore movements across eastern and coastal Massachusetts in autumn*

General movement	Direction	Time	Species (from echo appearance)	Probable objective
1. South-east-ward (Diurnal and nocturnal)	145°–165°	July to October	Offshore movement of waders	South America
2. Southward (Nocturnal)	175°–195° (by M.T.I. wedge)	Early September to mid-October	Offshore movement of passerines (wood warblers)	Antilles and South America; non-stop flight over West Atlantic
3. South-west-ward (Nocturnal)	235°–245° (by M.T.I. wedge)	Early August through mid-November	Passerines (thrushes, wood warblers, and buntings. General south-west movement of these species)	Some fly direct across the bight of the West Atlantic to the Carolinas

Drury and Keith (1962) distinguished three major movements of migrants over the sea south of Cape Cod that take place in the autumn (Table 7.1).

Radar has prompted theories as to the probable routes pursued by these south-bound passerine migrants which cross the sea south of New England, following the succession of cold fronts which advance southward from the north at this time. Drury and Keith suggested that this previously unrecorded movement consisted of millions of songbird migrants that winter in the Southern States, the Antilles and South America. They further suggested that the birds fly straight across the open Atlantic to their destination; they supplied evidence that such extended flights were well within the fuel capacity of the birds.

That this movement had hitherto escaped detection was because the track was wholly over the sea and so was inaccessible to the ground observer; but the failure of the ground watchers on this particular movement serves only to emphasize the remarkable success which they had achieved over the years in inferring the probable form and tracks of the main south west–north east movements. This success was due in part to the great length of the migrant track along the eastern seaboard of the U.S.A. By careful monitoring of the migrant falls along this long land route which occurred when unfavourable weather caused the migrants to land, a very fair sample of the species content and timing of the spring and autumn bird flows was obtained over the years. Ground monitoring by visual observation could not, of course, detect the passage at high altitude overhead of a heavy migration occurring during good weather.

Similar monitoring has gradually built up an integrated picture of migration in England but, as Lack has shown, these visual methods failed to detect the scale of overflying movements since the majority of them take place at night and carry the migrants well beyond the East Anglian zone of observation. In the English case, also, the fact that any movement from the Continent involves a sea crossing means that species identification by falls along the track cannot be continuous, while the comparative shortness of the sea crossing means that overflying of the coastal region of the eastern counties is the rule rather than the exception. For these reasons visual observers had not achieved as close a representation of the North Sea migration as in the American case. Although the distances involved in the England/Continent movements are much shorter than in the American case, this does not simplify the problem. For the weather states off continental Europe are very changeable, due to the succession of 'lows' derived from the Atlantic over which the air flow is mainly west to east. Periods of weather favourable to migration may, therefore, be brief, which means that the birds must be adapted to take advantage of weather states which are likely to result in a successful crossing occupying a few hours only. In other words, the time constants of the weather processes involved in the European migrations are short compared to those which obtain in the American case. That adaptations should be different in the Old World and New World families of birds is only to be expected, since they face such vastly different geographical and meteorological situations.

Nocturnal migration of songbirds off the New England coast during autumn

The detailed analysis of the directions of the autumnal migratory movements in the Massachusetts area observed on the South Truro radar was performed by Drury and Nisbet (1964). One of the major objects of this analysis was to study the orientational behaviour of nocturnal migrants in the presence of crosswinds. If track data of sufficient accuracy could be extracted from the radar films then it would be possible to determine bird headings under different wind states and so decide whether a bird could detect and correct for wind drift. Similarly, by study of migrant tracks under complete overcast or cloud cover at night, it might be possible to decide whether migrants could maintain good orientation even though sight of the stars was denied to them. It was not considered that viewing of the sea's surface would help the birds to maintain a constant flight track. These aspects of the Cape Cod observations are discussed in the next chapter; the present purpose is to describe the general form of the movements.

The radar picture of autumnal passerine migration was built up from p.p.i. film records secured over four seasons from 1959–62, and comprised a total of fifty-six observational nights. We have seen that the migratory pattern in North Europe is made up of an overlay of a number of broad front movements; this

TABLE 7.2   *Nocturnal passerine migration in south-eastern New England (autumn)*

Description of movement	Average track	Species involved
1. S.W. movement over the mainland of Massachusetts. Mid-August–November (Table 1 – movement No. 3)	219°	A wide variety of passerines including flycatchers, warblers, buntings and thrushes. This is the largest movement of the autumn, only the eastern fringe passes over Cape Cod
2. S.W. immigrant movement over the sea from Nova Scotia. Mid-September–November (Table 1 – movement No. 3)	236°	Thrushes and sparrows. Movements less dense then those over the mainland
3. S. movements, departure E. of S. (early evening at South Truro). Late August–early November. Peak in October (Table 1 – movement No. 2)	172°	Blackpol Warbler, possibly Yellow-billed Cuckoo, Bobolink, Barn Swallow, Bank Swallow, Connecticut Warbler
4. S. movements, departure W. of S. (after 21.00 h at South Truro). Late August–early November (Table 1 – movement No. 2)	186°	Thrushes, possibly some warbler species. Migration to the Bahamas and Greater Antilles

type of structure also characterizes the autumnal migrations which were observed during this New England programme. Each of these movements could be defined by the tracks or directions of motion associated with them and one of the most startling and impressive facts uncovered by Drury and Nisbet was the remarkable constancy of the bearings associated with these tracks. Because long persistence afterglow tubes were not employed in the South Truro radar it was not possible to measure movement direction from the afterglow trails on the echoes, instead, the M.T.I. wedge method, as described in Chapter Three, was brought into service. This technique, however, can only yield results when the distribution of migrating birds is extremely widespread – as is the case with the broad-front type of migration now under discussion. In addition, it is also necessary that the birds should fly along closely parallel tracks – which requires that the wind should be favourable. Four main types of passerine movement were identified and their features are listed in Table 7.2, together with their relationship to the broader descriptions given in Table 7.1.

A number of smaller nocturnal movements were also detected in the autumn on the South Truro radar which may be briefly described as follows:

TABLE 7.3   *Other autumn nocturnal movements in south-eastern New England*

General direction	Period of occurrence	Probable species
Southwards	Late October and November	Waterfowl
South-eastwards (130°–140°) (Table 1–movement)	Throughout autumn but densest in August (Bright echoes moving fast)	Shorebirds on direct migration towards eastern South America
Eastwards (70°–110°)	Densest in October (Bright echoes)	Species which winter off the New England coast, e.g. scoters, herring gulls, gannets
Eastwards (75°–100°)	Throughout autumn (Weak, flickering echoes. Warm side of high pressure systems)	Landbirds on reversed migration
North-eastwards (40°–60°)	Throughout autumn (Weak, flickering echoes on warm side of high pressure systems)	Landbirds on reversed migration

One of the interesting points about the M.T.I. wedge technique for average track determination is that the clarity of the wedges depends upon the parallelism of the tracks of the individual birds. If the quality of the orientation deteriorates the wedge becomes diffuse and reduces the accuracy of measurement of the average track of the movement. It was noted by Drury and Nisbet that the quality of the wedges deteriorated as the night progressed, suggesting that the orientation of the birds became more random. Linked with this observation is the fact that the orientation of the birds can never be absolutely parallel, but must be scattered about the average direction, with the result that in spite of drift correction some of the birds must fly along tracks which bring them to the coast of Massachusetts where they appear as falls; such falls, however, are clearly only a very small portion of the total broad-front movement. Drury and Keith suggested that this was because these errant members of the flock were immature individuals, which was in agreement with the falls observed. On the same principle, many such birds must be lost in the Atlantic because of variations in track to the east rather than to the west, but it is in just this manner that selection in a species operates so as to maintain it adapted to its total habitat which, in this case, includes the migration route to be followed.

Drury and Nisbet (1964) did not report the occurrence of the same radar wedge effects with the spring movements. This does not necessarily mean that the autumn paths are not the reciprocals of those of the spring, but rather that the spring movements do not fulfil the conditions that allow average tracks of mass movements to be derived, i.e. large areas covered by migrating birds flying on parallel paths. The spectacular displays of migrating birds which could be observed on the p.p.i. out to 70 miles, appear to have been characteristic of the autumn and not of the spring. It was estimated by Drury and Keith (1962) from measurements made by Nisbet, that several million birds must have passed over a 100-mile front on one of these busy autumn nights!

In a later study Drury and Nisbet (1967) confirmed the general north-eastward trend of the spring migration and determined the orientations of the migrants by the wedge method. They found that the migratory directions were less diverse than those of the autumn. It was concluded that some of the species which migrated south in the autumn must have followed a route in the spring which lay to the west of New England.

The dependence of New England migration upon weather factors

Radar provides the bare bones of the migration picture. It remains for the ornithologist to interpret what he sees in terms of weather and geographical factors, taking account also of the changing inner state of the bird itself, which is an indefinable mixture of physiological and psychological elements as indicated in the last chapter. This type of analysis has been applied to the radar records secured in both England and in America, with results that sometimes agree and sometimes apparently disagree – but the probable causes of the disagreement suggest some fascinating possibilities concerning the weather programming, or instinctive reactions of the birds to various weather situations.

In contrast to the highly variable weather which prevails over most of the year in the North Sea area (save in the presence of continental highs which produced a winter such as 1963, or the summers of 1959 and 1964), the weather cycle of New England is much more regular. Drury and Keith have shown how this stability of the annual weather pattern arises from the location of New England on the eastern edge of a huge continental land mass from which proceed the high and low pressure systems that move continuously over New England and out into the

Atlantic. Such pressure systems may take several days to cross the New England region, which, of course, is very much larger in extent than the radar cover of South Truro shown in Fig. 7.1. It is not suggested that the movements of such air masses are wholly predictable, not even by man, let alone by the birds, but the air masses and linear distances involved are so much greater in New England than those in north-west Europe, also the air masses are moving more slowly, that the succession of weather events consequent upon the air-flow fall into a more recognizable pattern – in other words, weather forecasting in New England is certainly possible over at least a few days.

In particular, Drury and Keith suggest that the birds can recognize a sequence of weather events which is likely to lead to a successful flight, i.e. that a code of weather stimuli can be defined which leads to the selection of a propitious air-mass movement, if not to an objective appreciation of the total weather situation. Two other macroscopic meteorological influences must be mentioned whose effects are not, of course, limited to the New England region. Firstly, there is the presence of the polar air cap, small in summer and large in winter. Secondly, over the mid-Atlantic there exists the 'Bermuda–Azores' high-pressure zone which expands and moves westward and northward in summer in anti-phase with the polar cap. In winter the polar cap sheds a series of cold fronts of more or less regular form. In summer, the cap recedes due to the heating of the polar regions and its dominant influence on the New England weather is then taken over by the movement of warm maritime air from the tropics moving round the western edge of the Bermuda–Azores high-pressure region, so creating an air stream directed north-eastward.

A greatly simplified view of the influence of the weather pattern in the east of the U.S.A. on the migrations of birds would be to say that the establishment during spring of the north-eastward flowing warm air creates a stream which the migrating birds can ride from their wintering sites in the southern states, central America, and northern South America. Similarly, the onset of autumn brings cooling and extension of the polar air cap towards the south, so that during September and October the warm maritime air is pushed back and these cooler south-westward flowing air masses again provide the moving medium that the birds, their breeding complete in eastern Canada, Labrador, Newfoundland, and the northern portions of the New England states, can now exploit in the return journey south and south-westwards back to their winter sojourning areas. Simultaneously, the Bermuda high-pressure region is reduced in area and recedes so that the stream of cool air from the north becomes dominant.

Accepting this broad pattern of meteorological and migratory events, Drury and Keith have analysed the radar records of movements against the background of the local weather changes in order to show that the birds move when the sum total of weather evidence available to them adds up to a situation which signals the fact that the air masses are moving in the manner best suited to the migration to be made. It will be noted that, according to this view, the bird is adapted or 'programmed' to react to the total weather situation, although the pointers to favourable air-mass movements are still the local weather effects. Thus, in spring, ideal conditions for migration are a rise in temperature of 5°–10° F, favourable winds not exceeding 20 knots and clear skies – and it is just these weather events which accompany the movement of warm maritime air up the Atlantic coast. Similarly, in autumn the weather circumstances that signal the movement of polar air to the south-west are a temperature drop of 10° F, a favourable wind from the north-east not exceeding 20 knots and clear skies.

These deductions by Drury and Keith from the radar/weather evidence are in substantial agreement with a review made by Lack (1960) of the influence of weather on migration in the U.S.A. In addition, there is also agreement on the general inhibiting effects on migration of strong winds, rain, and overcast; although the American workers suggest that overcast has little effect in the early spring.

Clearing rain as a stimulus to migration

One interesting feature of both the American and the British work is the emphasis laid upon the importance of a period of rain, not merely because it acts as an inhibitor of migration but rather that its termination seems to provide an almost irresistible stimulus to the birds to move. In Drury and Keith's view the maximum stimulus for migration appears to occur when a period of rain not only ceases but is accompanied by clearing skies, following winds of low speed and a temperature rise or fall according to the season, i.e. spring or autumn respectively. Such a sequence of events was reported by Drury and Keith (1962) during the autumn migration of 1959; this incident illustrates very vividly how carefully the radar data must be associated with both weather reports and the sightings of bird watchers if a correct interpretation of events is to be achieved. The period covered was 30 August–8 September 1959; radar showed only small general activity of seabirds and waders during this time except on the night of 4/5 September when the largest small-bird migration of the autumn took place with the p.p.i. obscured to a range of 70 miles. Weather details for this period were:

Rain
In north-western New England 30 August–3 September. Rain continued in southern New England until early on 4 September.

Pressure, visibility, and wind
High pressure centre in the region from 4 September bringing clear skies 4–8 September, wind veering to North on 4th/5th as the High moved across New England.

Temperature
Day Temperature   80° F
Minimum Night Temperature 60° F until 4th/5th when it fell to low 50° F

Bird Movements (Visual)

30 August to 4 September	– No migration observed
4 September	– Large movement of warblers and thrushes observed in New Hampshire
5 September	– Medium movements in most parts of New England
6–8 September	– Small numbers of various species observed

Drury and Keith interpreted these diverse pieces of information in accordance with the above pattern, suggesting that warbler migration over or through the New England area had been prevented by the presence of widespread rain. The partial clearance of rain from northern New England on 3 September prompted a movement southward of many birds but grounding resulted from the presence of the rain in the south of the region. Complete clearance of rain on the 4th and the presence of a northerly wind on the night 4th/5th, accompanied by a fall in temperature, produced conditions wholly favourable for a heavy movement of the birds to the south and south-west, which is what the radar recorded on the night of 4/5 September. It should be pointed out that the fall in temperature in this case was a consequence of the wind change. Lack has recorded many cases in Britain in which temperature may be regarded as a secondary effect resulting from the wind change and has shown that the existence of a favourable wind is the most important stimulus to movement.

Internal and external stimuli to migration

It is not the purpose of this book to discuss the vast subject of bird migration in general, which has been the special province of so many distinguished ornithologists, but rather to show only the part which radar is playing in furthering such studies. No matter whether migration phenomena are studied by radar or by visual observation, however, there has to be clear recognition that motivation within the bird itself is a vital element in the whole process. It has been shown by many workers (e.g. Marshall, 1961) that the migratory urge within the bird grows in intensity as a consequence of physiological changes, particularly within the bird's reproductive system, in consequence of the increase in day length with the onset of spring. Experiments with caged birds of migratory species have shown that this migratory restlessness occurs for a few weeks in the spring and autumn respectively, at the times which are usual for the species to undertake its journey to the breeding grounds and to return to the wintering region. If favourable weather factors present themselves to the bird in accordance with its programme of responses to the total weather situation, and at a time when its physiological state has produced an urge to migrate of sufficient intensity, then the bird will commence or continue its migratory journey. Unfavourable weather states will inhibit the bird's departure, but the detailed analyses of Lack (1959/63) and Drury and Keith (1962) of the radar movements/weather relation show that the longer the birds are forced to wait for departure because of inclement

137

weather, the worse weather state they are finally prepared to accept, because of the growing urge within them that cannot ultimately be denied, even though departure results in heavy losses en route. Clearly this balance point of opposing urges within individual birds must show a wide scatter throughout a community, and radar has shown that some birds, at least, will move at all times throughout the migratory period. It was pointed out in the last chapter that not the least important of the British radar results was the demonstration that days on which no migration at all occurs, either direct or reverse, are very rare indeed.

In accordance with this picture, Drury and Keith have found that whereas a 10° F rise or more is necessary for stimulus in the early spring, 5° rise may be an adequate stimulus in late spring. It was also found that reversal of the normal positive weather stimuli associated with spring or autumn can cause temporary reversal of bird flow, e.g. the incidence of northerly winds in spring coupled with a fall in temperature and clear skies can produce the similitude of conditions normally associated with the autumn, and the movements of the birds can be reversed for a time in consequence. Reversed migration effects are discussed in Chapter Eight; repeated reversals of bird flow during winter between Britain and the Continent were shown by Lack to be attributable to wind effects rather than temperature change in the case of European passerines and waders.

Comparison of radar movements in the U.S.A. and in Europe

In viewing the results of this radar migration analysis as a whole including both the work in the U.S.A. and North-western Europe, perhaps the sharpest difference between the interpretations offered for the two sets of events lies in the significance attached to the local and immediate weather situation. The American workers regard the bird's reaction to the local weather factors as being a lead to the *total weather situation*, which is itself indicative of the presence of favourable movements of air masses on the grand scale that will ensure success of the long flights to be undertaken. Lack and his collaborators, on the other hand, have adduced radar evidence which suggests that the European birds react to the *immediate weather stimuli*, i.e. temperature, speed, and direction of wind, the presence of cloud or overcast, as necessary and sufficient indications of conditions that will permit the successful completion of their much shorter flights.

As already mentioned, the migration observed at South Truro in spring forms the eastern wing only of the massive, broad-front movement of birds that flows up the eastern United States. On the eastern flank of the migrating birds is the broad Atlantic waiting to absorb those birds which have not 'assessed' the weather symptoms aright, and many sightings have been made over the sea and in Bermuda of birds borne by the air masses which have been diverted far to the east from their usual tracks. The adaptation achieved by the birds in America is, therefore, likely to be more specific than in Europe where the sea crossings are short and the consequences of error in assessing weather conditions favourable for departure are not so catastrophic. Viewed in this way the discrepancies between the American and European results appear reasonably reconcilable – the birds in the two regions have become adapted to their own peculiar weather conditions and geographical hazards. There is obviously much work to be done before we fully understand how the bird manages its highly complex migratory way of life.

Radar observations of migration in the Middle West of the U.S.A.

Radar observations on the flight paths of nocturnal migrants over the state of Illinois were made by Bellrose and Graber during the spring and autumn of 1960 (Bellrose and Graber, 1963). In this work a low powered 3-cm aircraft-type radar was employed which was mounted on top of a 100-ft tower (Fig. 11.4) and was scanned at the rate of 10 r.p.m. The objective was to measure both altitude and track direction of the birds accurately, in order to study the influence of wind and cloud. For such an investigation the precision of an X-band radar possesses many advantages which were well exploited in this study; the lack of range (4 miles only) was not a great disadvantage in an inland region such as Illinois, which is distinguished by its remarkable flatness and total absence of prominent physical features. It is true that only a short length of track could be observed and measured, usually 200–4,000 ft, so that it was, in effect, the direction of the tangent to the track at the position of the station which was measured, but probably this limitation was no great matter over such a flat terrain where it was reasonable to suppose that the tracks would be straight, though not necessarily parallel. Of importance also was the fact that it was the transits of individual birds that were observed and measured and not the echoes from flocks.

Directions of radar tracks in spring and autumn

Champaign-Urbana, where Bellrose and Graber carried out their work, is over-flown by masses of migrants proceeding from widely distributed and unknown wintering areas towards their equally numerous and unknown summer breeding grounds. This circumstance, combined with the fact that at least 150 species were involved, both passerines and shorebirds, made it inevitable that some spread of tracks should occur. Track directions during the month of May are summarized in the upper part of Fig. 7.3 in which each radial line represents the mean course of all migrants tracked on radar during one night. It will be seen that the majority of the vectors lay between 7° and 17°, although the total angular spread was from 332° to 43°.

The observations during the autumn were more extensive, covering the period from early August until November, and the corresponding flight directions are shown in the lower half of Fig. 7.3. Track spread in the autumn was from 124° to 204°, with most of the vectors lying between 160° and 175°.

Of particular interest in Fig. 7.3 is the fact that most of the tracks lie east of the north–south line in both the spring and the autumn, so that the flight direction of the return path in the autumn was certainly not the reciprocal of the outward course in the spring. This observation led Bellrose and Graber to suggest the theory that the complete migration route of many species of birds which

139

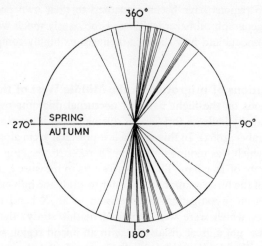

FIG. 7.3. True courses of nocturnal migrants during spring (upper semicircle) and autumn (lower semicircle) in 1960 at Champaign, Illinois. Each line represents the mean course of all migrants tracked on radar during one night. Note that most tracks are E. of the N.–S. line, both spring and autumn (after Bellrose and Graber, *Proc. XIIIth Int. Ornith. Congress*, 1963)

winter in Central and South America and breed in North America is in the form of a closed ellipse which the birds travel clockwise, northwards in the spring and southwards in the autumn. By this adaptation maximum advantage would be derived from the wind pattern of the North American continent, which is westerly above latitude 40° and easterly below latitude 30°. It was pointed out by Bellrose and Graber that such a migration path is known to be pursued by the Golden Plover (*Pluvialus dominica*), but only the use of radar has permitted study of the passerine migrations which occur mostly at night and which apparently also follow elliptical routes.

Correction for wind drift

Intensive study was made of wind effects in order to determine whether the birds were able to recognize the presence of drift and to correct for it, or whether they flew on constant headings. Careful measurements of track directions at different altitudes were made, a measurement for which the airborne type of radar was specially suited; bird headings were derived from the tracks by use of the parallelogram law and the appropriate wind vector, in the manner described in Chapter Two. It was found that shifts of the wind with altitude produced corresponding changes in the tracks, but the relation between wind shift and track displacement was not a simple one; it appeared that there was some compensation for wind drift but the compensation was far from perfect.

That drift correction was practised by the birds is suggested by the following figures, which compare the nightly average flight tracks during spring and autumn respectively with the average flight headings derived from them:

140

	Spring 1960	Autumn 1960
Spread of track	69°	72°
Spread of heading	113°	98°

It is clear that the spread in headings was substantially greater than the spread in tracks, i.e. each individual bird had endeavoured to adjust its heading in order to reduce the drifting effect of the wind; in this way a more nearly constant direction of track over the ground would be obtained (see Appendix).

A similar result was obtained from direct radar observations made during the day with the same radar apparatus on the tracks of migrating ducks during the autumn of 1961. The average daily flight tracks were spread over an angle of 36° while the derived headings spread over 63°.

More detailed analysis of the wind drift phenomenon suggested that the drift errors increased with the strength of the crosswind. While this is probably only to be expected it implies that it is high drift rates with which the bird fails to cope; this could well be of importance in any theory of bird navigation.

Orientation of birds beneath overcast

Of importance also to any theory of orientation is the behaviour of the birds beneath complete cloud cover or overcast at night, when sight of the stars is denied to them. Bellrose and Graber (1963) cautiously stated that their observations only permitted them to suggest that birds were not necessarily disoriented under such circumstances. More specifically, it appeared that during the autumn migration the mean directions flown by the birds, also the spread of tracks, on overcast nights, were similar to those measured on clear or only partly clouded nights. The birds usually endeavoured to rise above the cloud layer but if this were too high then they flew just beneath the cloud, although some of the simultaneous records of birds and clouds showed that birds sometimes flew within the cloud layer itself (see Chapter Eleven).

Evidence was given which suggested that when a migration was commenced under a clear sky, the journey could be continued beneath complete cloud cover, with good directional flight paths being maintained. Nevertheless, the track records suggested that other birds under the same overcast conditions failed to determine the direction as accurately as those birds to whom the sky was available for celestial guidance.

CHAPTER EIGHT

Flight behaviour of migrants

Long-range radars are ideal for the detection of broad-front movements because they can maintain continuous surveillance over large areas of land and sea. The patterns of bird migration in Europe and North America described in the preceding chapters were established in this way. Such radars have also supplied a large amount of information about the flight behaviour of birds and the manoeuvres which they execute during their migratory journeys. It is the purpose of the present chapter to describe some of the interesting features of these researches and to consider the significance which they possess for theories of bird navigation and orientation.

In this work, the fact that the radar 'sees' masses of birds in the form of angel groups is no disadvantage, but when it is required to examine the behaviour of the individual bird it is necessary to use a short-range radar, for the resolving power of a surveillance equipment at long range is too coarse for this purpose.

Radar identification

Objects in the airspace such as aircraft, birds, or raindrops which are capable of reflecting radio waves are shown upon the p.p.i. of the radar as bright points of light. These 'echo paints' on the phosphor of the tube do not directly reveal the nature of the reflecting sources, however, and so target identification is one of the main operational difficulties encountered in the use of radar; especially is this the case when it is desired to know the species of the birds producing a particular angel. It is true that radar provides other information which can be helpful in identification, such as amplitude modulation, speed and altitude for example, but it would be more convenient if positive identification of the identity of a scattering object were suggested by the appearance of the echo itself upon the p.p.i.

In the case of bird echoes, hints as to the species involved are not wholly lacking. These clues depend upon the size of the bird and also upon the manner in which the birds associate themselves into flights. As shown in Chapter Three, signal strength is determined by the echoing area of the target, but the constancy or otherwise this signal depends upon how the echoing area is made up.

Study of the characteristics of the signal from a target, whether single or multiple, is called 'Signature Analysis', and was considered in Chapter Five. It is sufficient for our present purpose to note that if the angel comprises only one large bird, then the fluctuations of the signal will be less than if the angel were composed of three or four smaller birds, for in the latter case the interference between the radio waves reflected from the individual birds would result in a varying or fading signal due to their changing relative positions. If a large number of birds were contributing to a single echo, then the fluctuation of the resultant signal might again be small, since the effects of the large number of random movements of the birds relative to each other would tend to cancel each other out. On the other hand, wide dispersal of small flocks of small birds would produce a mass of small signals, each of which would only just rise above the radio noise level of the equipment for part of the time, with the consequence that varying, low-level echoes on the p.p.i. would result, giving the appearance of a haze of light rather than an assembly of bright echo points. This appears to be the case during the night migration of warblers.

Identification of the masses of angels seen by surveillance radar is a judicious mixture of physics and experience. The operator learns to associate a particular type of echo with a species known to be airborne at the time and location in question, in this way a library of identified echo-types can be slowly built up and applied on future occasions; a few examples may be quoted:

Waders

In Plate 10 are shown the strong, discrete echoes typical of lapwing. This picture was taken on the morning of 23 December 1958, when a light easterly wind favoured a small-scale, hard-weather movement of these birds from Holland to England as in Fig. 8.1.

FIG. 8.1. Hardweather movements of lapwings westward assisted by a light easterly wind (Key to Plate 10 (*b*), 23 December 1958)

Swifts

Night-ascended swifts produce a semi-continuum of echoes as in Plate 20. This is a typical example of signals contributed by all the birds contained within the pulse volume, as compared to the bird-group echoes provided by diurnal flights of lapwing.

143

Warblers

The appearance of the p.p.i. at 21.00 h on 24 August, 1959, is shown in Plate 10 and a key to the movements in progress is given in Fig. 8.2. Commencing at 20.15 h a huge departure of fine warbler-type echoes took place in a direction slightly east of south. The movement started over land and the coastlines of Suffolk, Kent, and Sussex seemed to advance out to sea. On this same evening between 19.00–24.00 h, a small movement of wader-type echoes occurred, directed south-south-west across Kent, Sussex, and the Pas de Calais. Some of

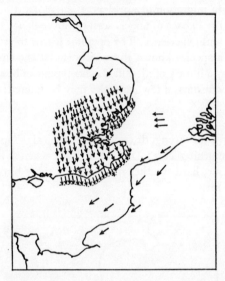

FIG. 8.2. 24 August 1959, 21.00 h. Anticyclonic with W.N.W. wind. Between 19.00 and 24.00 a small movement of wader-type echoes S.S.W. across Kent, Sussex, and Pas de Calais, some of them coasting W.S.W. to Cap Gris Nez, also a very few S.S.W. over East Anglia. From 20.15 a huge departure of very fine warbler-type echoes over land slightly E. of S., the outlines of the Essex and Sussex coasts seeming to advance out to sea like a wall, as indicated by the dotted lines. Around 23.30 a small W. arrival of wader-type echoes. (Key to Plate 10 (*a*) after Lack and Eastwood, *British Birds*, 1962)

these echoes can be seen at the bottom of Fig. 8.2, and are easily distinguished from the dense mass of warbler-type echoes in the centre of the picture. The movements on this pair of figures is typical of the first part of the night during late August and September.

Starlings

The ring angel echoes, characteristic of dispersing starlings, are shown in Plate 17.

144

Medium-sized passerines

A passerine movement during late November is shown in Plate 10 (24 November 1959) with a directional key in Fig. 8.3. This situation occurred during the night when a light wind was directed from the south-west. The easterly movement of

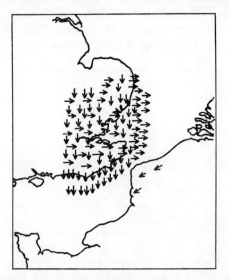

FIG. 8.3. 24 November 1959, early night. Transitional weather with S.W. wind. Over England a big departure E. and a fairly big departure just E. of S., and over Pas de Calais a small movement S.W. These movements started at dusk, the one E. consisting of moderate-sized echoes similar to those when thrushes are on migration. (Key to Plate 10 (*c*) after Lack and Eastwood, *British Birds*, 1962)

moderate-sized echoes is typical of the larger passerines such as thrushes. Both the easterly and southerly movements commenced at dusk.

Sea birds

The haphazard daytime movements of strong angels in the estuary of the Thames appear to be associated with movements of seabirds, since randomness is present even under conditions of good visibility, when there can be no question of disorientation (Plate 19).

Movements between Dover and Calais

A radar microscope picture of the distribution of angels within a rectangle of 20 × 15 n.m. situated between Dover and Calais at 23.00 h on 22 August 1958, is shown in Plate 11. A typical low density situation is illustrated with about one angel per 10 sq miles. The trails indicate the directions of movement as derived from the time-compression method of analysis and demonstrate how the English Channel is a region of mixed directions of bird flow. Very seldom is it that only a single direction of bird movement can be observed – a situation which is in marked contrast to the undirectional flows of migratory birds described by Drury and Keith (1962) for the dense movements that take place in the vicinity of Cape Cod in the autumn.

Departures from headlands and the wind drift effect over the North Sea
It has long been known that migrating birds frequently make use of headlands as preferred points of departure for a sea crossing. This phenomenon is well illustrated in Plate 11 (*b*) and Fig. 8.4 which show birds streaming from the

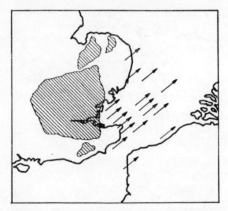

FIG. 8.4. Directions of the spring migratory movements shown on Plate 11 (*b*), 09.15 h, 5 March 1959

North and South Foreland on a wild March morning in 1959 in the presence of a strong south-west wind.

The marked northerly drift imposed on the birds by the wind is clearly shown. Headland departure is also shown in Fig. 8.5 for 1 April 1959, and took place from both the South Foreland and Dungeness, but the wind direction in this case was west-south-west and the drift to the north was markedly less than in Fig. 8.4.

The difference between the track directions of the movements shown in Fig. 8.4 and Fig. 8.5, which relate to birds of the same migration, in response to the wind states south-south-west and west-south-west respectively, suggests that any correction for wind drift that the birds might have made was not significant. In other words, the North Sea birds appear to maintain a roughly constant heading and make no correction for wind drift. The birds, therefore, make good a ground track which is the vector resultant of the wind velocity and the birds' air velocity. This conclusion is in accordance with the general findings of Lack (1958 and 1962b), also Lack and Eastwood (1962) for the North Sea region.

Studies of the diurnal overland migration of the chaffinch made in Holland (Gruys-Casimir, 1965) show that this bird is able to compensate for wind drift, at least for wind speeds under 8 knots, and provided that visible beacons are available. Similar results were obtained for the starling as a diurnal migrant. On

FIG. 8.5. 1 April 1959, 08.00 h. Rather disturbed weather with W.S.W. wind Moderate departure E. over land and sea, and marked coasting movement E.N.E. to South Foreland and smaller one to Dungeness, with concentrated departures from these headlands (after Lack and Eastwood, *British Birds*, 1962)

the other hand, it was found by Eastwood, Isted and Rider (1962) that many dispersal flights overland performed by starlings from their roosts, show no correction for drift, in spite of the clear view which the birds then have of the ground. Neither did analysis of the flight directions of the common scoter and the long-tailed duck across the Gulf of Finland by Bergman and Donner (1964) reveal any correction for wind drift.

During his radar study of passerine night migration over Northumberland, Evans (1966) paid particular attention to the influence of wind speed and direction upon the tracks of the migrants. He found that the autumnal movements of warblers, chats and flycatchers in this region occurred during August and September and took place mainly along tracks lying between south-east and south-south-east. Evan's method of assessing the effect of wind was to establish a mean track of the migrants for each night of his observations and to derive from this bearing the probable heading of the birds by 'taking out the wind.' He argued that if the migrants made no correction for wind drift then the scatter in the tracks should be significantly greater than the scatter in the headings derived from them. In fact, he found that the scatters in tracks and headings were about the same and suggested that this evidence supported his view that the migrants were flying on approximately fixed tracks rather than fixed headings (see Appendix).

Further evidence in support of drift correction by the birds was the fact that the average of the mean tracks on seven of the nights when the wind was observed from the left of the birds was 155·6°, while the corresponding average on twenty nights with winds from the right of the birds' path was 152·3°. Also, on certain

147

nights when a shift in wind direction took place, the mean track of the migrants was unaffected.

Similar results were obtained by Evans for the passage migrations of wheatears from Iceland or Greenland during early October and during the movements of songthrushes and Icelandic redwings in late October and November. The track directions in these cases were mainly south-south-east or south-east by south, but Evans suggested that his track, wind and heading data were compatible with wind drift correction by the migrants rather than with the occurrence of passive wind drift of the birds from preferred headings.

Correction for wind drift by migrants over New England

In the case of migratory flights over eastern New England the studies of Drury and Keith (1962) and of Drury and Nisbet (1964) have shown that the radar track directions of the major migratory movements of the autumn, as measured by the M.T.I. wedge method, were substantially constant in spite of changes in the wind. It was concluded that the birds must have been correcting for wind drift, since the spread in the tracks was much less than the spread in the bird headings (see Appendix).

In the case of the south-west movements over the mainland of Massachusetts, the total spread of tracks observed by Drury and Nisbet over the four autumns of observation was contained between 211° and 225°, the mean being 219°, and the standard deviation 3·7°. Track directions were measured at hourly intervals. The headings of the birds on these occasions were extracted by combining the track with the wind speed, using the triangle of velocities. For the purpose of this calculation a constant air speed of 22 knots was assumed for the birds, this being taken as typical of the species involved. These authors also considered that the most probable value of wind speed and direction was that derived from the spacing of the isobars at ground level, i.e. the geostrophic wind was employed. It was found that the bird headings corresponding to the above tracks ranged from 177° to 243° respectively, the standard deviation being 18·5°.

Although the above method of deriving the birds' heading cannot be regarded as wholly satisfactory, the results certainly suggest that the birds adjusted their headings so as to maintain the same track throughout the night, and from night to night, regardless of the direction of the wind. Perhaps more convincing was the simple comparison made by Drury and Nisbet of the tracks recorded in the presence of winds directed from:

(a) the right of the bird; measured direction of mean track was   217·8°
(b) the left of the bird; measured direction of mean track was   217·9°
(c) tail of the bird; measured direction of mean track was   220°

The substantial identity of the mean tracks flown by the birds under these three very different sets of circumstances strongly suggests that the birds were correcting for drift produced by the crosswinds. Partial correction for wind drift was also detected by Bellrose and Graber, as described in the previous chapter.

A correction effect was detected by Drury and Nisbet (1967) during a later study of the orientation of spring migrants off New England. The mean direction of migration is then roughly north-eastward but is deviated to left or right in the presence of crosswinds from right or left respectively. The magnitude of this deviation, however, appeared to be too small to be caused by wind drift from a constant heading. Drury and Nisbet suggested that an explanation of their observations might be that the 'programmed' direction which the birds wished to fly must inevitably vary somewhat in individual birds. In the presence of a cross-wind from the right the flight of those birds might be suppressed whose preferred direction lay to the right of the average direction. Thus, although the birds that flew might make correction for wind drift from their individual and inate pre-ferred direction, there could still be night to night changes in the tracks flown due to the selection effect produced by the wind.

A similar theory was also proposed by Evans (1966) in connexion with his observations of the behaviour of migrants over the north-east of England. He suggested that the theory might explain the flight behaviour of winter visitors leaving East Anglia in the spring, when, as reported by Lack (1958, 1960a) the birds tend to adhere to a constant heading and so suffer drift by the wind. It was pointed out by Evans, however, that a consequence of his interpretation of the drifting of East Anglian migrants was that 'one might expect a greater variation in track directions on calm nights than on windy nights, for under the former circumstances few, if any, migrants would be discouraged from departing, no matter what the track on which they intended to fly'.

It is interesting to note that M.T.I. wedges on bird movements in the East Anglian region as observed at Bushy Hill are most clearly distinguished when the wind is light and following. Wedges are not observed with strong winds. The evidence from Bushy Hill, therefore, hardly supports Evans' theory.

It should be added that M.T.I. wedges on bird movements are not commonly observed at Bushy Hill in either the spring or the autumn, with the clarity that would permit persistent directions to be extracted as in the work of Drury and Nisbet. This is not because the movements do not cover sufficient area of the tube; the reason must be the lack of parallelism in the bird tracks and because the tracks are not maintained constant in direction during passage through the radar cover.

Undoubtedly the greater air turbulence of the North Sea region is a contri-butory factor to this difference. It can also not be excluded that the requirement for more precise orientation in the American case, due to the long sea crossing and the presence of the Atlantic on the flank of the bird's movement, has caused the process of selection and adaptation in the species to be more severe than the European situation required. In the North Sea case, particularly in the autumn, the presence of easterly following winds from the Continent and a general orientation of the birds towards the west can lead to a successful sea crossing to the British Isles in the majority of cases, and so the mechanism of selection can be quite crude.

L

Orientation and disorientation

Closely associated with the above problem of wind drift is the occasional occurrence of 'disorientation' in migratory birds. Before the advent of radar the possibility of disorientation could only be inferred from the fact that falls of unusual species in a locality were often associated with such adverse weather factors as opposed wind, cloud, or rain, particularly at night; these are just the circumstances that would prejudice any conceivable form of bird navigation. Radar, and particularly the speeded film method of viewing the p.p.i., permits many occasions to be detected when the birds are seen to circle aimlessly; their tracks show a randomness which is in sharp contrast to the straight, purposeful tracks characteristic of birds on migration, and can only be indicative of directional uncertainty in the bird. Disorientation is not a common occurrence and is of limited extent in both time and space, being confined to regions of fog, total cloud, or rain, and persists only for the duration of the adverse weather state. Such an incident was described by Lack and Eastwood (1962).

The situation just after sunrise is shown in Fig. 8.6 and indicates the presence of the normal springtime movements towards the east, north-north-west, and north-north-east respectively, but only in the southern part of the region. Hardly any migration was detected in East Anglia, which was covered by widespread fog. Disoriented movements of birds took place off the coast of East Anglia in the dotted area; Fig. 8.6 also shows the presence of a cold front moving eastwards which quenched the migratory movements overland. By 10.30 the fog over the sea had dispersed and the birds in the disoriented region appeared to be moving south-south-west. This was interpreted as a reverse movement of migrants previously travelling north-north-east consequent upon reorientation after some time had been spent in a confused and disoriented state.

That disorientation should sometimes occur is not surprising; what is remarkable is that it should occur so infrequently. Accepting the findings of Kramer (1950, 1952, 1957) and Sauer (1956, 1960) on the parts probably played by the sun and the stars in facilitating orientation by day and by night respectively, it might appear reasonable to assume that birds having a clear view of the sky can maintain orientation, while birds denied this sky view because of the presence of complete cloud cover must inevitably be disoriented, particularly at night. Alas, the accumulation of radar observations shows that birds do not always behave in accordance with this clear-cut theory of orientation by visual reference.

In a fascinating review of radar evidence on migratory orientation, Lack (1962b) pointed out that birds normally fly along straight tracks both by day and by night, no matter what the wind state, and that in the transition from day to night the continuity and direction of a bird track is maintained. These facts demonstrate that the migrant has a capability for orientation which is operative both by day and by night without discontinuity between them. On the assumption that the exercise of the bird's 'orientational' faculty requires a clear view of the sun or the stars, then the presence of complete overcast should produce

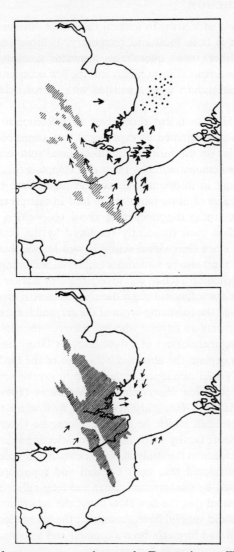

FIG. 8.6. 24 March 1959, 07.00 and 10.30 h. Depression to W. of Ireland, cold front moving E. as indicated by cross-hatching, wind S.E. ahead of front and S.W. behind it, widespread fog over northern part of area in early morning. Between 05.30 and 07.30 in S. of area there were the three typical spring movements, (i) E., (ii) N.N.W., and (iii) N.N.E., but in East Anglia extremely few birds were moving E. and none in the other direction, presumably because they had been grounded by fog. Over the sea off East Anglia there was an area (shown dotted) where all directions were random and migrants were presumably disoriented in fog. Movements (i), (ii), and (iii) faded rapidly between 08.30 and 09.00 as the cold front moved across, but between 08.30 and 10.30 there was a movement S.S.W. over the sea off Suffolk and Essex, presumably due to the birds disoriented earlier returning when the fog dispersed. Behind the front, a N.E. movement started at 11.00 and was dense over the whole area in the afternoon (after Lack and Eastwood, *British Birds*, 1962)

disorientation over a wide area. In general this is not observed; as Lack points out, disorientation is both local and temporary. Bellrose and Graber (1963), also Drury and Nisbet (1964), quote radar instances of orientation being maintained under fully overcast skies at night, and the few occasions of disorientation quoted by the latter authors were associated with overcast skies, rain, fog, and stationary fronts.

The ability of birds to orient themselves by reference to the sun or stars appears to be fully substantiated by experiment with caged birds. Nevertheless, the findings of radar on the rarity of the disoriented state under natural flight conditions, also the demonstration by radar that complete overcast by itself does not necessarily result in disorientation, even at night, both suggest that some unknown factor is also of importance to the bird in this process of orientation. Drury and Nisbet (1964) suggested that visual observation of the landscape might be the method most frequently employed by the birds in maintaining their flight tracks, since their visual acuity is well known, but they considered that other methods must also be sometimes employed, including possibly a simple form of inertial orientation such as was investigated by Barlow (1964) in the case of animals. This is not a fanciful suggestion, since inertial control is well developed in man through the balancing organ of the ear, and is even better developed in a bird, as is apparent to anyone who has admired the flight operations of a swift or the hunting manoeuvres of a flycatcher. As Drury and Nisbet observe, 'It is preferable to explain the observed behaviour of the birds as a refinement of a system already well developed, rather than to invoke new senses.' On the other hand, the intriguing observations of Matthews (1961), on the strong tendency of the Mallard (*Anas platyrhynchos*) to fly towards the north-west on release, the phenomenon which he termed 'Nonsense Orientation', is surely indicative of some inate faculty in the mallard for selecting a direction which may not be without relevance to the study of bird orientation in general. Bergman and Donner (1964) considered that both celestial and topographical methods of orientation were used by the common scoter and long-tailed duck.

It has to be admitted that the new facts about the behaviour of birds in flight, which only radar could supply, have shown that the orientation problem is even more complex than had formerly been supposed and a solution can only come from much more observation and experiment.

Coasting and turning

An impressive feature of the radar films of migration recorded at Bushy Hill is the manner in which the birds fly across the coastline without any deviation in their tracks. This occurs for both emigrant and immigrant movements and by night as well as by day. On some occasions, however, quite spectacular coasting movements have been observed and two very interesting examples are shown in Plate 12 for 3 February 1959 and 6 October 1959 respectively; Figs. 8.7 and 8.8 provide the keys to these p.p.i. photographs.

Plate 12 (a) illustrates a hard-weather movement of birds into south-eastern

FIG. 8.7. 3 February 1959, 09.00 h. Anticyclone in North Sea, dry, cold, with easterly wind. Departure W. from Continent started well before first light, with peak around sunrise. Reached Kent and Sussex earlier than Essex or Suffolk because of shorter sea-crossing. Birds coasted W.S.W. to Cap Gris Nez, where concentration put out to sea W.S.W. between 08.00 and 09.00, turning gradually W. in Channel and later W.N.W., chiefly after passing Beachy Head, and so in to land. Later in the morning the W.N.W. turn came further E., so that most birds were flying in over Beachy Head, and yet later over Dungeness. A similar turn W.N.W. was seen off North Foreland, and later in the morning by some of the birds off Essex and Suffolk. (Key to Plate 12 (a) after Lack and Eastwood, *British Birds*, 1962)

England; the weather was dry and cold with an anticyclone centred on the North Sea. Departure from the Continent was stimulated and assisted by an easterly wind and commenced in the later part of the night, reaching a peak about sunrise. Arrival of the lapwing-type echoes into Sussex and Kent preceded the crossing into Essex and Suffolk because of the shorter sea crossing. More interesting was the coasting movement west-south-west along the coast of France to Cap Gris Nez at which point the birds moved straight out to sea without change of direction. There was no sign of a sharp turn to the north-east in order to make the shorter crossing between Calais and Dover, even though the English coast would be clearly visible to the birds, since they were at an altitude of approximately 2,000 ft and the crossing was made in daylight. As the birds advanced over the Channel a gradual turn to the right was made away from the initial direction of west-south-west, so that the track became westerly and later west-north-west. On reaching the English coast the first birds crossed at Beachy Head, but the turn of track was made earlier as the morning advanced, so that the later birds crossed the coast more to the east over Dungeness. A similar turn west-north-west was made off North Foreland, by some of the birds heading towards Essex and Suffolk but occurred still later in the morning.

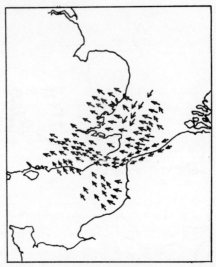

FIG. 8.8. 6 October 1959, morning. Anticyclone in southern Scandinavia, S.E. wind. Small movement S.S.W. off Suffolk and Essex, presumably from Scandinavia, and dense morning departure westward from Holland and Belgium, presumably mainly of chaffinches. The presumed chaffinches in the North Sea flew either W. or between W.N.W. and N.W., giving the impression of two distinct movements, but probably this was merely due to individual birds making the change from W. to N. of W. at different points on their journey; after reaching East Anglia most flew N. of W. but some still W. In the eastern Channel and over Sussex, all flew between W.N.W. and N.W. In between these two areas a thick band coasted W.S.W. to Cap Gris Nez and put out to sea as a concentrated stream which gradually changed direction to W. and then W.N.W.; this concentration was still easily noticeable far inland over Kent. (Key to Plate 12 (b) after Lack and Eastwood, *British Birds*, 1962)

An even more spectacular coasting movement is shown in Plate 12 (b) for 6 October 1959. This general migration was directed west-north-west, which is usual for an autumn westerly-oriented movement made in the presence of a south-easterly wind. The appearance of the echoes and the time of their occurrence suggests that medium-sized passerines, probably chaffinches, were involved and should be compared with those of Plate 12 (a), which were presumed to be lapwings. The key of Fig. 8.8 shows that a small movement was present off the coast of Essex and directed south-south-west, probably of birds arrived from Scandinavia. More obvious is the heavy morning departure from Holland and Belgium, and of special interest is the concentrated stream of echoes moving west-south-west along the Belgian and French coasts towards Cap Gris Nez, there to put to sea in a manner very similar to the movement in Plate 12 (a). Again, there is the change of direction from west-south-west through west to west-north-west and the speeded film shows that the stream continued well into Kent before dispersal occurred; the turn to the right was also made earlier in the crossing as the morning advanced, precisely as described above for the lapwings.

This gradual change in direction of the presumed chaffinch stream is reminiscent of the observations of Tinbergen (1956), Deelder (1949), and Van Dobben (1953) on the movements of migratory chaffinches through Holland. The extensive studies of the autumn migration of this bird through north-west Europe have been conveniently summarized by Gruys-Casimir (1965). The chaffinches which pass over the western and central part of Holland are of Scandinavian origin and winter in Britain and Ireland. Leaving Norway and Sweden in a southerly direction the birds sweep down through Denmark into Holland, where the standard direction of their broad-front movement is west-south-west. If the weather is favourable the birds cross the coast without deviation; but in the presence of unfavourable winds they proceed along the coastline in the direction that deviates least from their standard direction. A concentration of birds builds up at the coast under these circumstances, the stream leading down to Cap Gris Nez where the crossing to England is made. Over Holland the chaffinch has a tendency to overcompensate for wind drift, with the result that in the presence of northerly winds the track of migrants changes direction towards the north as the day advances. In the presence of southerly winds the shift is towards the south.

Not all the birds made the complete coasting run to Cap Gris Nez; many spilled off the Belgian coast to the north-west as shown, so that there is little doubt that the coast was not providing a guide line to the point where the shortest sea crossing could be made. Lack (1959) has shown from other radar evidence that Van Dobben (1953) and other Dutch workers were probably correct in their view that coasting movements in autumn are without any guiding significance but are probably due to an urge to travel in the migrants which is insufficiently strong to take them out to sea unless there is a favourable wind.

Drury and Nisbet (1964) reported that their southbound autumn night migrants, moving over and near the mainland of Massachusetts, turned towards the right during the progress of the night by about 1·5° per hour. This evolution was a turning away from the Atlantic ocean stretching out on the birds' left flank and so the directional change had survival value. But if survival is the simple objective of the continental birds crossing to England, it is not clear why they do not turn north-east at Calais, particularly as the English coast must be visible to them. Lack and Eastwood (1962), from a review of these and similar movements, have suggested that these birds have an innate tendency to head towards the west, but are also prompted by sight of the land to head into the land, with the result that the flown track is a compromise between the two tendencies. That the birds turn to the right progressively sooner as the day advances might be interpreted to mean that the tendency to migrate on their innate westerly heading weakened as the day wore on, while the urge to make for land strengthened. It must be admitted that this problem of track change over the sea is still largely a mystery.

Changes in flight direction of diurnal migrants over Switzerland were measured by Gehring (1963) using the Kloten radar. In calm, fine weather, the flight direction turned clockwise through an angle of about 12° during the course of the morning, but returned to the standard direction in the afternoon. Gehring explained this phenomenon in terms of errors in the birds' interpretation of the 'sun-compass'.

A long, slow track change by night is illustrated in Fig. 6.1. A wader-type movement south-south-west from the Wash took place in the first part of the night but had ceased by about 23.00 h. At 24.00 h a thin stream of strong echoes came in from the sea and crossed the east coast of Norfolk. They continued to move westward across Norfolk, but turned very gradually in a great arc over the land until the stream headed south at the point of dispersal, which occurred in a region about 100 miles west-south-west from the point of crossing the coast. These echoes were very slow moving, slower than lapwings, and perhaps were produced by gulls; the manner in which the birds described the same path over the country, even though well separated from each other in time and distance, was very remarkable, and must surely be indicative of a navigation process which is extraordinarily precise.

Fig. 8.9 has been inserted for comparison with Fig. 8.8. Both these p.p.i. records were made in October 1959, and although they are separated in time by only one week, the appearance of the movements are quite different. Both dia-

FIG. 8.9. 13 October 1959, morning. Anticyclone over Scandinavia and Germany, small depression over north-east England, wind variable but N.W. to N. This shows the three main autumn movements: (i) departure S.S.E. over land, in this instance chiefly to the west of the station, (ii) small S.S.W. arrival from Scandinavia and (iii) W. arrival from Low Countries, the birds on the last movement as usual proceeding W.N.W. or N.W. from France south of Cap Gris Nez. In marked contrast to the position in Fig. 8.8, there was no coasting movement to Cap Gris Nez, and no concentrated departure from it (after Lack and Eastwood, *British Birds*, 1962)

grams refer to a migratory movement from the Continent performed by birds presumed to be of the same species, motivated with the same urge, viz. to achieve winter quarters in the British Isles via a sea crossing towards the west. The marked difference in the form of these two movements was prompted by the difference in wind states on the two occasions. In Fig. 8.9 which refers to a morning situation, as does Fig. 8.8 the winds were variable, but came mainly from between north and north-west. Fig. 8.9 shows that the three main movements characteristic of the autumn in this region were simultaneously present, i.e.:

(*i*) departure south-south-east over land;
(*ii*) small south-south-west arrival from Scandinavia, and
(*iii*) westerly arrival from the Low Countries accompanied by a north-west departure from France south of Cap Gris Nez.

On this occasion there was no coasting movement to Cap Griz Nez as in Fig. 8.8, neither was there a concentrated departure from it.

An interesting example of a fairly sharp change in direction made during the course of a migratory flight over the sea has been reported by Lack (1962a). During the course of radar studies of the tracks pursued by Scandinavian thrushes moving south-south-west during the autumn migration, it was noticed that these birds, if in the presence of an easterly wind, change their tracks to south-south-east after dawn and while still over the sea. In discussing the navigational significance of this manoeuvre, Lack considered that it could not be a true compensation for drift arrived at by a process of bi-co-ordinate navigation based upon a view of the sun that was then possible, since the directional change appeared to be independent of the amount of drift that had been experienced. Lack made the very tentative suggestion that the Scandinavian thrush might have an innate reaction to a view of the sea at dawn, which prompts the change of heading from south-south-west to south-south-east, but this response is only operative if the birds are aware of the westward drift. Lack recognized that this hypothesis was highly speculative, but pointed out that it would be a valuable adaptation in birds making journeys from Scandinavia to France or the British Isles, since it would tend to prevent passage over the Atlantic.

It is significant that similar behaviour in this same species was observed by Myres (1964), during his radar observations in the Shetlands (see Fig. 6.4). He noted the occurrence of the dawn ascent phenomenon discussed in Chapter Six, followed by changes in the flight tracks of the migrants from the overnight bearing of west-south-west to one of the three main directions of movement E.S.E.–S.E., N.–N.N.E., or S.–S.S.W. Again, Myres considered that this south-eastward reorientation of the Scandinavian thrushes was an adaptation which would ensure that migrants should not fly out over the eastern Atlantic but should regain Ireland, the British Isles, or the coast of North-west Europe. It is a movement which is the inverse of that reported by Drury and Keith (1962) where the hazard to the birds was the presence of the Atlantic on their eastern flank when moving southwards in the autumn.

A turning movement of migrant birds on a grand scale was described by Evans (1966) from his radar study of passerine departures from eastern Scotland and north-east England during the autumn. These take place in directions east of south, yet the ultimate objective of many of these small birds is the Iberian Peninsula. An average track of south-south-west would have to be flown if the birds were to attempt a direct journey, and this would cause the birds to be opposed by unfavourable winds. Evans pointed out that a departure east of south from the east coasts of England and Scotland permits the birds to take advantage of the speed and directions of the upper-air winds which prevail at this time of the year and so the birds perform a wide circling movement which ultimately brings them through southern France into Spain.

Hard-weather movements and reversed migration

One of the more surprising discoveries made by radar surveillance of bird movements off the east coast of England is that some migration takes place on every day of the year, although the volume varies greatly from day to day. Equally important has been the recognition that movements in directions opposed to the so-called normal direction of migration for the time of year are very common indeed. When such reversed movements are prompted by a worsening of weather, for example, by falls of snow making food finding difficult for the birds, it is usual to describe the migration as a 'hard-weather movement'. The birds move to a less weather-bound region and the change is wholly favourable to the birds' way of life. Such movements may be of quite short duration, but the interesting point is that movements of the same general form have been detected at other times of the year when it seems more appropriate to refer to them as 'reversed migrations'.

In the case of the North Sea area, the frequency of occurrence of reversed movements is so high that it would appear more natural to regard the sea as an enclosed lake across which the indigenous birds of the region, such as lapwing, starlings, and thrushes come and go according to the local weather situation. It is obviously advantageous to the birds to leave a region of frozen ground, and to return when it has thawed and the snow has disappeared. Vleugel (1948) has described the 'frost flights' of lapwing in this way in Holland. This situation, of course, does not apply to the 'long haul' migrants such as the warblers, except that during their arrival and departure phases signs of similar reversed movements prompted by weather changes have been found for them also (Lack 1963).

The departure and return phases of a hard-weather movement are well illustrated in Plate 13 and in the associated diagrams of Figs. 8.10 and 8.11. These photographs actually refer to two separate movements which took place in January 1959 and January 1962 respectively, but between them they describe completely the outward progress of a reversed winter movement, and the return of the birds to their normal winter habitat when the period of inclemency has passed. The weather on 9 January 1959 was cold, with snow showers in the areas indicated by the cross hatching on Fig. 8.10; a depression was located in the

FIG. 8.10. 9 January 1959, noon. Depression over North Sea, cold with snow showers as indicated by cross-hatching, N.N.W. wind. Extensive departure of large lapwing-type echoes just E. of S., ahead of snow showers moving S. over Norfolk. First birds crossed Sussex coast at 09.30. No change of direction over sea. (Key to Plate 13 (a) after Lack and Eastwood, *British Birds*, 1962)

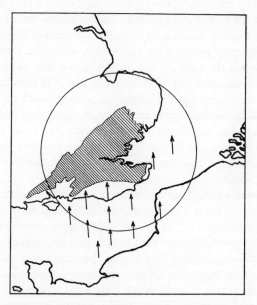

FIG. 8.11. Warm front advancing northward from France followed by returning lapwing after a hard weather sortie. (6 January 1962. Key to Plate 13 (b) after Eastwood and Rider, *British Birds*, 1965)

North Sea and the wind was from the north-north-west. A heavy exodus of lapwing-type echoes took place slightly east of south; on the time compression film it appeared as if the birds were fleeing before the southward moving snow clouds. The sharp bottom edge to the galaxy of lapwing in Plate 13 (a) corresponds to the limit of the radar cover and does not mean that the birds fell into the sea on this occasion! In Plate 13 (b) and Fig. 8.11 the wintry spell is over in Britain and a warm front is moving north, closely followed by the lapwing returning from France to the English countryside.

It will be noted in the above examples that the birds led the cold front but followed the warm front. This is an example of the fact that the main stimulus to such movement is usually the direction of the wind. Lack and Eastwood (1962) have shown that hard-weather winter movements across the North Sea correlate very firmly with the wind direction and that fall in temperature is only a secondary effect. Plate 12 (a) and Fig. 8.7 illustrate a hard-weather movement directed westwards from the Low Countries which is, in many ways, typical of the more pronounced movements of this type. The wind direction appears to be sensed by the birds and accepted as an harbinger of the inclement weather which is to follow, the birds, therefore, move in response to its prompting. But the birds may sometimes be misled and a case was described in Lack and Eastwood (1962) when the birds moved north into England in response to a southerly wind but later encountered a region of snow and north-easterly winds (29 December 1961).

'Hard-weather movement' in the winter is a form of bird behaviour which seems to be wholly reasonable; the reversed migrations which occur during the other months of the year are not quite so easy to understand. Lack (1963b) has pointed out that westerly movements from the continent of Europe into England occur quite frequently even during springtime, when the normal direction of migration is towards the east. He has further shown that the main stimulus to such reversed movements is the wind direction, just as in the winter. To indulge in an unnecessary sea crossing during the late spring would appear to be much more of a hazard to the bird newly arrived on the Continent from England than to wait until the wind has changed to a direction favourable to its continued migration. Nevertheless, the frequency with which reversed movements occur suggests that the 'retreat' manoeuvre must be the more favourable to survival of the species as a whole.

Fig. 8.12 illustrates a small but well-defined reversed migration which occurred during the autumn of 1961. The movement was directed north-north-west from the continental coast, east of the Pas de Calais. This movement was made in response to a light south-easterly wind in Belgium. Simultaneously, there was a small eastward movement from East Anglia, the wind being south-westerly.

Mascher and his co-workers in Sweden (1962) have shown that reversed movements during the spring migration are daily occurrences and can take place simultaneously with migratory flights in the normal direction by other birds. In this case the reversed flights were observed in the field and were made at low altitude against the wind, so that they were not visible to the radar; the normal

FIG. 8.12. 26 September 1961, early night. Transitional weather with high pressure to the E., a light south-westerly wind W. of East Anglia, a light south-easterly wind in Belgium, and a S. wind in between. Small eastward departure (locally S.E. or E.N.E.) from eastern England, very small movement W. from France S. of Cap Gris Nez, and small but clear-cut reversed migration N.N.W. from coast between southern Belgium and Pas de Calais (after Lack and Eastwood, *British Birds*, 1962)

flights were performed at high altitude with the wind. Drury and Keith (1962) refer to the occurrence of reversed movements on the radar records of their New England birds in the presence of cold fronts and snow showers, i.e. under hard-weather circumstances, but reversal also occurred in the late spring when the weather situation approximated to that which normally accompanies the autumn migration. Similarly, Drury, Nisbet, and Richardson (1961) report occasional large northerly movements in Massachusetts in the presence of southerly winds in the autumn, i.e. weather conditions normally characteristic of the spring produce a spring-like response in the migrating birds of the autumn.

One important and interesting aspect of the reversed migration phenomenon again relates to the method of orientation or navigation employed by birds. The radar evidence shows that reversed movements are made with all the confidence and precision that mark the normal migratory flights. This observation implies that a bird engaged on a reversal movement possesses the ability to select and fly a track which is the reciprocal of the one it would normally pursue in the presence of the particular configuration of sun or stars associated with its usual migratory direction. If the bird indeed employs celestial means of orientation it has become amazingly adept in the interpretation of stellar positions! Again, radar evidence has not solved the problem of orientation during reversed migration; but it has shown that there are additional demands to be made of the bird's navigation equipment. In fact, the memory store and programme of the bird's innate navigation computer required to accomplish all these migratory manoeuvres has become bewilderingly complicated. One feels intuitively that a simplification of the theory must be possible somewhere.

Bird tracks near clouds

The flight behaviour of birds in the vicinity of dense clouds, and particularly the avoidance tactics adopted by birds near regions of heavy rain, can often be followed by radar, since a centimetric radar can see both the birds and the rain. Fig. 8.6 illustrates the easterly passage of heavy clouds associated with a cold front across south-east England and shows the resumption of flight activity in Sussex directed to the north-east after the clouds had cleared from the area. An example of cloud avoidance which occurred during a winter hard weather movement of lapwing is shown in Fig. 8.13. The birds moved south in response to a

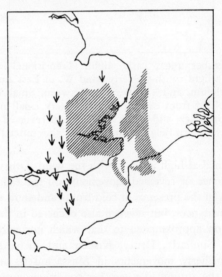

FIG. 8.13. 7 January 1959, noon. Depression over Low Countries, cold with snow showers as indicated by cross-hatching, wind N. earlier and in N. of area, N.W. later, especially in S. of area. Departure of large lapwing-type echoes S. over land, changing to S.S.E. over sea, probably due to drift by wind. First detected inland when thick cloud dispersed between 09.00 and 10.00, first birds crossed Sussex coast at 11.40, highest density 12.30. None detected in E. of area, where much cloud remained (after Lack and Eastwood, *British Birds*, 1962)

northerly wind which became north-westerly in the coastal region. A region of heavy snow showers was skirted by the birds whose direction of movement changed from south to south-south-east after crossing the coast – probably due to the drifting effect of the north-west wind. Bird activity quenched by the passage of a cold front is illustrated in Fig. 8.14.

A vivid example of the influence of rain upon the flights of birds is shown in Fig. 8.15 which is adapted from drawings of the Bard Hill p.p.i. made by Parslow

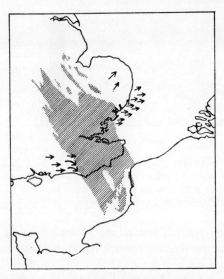

FIG. 8.14. 11 March 1959, 10.40 h. Depression off north-west Ireland, cold front moving N.E. over area as indicated by cross-hatching, S. wind ahead of front and S.W. wind behind it. Very small movement N. of E. in Norfolk and dense departure from Suffolk coast a little N. of E., birds presumably flying too low over land to be detected by radar and rising at coast, or starting from coast after earlier concentration there. No bird-echoes detectable near front, but behind it in Sussex a moderate E. movement, some turning S.E. along edge of front but many disappearing into it (after Lack and Eastwood, *British Birds*, 1962)

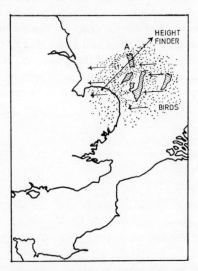

FIG. 8.15. Absence of bird-echoes on the lee side of hail or rain clouds, due to the birds descending to pass beneath them but rising again later. Wind direction N.E., 20.30 h, 15 October 1960 (after Parslow, in Lack, *Ibis*, 1963)

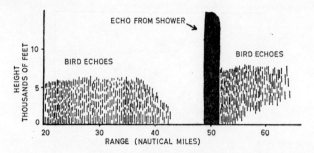

FIG. 8.16. Drawing of height-finder radar display looking N.E. across cloud at *A* in Fig. 8.15. Bird-echoes extend to a little over 5,000 ft except in the lee of a hail shower where there are at first none and then a gradual rise in height to nearly the previous level (after Parslow in Lack, *Ibis*, 1963)

and reported in Lack (1963). The wind was blowing from the north-east and the main bird movement was directed towards the west. A number of clouds are seen to have a region free from bird echoes on their western flanks. Lack and Parslow explained this effect as in Fig. 8.16 which is a drawing of the height-radar display tube. The radar echo from a heavy rain shower is shown at a range of 50 miles. Beyond this range the bird echoes extended in altitude up to 5,000 ft, but at shorter ranges the birds evidently dropped down to near the sea's surface and so became invisible to the surveillance radar. The height finder showed that the birds gradually regained altitude after passing beneath the cloud and through the rain shower. On the other hand, the actual passage of birds through cloud at night has been reported by Bellrose and Graber (1963) and by Eastwood and Rider (1965).

Radar pictures of hurricanes off the coast of Florida have been taken by a number of workers, for example, Senn and Hiser (1957), but it has proved extremely difficult to detect birds in any of these pictures. Nevertheless, birds are undoubtedly swept up by such storms and were seen in the eye of hurricane Carla in 1961 by the weather planes which flew in proximity to it.

CHAPTER NINE

Ring angels

The starling is not a well-loved bird. Many people regard it as aggressive, greedy, and voracious and it must be admitted that its bird-table manners are not of the best. Even its iridescent plumage excites no favour; it is true that it is grudgingly conceded that the starling is an excellent vocal mimic, witness Hotspur's threat to Bolingbroke in *Henry IV*:

> Nay, I'll have a starling shall be taught to speak
> Nothing but 'Mortimer' and give it to him,
>   To keep his anger still in motion.

But its performance as a ventriloquist gains no affection for the bird, indeed it is held to prove its essential deceit while the roosting habits of the species, whether in copses in the country or on buildings near Trafalgar Square, have created widespread antipathy and aversion towards the starling which is sad to contemplate. In spite of its ill reputation the starling is an interesting bird, not least to the radar ornithologist, for its habit of flocking and dispersal creates a pattern of radar echoes which have helped to reveal many aspects of starling behaviour hitherto unknown to the bird watcher in the field.

The starling is also a successful bird, as the extension of its range during the last 100 years amply testifies – including the colonization of North America since its release in Central Park, New York, in 1897. How much of this success is attributable to its social habits, and particularly to its peculiar roosting behaviour? We do not yet know the answer to these intriguing questions but it is certain that an understanding of these matters will help towards the better appreciation of a remarkable bird. In the account of bird migration given in the previous chapters the starling has been mentioned as a successful practitioner of the art and many orientation studies have been based on caged starlings. Detailed radar studies of this bird may well lead to clues on orientation phenomena during flight which may have application to migratory birds as a whole. The starling is specially suited to such a study for this bird possesses one inestimable advantage to the radar bird watcher – it is a self-identifying species on the p.p.i., by reason of the flight patterns which its social behaviour leads it to create.

Ring angels
All the displays of angels considered in earlier chapters of this book have been composed of randomly dispersed point echoes distributed over the face of the tube. It is true that the density of the echoes has usually been greater near the centre of the tube, as shown in Fig. 5.1, but the general mass of echoes has not

been characterized by any form of pattern. Sometimes, however, a group of angels may be so associated together as to present a recognizable shape, such as a line or hollow ring. Line angels will be discussed in the next chapter; here we are concerned with the 'ring-angel' phenomenon and its explanation.

A typical and fully developed radar ring angel which was recorded at Bushy Hill on 17 February 1959 is shown in Plate 14 (Eastwood, Bell, and Phelp, 1959). This illustration shows a random mass of ordinary migrant bird type angels in the Thames Estuary together with a ring angel located at Mereworth in Kent; the ordered geometric structure of the latter will be apparent. Such a ring angel is first observed on the p.p.i. as an intense point echo; it then extends into an annular 'ring of pearls', to be followed by other rings at approximately equal intervals of time, usually in the order of 3 min. When the ring is viewed upon the ciné projector, the whole phenomenon has an appearance similar to the outward moving ripples upon a pond after a pebble has been tossed into the water. The Bushy Hill ring angels were observed to occur around sunrise and in most cases the presence of the ring centres was detected on the p.p.i. a few minutes before sunrise. This correlation with sunrise is vividly apparent on the radar display since the sun radiates quite strongly at 1,300 Mc/s and so shows itself as a bright radial line upon the p.p.i. as soon as it tops the horizon. Plate 14 illustrates the rising radio sun effect and shows also the large number of simultaneous ring dispersals that may occur from a number of centres widely spread over the countryside.

Ring angels were first observed in January 1956 by Elder of the University of Michigan (Elder, 1957). He it was who gave the appropriate name of 'ring angels' to the peculiar echoes which he observed upon his L-band radar at Ypsilanti. In contrast to the Bushy Hill rings, the Michigan rings occurred only in the late afternoon between 14.50–17.00 h and the impression of the observing staff was that occurrences were more frequent in the winter than at other seasons of the year. Again, the ring was observed to start as a bright blob which formed into a diffuse ring that expanded outwards at a speed of about 43 knots; some of Elder's observations suggested a movement of the ring centre in the direction of the wind. In seeking for the cause of these curious afternoon echoes Elder made a careful examination of the topography of the region in which the rings were observed, including inspection from the air, and particular attention was directed to the possible coincidence of a ring centre with any large industrial establishment or heating plant capable of emitting large volumes of hot, moist gas such as the cooling tower of an electrical power generating station. Such a rising column of gas could conceivably give rise to radar echoes. No such obvious reasons for the production of the ring echoes was detected, nor did any topographical feature suggest a feasible explanation. Elder tentatively suggested that the ring structure might be attributable to reflections from the consecutive wavefronts of a shear-gravity wave moving through the atmosphere; curiously enough, the velocity of such a wave as derived by Elder from an analysis by Haurwitz (1951) was about 33 knots, but this rough correspondence was not interpreted as proof of the origin of the rings. Indeed, Elder concluded that many more records of ring angels over an extended period of time would have to be secured, together with full information on the atmospheric circumstances associated with their occurrence before the cause of the ring echoes could be established with certainty.

Another form of ring angel was detected by Ligda (1958) on films of the p.p.i. associated with a United States Air Defence Command Radar situated at Texarkana, Texas. These ring echoes were recorded during the summer of 1957 and showed many points of difference when compared with Elder's rings. Thus only one active centre was detected on each day and a single ring only emanated from the initial point echo – not a succession of rings. Again, the speed of radial growth was only about 14 knots, and the ring did not remain sharp as in Plate 14 but became progressively thicker and more diffuse as it expanded. The maximum radius achieved was about 15–25 miles. The first appearance of the centre echo roughly coincided with the occurrence of local sunrise and, very significantly, some of the films showed the presence of a weak, irregular-shaped echo at sunset which appeared to approach and converge upon the point of origin of the morning ring. It was the detection of this late afternoon echo which led to the suggestion that the explanation of both the morning ring angel and the evening diffuse echo might be found in the movements of the Redwinged Blackbird (*Agelaius phoencieus*), a species which is indigenous to eastern Texas, Arkansas, and Louisiana. As sunset approaches millions of these birds return from their feeding grounds to spend the night in communal roosts located in swampland thickets of giant cutgrass and willow, where they are safe from their predators. At sunrise the birds leave the roost and disperse over the countryside, flying over roughly radial tracks for the early part of the exodus, thus producing an expanding, annular ring of birds; the thickening of the ring with time was attributed to the wide difference in air speeds between the various members of the giant flock. When the birds have cropped the available feed in one area they move on to a similar region elsewhere and so the morning ring is only observed for a few weeks and, for radar detection, the roost must be at a favourable point within the cover of the radar station.

Ring angels in England

Radar echoes in the form of expanding arcs of circles were observed by Harper in December 1956, and were associated by him with starlings erupting from a roost which was situated 6 miles south of his meteorological radar station at East Hill, Hertfordshire (Harper, 1959). The starlings left this roost just before sunrise in two great waves which were separated in time by an interval of about 2 min. Observers at the roost reported that the birds left in all directions, although unevenly dispersed, and flew outwards along radial tracks. The centre from which the arcs on the radar p.p.i. were expanding coincided in range and bearing with the known position of the roost, so that there was little doubt that these arcs were produced by the erupting starlings. The fact that only incomplete

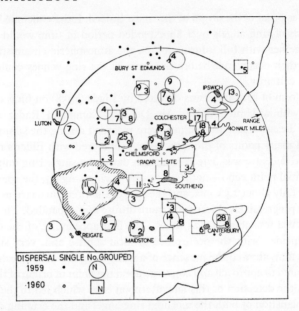

FIG. 9.1. Geographical distribution of ring-angel centres 1959–60 (after Eastwood, Isted, and Rider, *Proc. Roy Soc.*, 1962)

arcs of birds were observed proceeding towards the north-west was attributed to the screening action of the Chiltern Hills to the south of the roost, while the radar echoes of birds flying towards the north were obscured by the permanent echoes in this region of the p.p.i.

A complete demonstration that expanding radar ring angels were produced by birds dispersing from a roost was finally given by Eastwood, Isted, and Rider (1960). Observations and recordings at the Bushy Hill station of ring-angel occurrences commenced in 1958 and were continued over a period of some years, photographs usually being taken at least once per week. From the ciné films of the p.p.i. it was possible (by projection on to a graticule) to extract the positions of the ring angel centres and to plot them upon a chart, as in Fig. 9.1. This map records the positions of 454 ring eruptions which were observed during 1959 and 1960 (Eastwood et al., 1962). Some of the rings derived from sources proved to be active on several occasions and these centres have been plotted as large open circles and squares corresponding to records taken in 1959 and 1960 respectively. The number within the circle or square corresponds to the number of observed dispersals. Many rings, however, were observed on one occasion only and the small circles show the locations of these sources (solid for 1959 and open for 1960). As the number of observations accumulated during 1958/9 it became possible to pinpoint the centres of the persistent ring-angel sources more accurately and field investigations established that starlings' roosts were indeed sited at these map reference points.

Although the identification of these various roosts was fairly convincing proof

168

of the starling explanation of the ring-angel echoes it was still considered desirable to establish direct correspondence between visual observations of bird movements at these roosts and the appearance and movement of the ring angels upon the p.p.i. This correlation was achieved by placing a number of observers at certain of the ring-angel sources selected from Fig. 9.1. These observers were equipped with radio telephones with which they could signal to the radar station the precise moment of emergence from the roost of the successive waves of starlings. This information was impressed directly upon the film which was recording the radar picture as in Plate 15, where the numeral '4' on the left indicates that the fourth wave was about to leave the southern roost at Frating, Essex. Subsequent projection of the films established perfect time correlation between the emergence of radar rings from an active centre on the p.p.i. and the eruption of the birds from the roost as seen by the field watchers.

But if starlings leave home in the morning in this very orderly fashion why are they not seen returning in the evening? In fact, they *are* seen by the radar but the pattern of this movement on the p.p.i. is not quite so obvious as the morning dispersal. In order to detect and study the form of the evening assembly on the Bushy Hill radar use was made of the radar microscope device described in Chapter Two. It was arranged that the microscope display should cover the area of the p.p.i. around a selected ring-angel centre. Ciné records were made of the microscope tube and showed a heavy movement of birds into the roost region during the hour preceding sunset. Plate 16 shows the radar microscope picture of one form of evening assembly of starlings in progress at Matching Green, Essex; the majority of the birds approached the roost from the south-west and were extended over a funnel of 5 miles in length. The appearance of a ring which occurred at sunrise on the following morning is shown in Plate 16 and the thickening of the ring towards the south-west will be noted, i.e. more birds departed in the reciprocal direction of the evening approach line than in any other direction. The elliptical form of the ring is a consequence of the change of co-ordinates from polar on the p.p.i. to Cartesian on the B-scope, as discussed in Chapter Two. It will also be noted that the centre of the ellipse is slightly displaced from the apex of the assembly. This is in accordance with the well-known fact that when starlings progress towards their roost in the evening their flights normally terminate at a pre-assembly point near to the roost and this process of assembly or integration of the members of the community may take as long as an hour (see, for example, Witherby, Jourdain, Ticehurst, and Tucker, 1940). Final entry into the roost normally takes place about sunset and is completed within a few minutes.

The radar microscope also shows that the pre-assembly phase may often be a very ragged affair with a convergence upon the roost region from many directions, so that the whole occurrence is similar to that described by Ligda for the redwinged blackbirds. Finally, it is pleasant to be able to conclude this general discussion of the ring angel phenomenon with a brief comment on two films shown to the author by the kindness of Mr M. S. Kuhring and Dr W. H. Gunn

169

of the National Research Council of Canada. These films showed ring dispersals of starlings as recorded at a radar station in mid-Canada and also at the Canadian/N.A.T.O. station at Metz, France. The appearance of the rings was in all essential respects similar to those seen at Bushy Hill. A bird explanation would also appear more than likely for Elder's rings, but the fact that the dispersals took place in the late afternoon seems to rule out the starling as the species responsible.

Radar rings in starling research

With the proof established that radar rings are produced by starlings it becomes possible to use the radar as a means of furthering our knowledge of the roosting behaviour of the starling. Two important problems which can obviously be tackled by the ring method are the seasonal variation in roost activity and the changes in the geographical distribution of roosts throughout the year and from year to year. The power of the radar method of starling study will be obvious when it is remembered that the Bushy Hill radar is seeing roosting movements over an area of at least 5,000 sq miles – sometimes much more than this – since ring dispersals have been observed in Northern France when anomalous propagation conditions prevail. The radar supplies precise information on the times of occurrence and the positions of ring events, so that if radar watch could be made every morning of the year then a comprehensive record of roost activity within the cover of the station would be obtained. Bushy Hill radar station suffers no radio screening from high ground in any direction, since it occupies the summit of a low hill (204 ft above sea level) in the predominantly flat and low-lying county of Essex, thus the radar cover is substantially complete in every direction. Unfortunately for the starling record Bushy Hill is an experimental station engaged on non-routine work, therefore only one day per week could be devoted to ring-angel recording. Nevertheless, this weekly sample was taken systematically throughout the year and so provides a good picture of the variations in ring activity.

The geographical distribution of the rings recorded during 1959 and 1960 is shown in Fig. 9.1. It is clear that no ring centres occurred over the sea. It was the gradual recognition of this fact during the early compilation of the record in 1958 that caused the attention of Eastwood and his colleagues to be focused upon starling roosts as a possible explanation of the rings after it had proved impossible to associate any distinctive topographical features of the countryside with the persistent ring centres. The ring source located in the centre of London is particularly interesting and merits special comment, since it corresponds to the roost made up of the birds which cluster round the great buildings in the vicinity of Trafalgar Square, a type of roost which is now unfortunately to be found in many city centres. That this roost should be seen by the radar at all is of great technical interest in view of the mass of permanent echoes produced by the buildings in the London region and the device that made it possible was the Moving Target Indicator described earlier.

The comparative permanence of many of the ring angel centres is remarkable, particularly in the case of the larger roosts, but changes do occur and are immediately apparent on the radar, which permits the successive changes in location of a roost community to be followed. An interesting example of this was provided by the huge Frating roost, near Clacton-on-Sea, which made three changes of location during December 1959 and January 1960. The first of these 'flittings' occurred after a big shoot conducted by the local farmers against the starlings. It is well known that some roost sites are occupied by starlings over many winters and this essential continuity of occupation by the birds of an extended area of the country is well illustrated in Plate 17. This figure compares the pictures of the morning dispersals as recorded on 1 September 1959 and 31 October 1964 respectively. The general similarity between the pictures is obvious; that the scale and distribution of the activity should be broadly similar after an interval of five years is very impressive – the continuance of the ring centre at Canterbury is particularly noteworthy.

In making the comparison of Plate 17 between different years, it was necessary to select p.p.i. pictures which were taken in corresponding seasons of the respective years, because the number of ring angels which may be observed on any morning is not constant throughout the year but shows a definite seasonal cycle. Fig. 9.2 shows the variation in the number of ring dispersal centres observed on each of the operating days. It will be seen that the greatest number of centres occurs during July and August. During 1959 no ring dispersals were recorded during the four weeks mid-April to mid-May, while in 1960 there were none for the six weeks between mid-April and the end of May. Some ring activity was observed for all other weeks of the year.

The complete but temporary cessation of the ring form of dispersal during April and May is presumably related to the breeding habits of the starling. At this season of the year, not only has the total starling population in England been greatly reduced by the return of the many winter visitors to the Continent, but

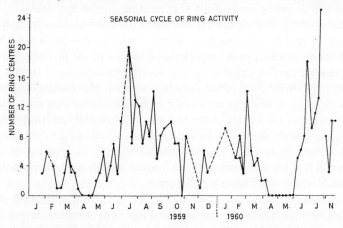

FIG. 9.2. Seasonal variation in the number of roosts observed during 1959 and 1960 (after Eastwood, Isted, and Rider, *Proc. Roy. Soc.*, 1962)

the breeding birds have also left the roosts. Although many roosts continue in being during this period, their populations are greatly reduced, and the radar evidence demonstrates that the periodic form of ring dispersal to the feeding grounds does not then take place. It is interesting to speculate that wave or periodic dispersal appears to be a characteristic of larger roosts and may perhaps be related either to the mechanics or to the procedures required for the evacuation of masses of birds from the confined region of a roosting site, cluttered as it often is with masses of closely packed trees.

The marked increase in the number of ring occurrences which takes place during July and August corresponds to a return to communal roosting by the birds after breeding is completed, and the main centres occupied then continue in being until the start of the next breeding season. The roost populations appear to grow by the accretion or fusion of the small flocks, by the addition of the young birds, and by recruitment from the continental visitors entering the country during these months. October and November, however, are the months when winter visiting starlings are chiefly added to the roost communities.

The occurrence of occasional roosts, i.e. the detection of a centre from which a well-organized ring dispersal took place on only one occasion on the film records, must correspond to the location of a heavy concentration of starlings at a roost occupied for one night, or at the most six, since the Bushy Hill observations were repeated at seven-day intervals. The relationship between these occasional roosts and the semi-permanent roosts is far from clear. The obvious suggestion is that the occasional roosts are due to flocks of birds on passage between their summer and winter places of residence. If this were the case then they would tend to occur more frequently during the spring and autumn migratory periods. However, Fig. 9.3 shows that these occasional roosts, like the persistent ones, are most frequent in July and August, long before the main arrivals of winter visitors in October. Presumably, therefore, the temporary roosts in July and August are due primarily to young birds of the year roosting for the first time.

Migrant starlings moving eastwards towards the Continent in spring do set up temporary roosts however, and some of these have been seen on radar but not nearly as many as might have been expected in view of the probable number of starling emigrants. The migrant roost is readily distinguishable from a normal recurrent roost by the form of the morning dispersal. Movements to the feeding grounds by resident starlings are usually of the expanding ring type but a dispersal of migrants takes place in the presence of a favourable westerly wind and is directed eastwards, the successive waves of birds fanning out to join the general migrant stream. Plate 18 is a good example of such an eruption of migrant starlings and is in marked contrast to the roughly circular movements to the feeding grounds which occur from a stable roost.

It was noted by Lack (1959, 1960) that in Norfolk during springtime starlings sometimes left their roosts near the shore and moved out to sea in extended flocks, which produced long line echoes on his radar. Such movements took place at sunrise, just as for an ordinary starling dispersal, but line departure of birds have

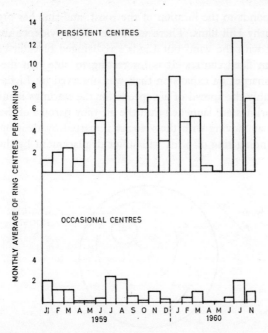

FIG. 9.3. Seasonal variation in the number of (*a*) persistent and (*b*) occasional roosts (after Eastwood, Isted, and Rider, *Proc. Roy. Soc.*, 1962)

also been detected at night and from their speed of flight it is practically certain they were starlings (Lack and Eastwood, 1962). A nocturnal departure eastwards is shown in Plate 18 and took place at midnight on 31 March 1966.

The upper part of Fig. 9.3 shows that there is also variation in the occupancy of roosts used on more than one occasion, and that more roosts are occupied in the late summer than at any other time of the year. The main seasonal variations in the occupancy of roosts, as deduced from the radar observations of Eastwood *et al.* (1962), fit well with what has been found by bird watchers in the field, including the numerous roosts in late summer, the many changes in location between then and the first part of the winter, and a general tendency for small roosts to amalgamate into larger ones at this season (see North 1933; Marples 1934; Cramp, Parrinder, and Richards, 1957).

Starlings and the wind

The influence of wind speed and direction upon the flight paths of migrating birds has been touched upon more than once in this book but in no case is the interaction better illustrated than in the ring dispersal flights of the starling. This roughly circular formation of the flocks of departing birds is clearly a consequence of the approximately radial flight lines which are pursued by the birds, all flying with about equal velocities. The position of the ring angel source upon the p.p.i. should, of course, remain fixed and independent of the wind, since it corresponds to the location of the roost, and this has proved to be the case on the Bushy Hill films. There was some slight evidence that Elder's ring centres shifted with the wind but Ligda's redwinged blackbird dispersals also took place from fixed centres. It is interesting to note that the starling rings remain much sharper on expansion than was observed by Ligda for his blackbirds; presumably the spread of air speeds for the starlings is much smaller.

Once the starlings are launched into the air they partake of the movement of the air as well as moving with the velocity imparted by their own wing beats. Thus the expanding ring of birds will suffer displacement by the wind relative

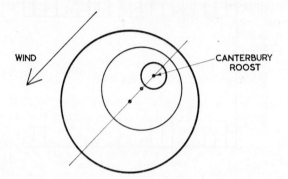

FIG. 9.4. Displacement of rings downwind; birds carried by the wind without drift correction

to the fixed point of emergence, which is the roost itself. This effect is beautifully illustrated in Plate 15 which records the ring structure formed by starlings erupting from a roost near Canterbury and clearly shows displacement of the successive rings to the south-west. A number of such cases have been examined and the ring displacements prove to be in good agreement with the directions and speeds of the local wind, i.e. the centres of the displaced rings lie on a straight line parallel to the wind direction while the rate of displacement of the apparent centres of the rings agrees with the wind speed according to the scheme shown in Fig. 9.4. Of particular interest in Plate 15 is the fact that the circular forms of the displaced rings were substantially preserved, even after some ten minutes of flying, which indicated that all the birds flew on constant headings at the same speed; also, they apparently made no significant correction for wind drift in spite of their presumed knowledge of the local topography. In view of the importance to any theory of orientation or navigation of the question 'Do migrating birds correct for wind drift?' this radar observation on the daylight flight paths of dispersing starlings is of great interest.

Plate 17 illustrates a common form of ring distortion which may be explained by wind effects. The emerging birds are apparently concentrated in a small sector to one side of the roost, e.g. the two roosts 17 miles north-west and 7 miles north-north-west respectively. In these two cases, and in many others where the local wind has been known with certainty, it transpires that the sector dispersal takes place downwind. This suggests that the real explanation of such a form of dispersal is not that the birds are totally absent in the upwind direction but that there is a tendency for these birds to fly at a low altitude in the face of the wind and so remain invisible to the radar. Support for this view is found in the fact that a number of cases have been observed where the direction of sector dispersal from a roost changes with the wind. Although sector dispersals appear to take place predominantly downwind they can be caused by other factors, such as the presence of the sea to the east of the Frating roost (18 miles north-east), thus causing the feeding flights to be directed inland towards the west. Boyd (1932), Marples (1932), Whitehouse (1937, 1938), and other observers have noticed that, whereas at some roosts the birds returned from or dispersed in all directions in similar numbers, at certain other roosts there appeared to be preferred directions of arrival and departure.

A study of the wind states associated with three forms of starling dispersal shows that concentric ring dispersals only occur when the wind speed is comparatively low, i.e. less than 6 knots. For slightly higher winds, i.e. about 6–12 knots, the circular form is substantially preserved but the successive rings are drifted downwind relative to the roost centre. With further increase in wind speed complete rings are rare, instead, the sector form of dispersal occurs with arcs of birds visible to the radar only on the downwind side of the roost.

Starlings and light

The role of the domestic cock as the herald of sunrise has been familiar to man from time immemorial; equally familiar is the dawn chorus of song birds which is one of the great thrills of springtime. So perhaps it is unnecessary to point out that birds are stimulated to various activities by light and that the quenching of the light suppresses these activities – as is evidenced so vividly by bird behaviour during the onset of a total solar eclipse. General recognition of this relationship between bird activity and light intensity became so commonplace through the ages that it is only in comparatively recent times that it has appeared to be desirable to seek for a better understanding of the physical and physiological processes involved.

In common with other birds the starling also reacts to variations in light level, but the effects in this case are particularly interesting since they produce easily recognizable changes in the characteristic dispersal and assembly behaviour. Mention has already been made of the fact that ring dispersals always occur about sunrise and Plate 14 illustrates the point that the onset of the ring occurs almost simultaneously over the whole area covered by the radar. This approximate coincidence with sunrise is maintained throughout the year; there is a similar correspondence with sunset for the time of final entry into the roost from the area of preassembly (Eastwood et al., 1962).

A simple though reasonable view of the dispersal phenomenon is to suppose that the growing intensity of light at sunrise triggers off the birds which are stimulated to leave the roost when the light has achieved a certain threshold level.

This explanation is incomplete, however. If the time interval between the appearance of the first radar ring and sunrise is plotted throughout the year, as in Fig. 9.5, it is seen that the birds tend to leave the roost early relative to sunrise in winter, and late in the summer. Detailed analysis by Eastwood *et al.* (1962) has shown that the birds do not leave the roost at the same light level throughout the year. On the contrary, the tendency is to leave early in the winter when the longest time has been spent in the roost, when the temperature is lowest and when the number of daylight hours available for feeding is least. It seems clear that in the ordering of their dispersal the starlings are sensitive to other stimuli as well as to the intensity of the light. Wynne-Edwards (1929) and Brown (1946) also observed visually that the time of departure from the roosts was earlier,

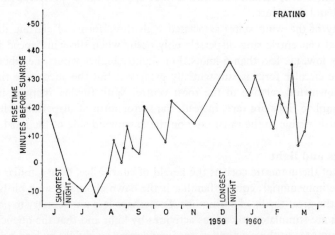

FIG. 9.5. Seasonal changes in time of first ring event relative to sunrise. Frating roost 1959–60 (after Eastwood, Isted, and Rider, *Proc. Roy. Soc.*, 1962)

relative to sunrise, in midwinter than it was in February or March, and Wynne-Edwards (1929) noted that the time of return at dusk was later, relative to sunset, during the mid-winter.

That light intensity is one important factor determining the time of emergence of the birds from the roost, however, is shown by some of the Bushy Hill results in which a direct correlation was established between the extent of cloud cover prevailing on selected mornings throughout the year, and 'lateness' of emergence of the first ring relative to the normal time of occurrence under clear skies for the season in question. Wynne-Edwards (1929) recorded starlings leaving their roosts in the morning later than usual on cloudy and dark days, while Whitehouse (1937, 1938) similarly observed the birds returning earlier to their roosts at dusk on cloudy and windy days.

Ring dispersals have been observed from Bushy Hill on some mornings when ground mist appeared to be widespread, but there was no means of determining whether the active roosts were also enveloped in mist or, if so, to what altitude the mist extended. Harper (1959) reported a radar-observed dispersal of starlings from a roost in dense fog and noted that the onset of the dispersal was delayed about an hour. Several field observers have also recorded starlings failing to return to their roosts on foggy nights, and in some cases the birds were found roosting where normally they did not (Bourne, 1951; McMeeking, 1953; and Bagnall-Oakley, 1959). On the other hand, in foggy weather Wynne-Edwards (1929) recorded a starling flight heading on the normal bearing for the roost at dusk, and two others which headed in nearly the right direction, while Bagnall-Oakley (1956) recorded that starlings often reached their roosts successfully in foggy weather.

Further radar research on the influence of fog upon the flight patterns of starlings is very desirable and must surely make a valuable contribution to the understanding of the orientation and navigation capability of this one species at least.

The behaviour of starling waves
It was the periodic and wave-like form of the ring angel which led to its detection on the p.p.i.; these effects are even more spectacular on the speeded film and demonstrate a regularity in the process of starling roost evacuation which could not be apparent to a field observer. The remarkable nature of the wave emission effect is well shown in Fig. 9.6, which presents in histogram form the relation between the time interval between successive rings and the number of occasions on which such an interval was observed. Four hundred and twenty-five measurements of the lapsed time t between consecutive rings were made for a number of mornings distributed throughout the year, and for a group of eleven roosts. The number of measurements which corresponded to values of t lying between 1 and 2 min, 2 and 3 min, etc., were plotted. It is seen that the most frequently occur-

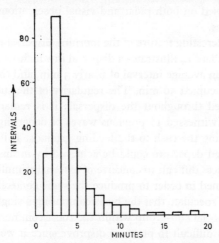

FIG. 9.6. Histogram of the time intervals between successive rings (after Eastwood, Isted, and Rider, *Proc. Roy. Soc.*, 1962)

ring interval was 3 min. Statistical treatment of these results suggested a Gaussian distribution for the logarithm of the time intervals; this is a common form of distribution for many biological variables but it is not clear what factors in the starling's sensory equipment might be involved to explain it in this context. Certainly, the time determining mechanism which results in the 3-min average interval between successive rings appears to be contained within the bird itself for there is no evidence to suggest that this time constant of the dispersal phase is determined by any physical factors within the roost environment.

It is of interest to note that the acoustic or chatter noise level of a roost also varies periodically at sunrise. The Bushy Hill radar observations were supplemented by sound recordings of a major roost made with the aid of a 4-ft paraboloidal mirror fitted with a microphone at its focus, as in Fig. 1.2. It was noticed that the chattering of the birds within the roost and the general excitement were both intense in the minutes preceding the commencement of the dispersal, but with the launching of the first wave came an immediate, sudden quenching in the noise level by as much as 10 db. Rapid regrowth of the noise then followed, only to be quenched once more at the moment of departure of the second wave. The total noise emitted decreased with the departure of the successive flocks, as would be expected since the total number of birds was being reduced progressively, but it was the sudden quietness at the moment of departure of a wave which was the most impressive aspect of the phenomenon.

It seems clear that the periodic eruption of starlings in rings from the roost possesses many of the features of a relaxation oscillation, and is evidently related to an excited, emotional state in the birds. Not all dispersals, however, exhibit such periodicity in their progress, for the radar record has shown that on many occasions small flocks leave the roost at random so producing a radar pattern which is the inverse of the commoner form of assembly at sunset. Only further research based on both radar and visual observations can unravel these intriguing anomalies.

A particularly interesting feature of the morning dispersal is the length of time which it occupies. Plate 14 illustrates a dispersal in which 18 waves were emitted from the centre at an average interval of nearly 3 min, and the complete evacuation of the roost occupied 50 min. The regularity of the successive departures was well maintained throughout the dispersal; it is remarkable that the last flocks to leave had witnessed 17 previous waves of departing birds and yet had withheld from joining the rush to the feeding grounds. It is difficult to believe that such an ordered departure could be achieved by means of a form of flock discipline; it is no less difficult to conceive of external stimuli to which the birds might be programmed in order to produce the same controlled departure.

It is tempting to speculate that the birds composing a single ring or departure wave constitute a social sub-group within the roost community. Such an hypothesis, of course, is difficult to prove or disprove since it would be necessary to establish not only that the membership of the sub-group is maintained from day to day throughout the communal roosting season, but also that some distinguishing characteristic of the sub-group members can be identified, e.g. age, place of origin, or breeding association. A detailed ringing study to investigate this question was beyond the capacity of the Bushy Hill Radar Research Laboratory, even if it were considered possible for expert field ornithologists to acquire the formidable mass of data that would be necessary to allow definitive conclusions to be drawn. Instead, the Bushy Hill team concentrated upon the one parameter of the ring dispersals that was accessible to radar measurement – the speed of expansion of the successive rings. As discussed in Chapter 4, the still-air speed of ring expansion averaged over all rings measured was 37 knots. When the first rings of all events were grouped together to give an average velocity of first ring emitted, and the result compared with that of the second and later rings, it was found that there was a tendency for successive rings to expand progressively more slowly, the speed reduction being in the order of 1 knot per ring.

What is the significance of this speed change? Is it indicative of some sub-group structure? It is impossible to say until much more evidence has been accumulated. Conceivably, the first birds to leave the roost have the strongest urge to depart and so fly the fastest, but this is mere speculation and incapable of being tested. Boyd (1932) suggested that the starlings which feed farthest away leave the roost first, but the Bushy Hill radar records do not indicate that the first radar ring achieves a diameter greater than the following rings. Observations made by Wynne-Edwards (1931) on one roost and its subsequent divisions, certainly suggested that there were recognizable differences between the behaviours of the different exodus groups, but the evidence was much too sparse to prove a sub-group structure to the roost.

Positive radar evidence was obtained upon the related question of the identity of a roost community as a whole in the presence of neighbouring roosts. Plate 15 shows the B-scope picture of expanding rings from two adjacent roosts at Frating and Ipswich, the ring centres being separated by a distance of 12 miles. Interpenetration of the rings from the two roosts is seen even on this still picture, but with the ciné film the effect is vividly apparent. The two sets of rings are then seen to flow through each other and to expand to normal ranges without any mutual disturbance, i.e. the starlings continue the missions normally associated with their respective roosts, unaffected by the other flocks of starlings flying in the reverse direction.

This radar result also suggests that a given parcel of ground is not to be regarded as the peculiar feeding territory of one special roost but may be occupied simultaneously by starlings from different roosts. That such overlapping of feeding parties must be commonplace is apparent from Fig. 9.1, which plots the positions of the various roost centres. If around each of these points is drawn a circle of 10 miles radius, then intersections of regions cropped by birds from coexisting roosts must obviously be a common occurrence, yet the roost identities are substantially preserved over many weeks in the period August to December, although some small interchange of roost members doubtless occurs from time to time. A daily penetration into the surrounding countryside from a roost has been taken as approximately 10 miles because the usual figure for maximum ring radius as observed at Bushy Hill is 5 miles, although the maximum radius ever recorded was 10 miles. During the course of the outward expansion a starling ring attenuates and breaks up into discrete fragments which continue to move outward with the same radial velocity. Radar and visual observations both agree that the wave of birds spreading outwards from the roost undergoes depletion of its numbers by small groups of birds flying down to the ground and commencing the day's foraging. It seems fair to assume that if the average ring radius is 5 miles then the additional travel of small flocks which continue beyond this point, but which have become indistinguishable from ordinary angels on the radar, must be about 5 miles also, i.e. a total penetration of 10 miles.

The greatest distance to which starlings have been reported flying to a roost is about 30 miles (Marples, 1936; Bagnall-Oakley, 1956). In a general survey of roosts in Devon, Wynne-Edwards (1929) reported that the birds from most roosts spread for some 5–15 miles into the surrounding country, with a maximum of 24 miles, and the records of other observers fit well with this generalization, and also with the radar figure discussed above.

Interpenetration of rings must therefore be a common occurrence, but roost identity appears to be fully preserved. If roosts can maintain identity in this way it seems not unreasonable to suppose that sub-groups may exist within the roost. The bees of a hive community are labelled as members of that hive by bearing the queen's scent – an odorous chemical secreted by the queen and transferred by contact to every hive member. Perhaps the members of a starling roost, or even animals or birds of other similar communities, may one day be shown to possess some form of chemical identification like that possessed by the bees. But whereas the biological function served by the hive and its social organization are now both fairly well understood, the same cannot be claimed for the starling roost, and much more research will be needed to solve this problem. The seasonal and diurnal variations in roosting behaviour suggest a high level of organization within the starling community, which must be indicative of some special advantage conferred by this form of community living – but what it is still remains unknown, in spite of the contribution which radar has made.

Echoes from rooks

Other birds which flock in large numbers and which should produce recognizable echoes upon a radar are Rooks (*Corvus frugilegus*) and Jackdaws (*Corvus monedula*). These birds form roost communities at the beginning of October which continue in being until March (Witherby *et al.*, 1940). Movements of rooks and jackdaws into a large winter roost in Bedfordshire were observed on radar by Harper (1959) and the procedures for preassembly and flight into the roost were not unlike those described above for starlings, although final entry into the roost took place about half an hour after sunset. A dawn departure of birds from a temporary roost near Bishop's Stortford was also observed by Harper. Two waves of birds were plotted from their roost and moved in a direction west-south-west. A continuous track was maintained over a distance of 40 miles which suggested a migration rather than a feeding flight. Although the birds were stretched out in an irregular line some six miles in length the departure had none of the characteristics of a starling dispersal and this fact, coupled with the measured still-air average flight speed of 30 knots, caused Harper to attribute the echoes to migrant rooks.

Echoes from migrant rooks over the North Sea were also reported by Lack (1959, 1960). Winter assembly and dispersal patterns attributable to rooks have also been observed from Bushy Hill but systematic radar behaviour studies of this species have yet to be made. Nevertheless, the radar evidence so far suggests that rook dispersals do not show the symmetrical and periodic effects which are so remarkable in the case of the starling.

CHAPTER TEN

Soaring and gliding

The art of gliding possesses special interest for the ornithologist, for it is when controlling a glider that a man comes closest to the experience of a bird in flight. Many of the manoeuvres consciously undertaken by the glider pilot to maintain himself airborne and to extend the duration of his journey are also instinctively practised by the bird in order to achieve the greatest economy in its flying operations; the soaring of the eagle and the climbing of the glider are all one.

The bird has need to conserve energy, which it derives from the body fat which is its fuel, and so it seeks for maximum lift from the air in order to overcome the ever-present enemy – gravity. The glider pilot is matched against the same relentless opponent, but in one respect at least he is at a disadvantage relative to the bird, for when co-operation from its element proves too illusive the bird may resort to powered flight like an aircraft. The glider possesses no motive power and so must pursue the inevitable cycle of lift and glide, success being conditioned by the pilot's handling skill and his experience in interpreting his simple instruments. His flying aids fulfil the same functions as the sensory equipment of the bird, but not so effectively, since the inbuilt instruments of the bird are directly included in the servo loop which controls its flight manoeuvres.

Excellence in any occupation requires dedication in the devotee; particularly is this so in the case of gliding where the pilot must become skilled not only in the handling of his machine, but also in map reading and navigation. In addition, he must become versed in the finer points of meteorology, for it is upon these various skills that his life as well as his pleasure may depend. The fact that the glider pilot is emulating the silent flight of the bird permits him sometimes to make observations upon birds in flight which could be made in no other way. True, such close-up reports by pilots are not frequent, but they are most valuable and sometimes they throw additional light on the results of other methods of bird observation.

Air waves
It is clear that neither bird nor glider can obtain 'lift' or upward flight, from still, stagnant air. There must be rising currents of air for a bird to achieve higher altitude without making use of wing flap. Similarly, the glider is also dependent upon rising currents of air, and so we may ask how these upward currents are produced and where they may be found.

We are all familiar with the effortless soaring of gulls at a cliff located by the sea's edge where the air, moving from the sea, impinges on the rock face and so creates upward air currents which the bird rides with such skill. A sea cliff is not a location conducive to the health of the glider pilot, but he commonly utilizes a similar effect which is produced inland when an air stream flows over a ridge of hills lying across its path. Lift can be secured by a glider from such an undulating air stream, but the degree of lift will be dependent upon the speed of the wind, the shape of the hilly obstruction, and the nature of its surface – whether wooded or rocky – since upon the roughness of the surface depends the friction offered to the air flow, while the presence of trees can materially affect the local humidity, which is an important factor in determining the buoyancy of a 'foreign' parcel of air.

An air stream surging over a mountain ridge can even create a standing wave pattern in the lee of the obstruction, in a manner similar to the rills produced in the surface of water flowing over pebbles lying in the bed of a stream (Fig. 10.1).

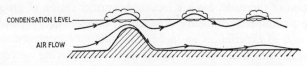

FIG. 10.1. Air waves in the lee of a mountain and lee-wave clouds

The presence of such 'lee waves' as they are termed, are frequently revealed by 'lee-wave clouds' produced by condensation of water vapour due to adiabatic cooling of the upward rising air. The converse effect is produced at the falling part of the wave where the downdraught produces compressive heating, so causing re-evaporation of the cloud droplets with consequent disappearance of the cloud at the trailing edge. Thus the clouds are in a state of continuous formation and dispersal, and so appear to be stationary in the lee of the mountain, hence their name (Wallington, 1961).

Such stationary clouds in the presence of a rapidly moving air stream were observed in the lee of the Ardennes by the author on an S-band radar situated near Metz, during the summer of 1958; angels, corresponding to flocks of birds, could be observed in the gap between the lee-wave clouds, but they were making good use of the quickly flowing air stream and so were moving swiftly to the north-east. It was the presence of the rapidly moving angels near to the stationary clouds which called attention to the phenomenon – radar, birds, and meteorology often appear to be inextricably mixed! In this case the birds were literally riding the air waves and their altitudes must have been varying in consequence. Schaefer (1966) has shown that the fluctuation in the height of a migrant due to this effect can be as much as 600 ft for an average height of 5,400 ft.

'Thermals' for birds and gliders

A component of lift can arise at very low wind speeds on sunny days over hill slopes so oriented as to receive the sun's rays. This so-called anabatic wind effect arises from winds induced to flow up the slope of a heated hill-side by reason of

183

the lower density of the air there compared with that of the air at the same altitude over the level plain. The air-lift phenomenon most frequently employed by bird and glider, however, is the 'thermal' and the good glider pilot could be described as a skilled locator and chaser after thermals. Not the least frequent clue to the vigilant pilot of the existence of a good thermal is the sight of soaring birds already putting it to good use. The formation of a thermal or upward rising air stream is a complicated physical process which it would hardly be appropriate to describe in detail here, but a brief account of its structure will serve to indicate how it can impart lift to a bird or glider.

The source of a thermal is commonly a patch of ground warmer than the surrounding areas of ground; a village or small town, a building or the water cooling tower of an electricity generating station may act as generators of thermals. Large temperature differences are not required, even fractions of a degree centigrade over horizontal distances of half a mile, are sufficient to cause the formation of thermals. Such a localized, warmer region of ground imparts heat to the air immediately above it which, in consequence, expands, becomes less dense and so experiences an increase in buoyancy in accordance with the Principle of Archimedes. But this idea of an upward moving convective stream of air lifting the glider with it is much too simplified a picture of what is really happening. A glance inside an electrical kettle before boiling commences reveals the turbulence of the water contained in it and suggests that a mixing process is at work. This is easily confirmed by placing one or two small crystals of potassium permanganate in a glass of water on a hot-plate; the dissolving crystals mark the upward moving warm water and show that this stream interacts with the cooler water above to produce a rising ring of turbulence in a form roughly similar to a doughnut. Careful and more detailed experiments by Scorer and Ronne (1956) showed that the thermal may, in fact, be regarded as an ascending and expanding vortex ring like a smoke ring (Fig. 10.2). It will be seen that although lift may be regarded as coming from the interaction of the glider's wing surfaces with the rising air, the circulation of air within the vortex ring itself means that the rate of lift in the centre of the ring can be much higher than the rate of rise of the ring as a whole. The head of the thermal located at the stable air level is frequently capped by cloud, and this often guides the glider pilot to the thermals that will give him the upward lift he is looking for.

It is thermals such as these which birds and gliders use. The distribution of thermals is dependent upon many factors, such as the configuration and nature of the ground, while sun, time of day, and wind state all play a part. A thermal is also disturbed by wind sheer, as suggested in Fig. 10.2, i.e. change of wind speed with altitude, and associated with the thermal is what may be described as a reversed thermal or downdraught which produces negative lift – obviously a region of space to be avoided!

While the soaring of birds in thermals is the most likely explanation of the stationary angels often seen upon the p.p.i. of a powerful radar, it is not easy to detect the birds with certainty upon the radar picture. It sometimes happens,

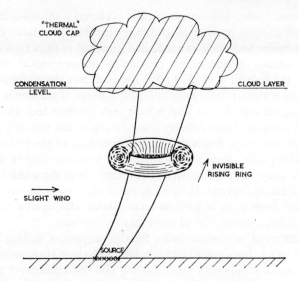

FIG. 10.2 The 'Thermal' as a rising vortex ring of heated air

however, that a succession of thermals can be generated from a group of sources and shed downwind to form a number of so-called 'thermal streets', aligned in the wind direction. Thermal streets, unaccompanied by precipitation, sometimes occur during the summer months and may be detected on the p.p.i., as was first observed by Harper (1958).

Harper attributed the radar visibility of these streets to the swifts that work the thermals, foraging for the insects that are borne upwards by the thermal stream. Many bird species make use of thermals, including gulls and swallows, but the swift appears to be the most adept in identifying and utilizing thermals and other convective sources of lift, recognizing them as sources of insect food as well as suitable locations for the exercise of its incomparable flying skill. The narrow belt of turbulent air associated with the line squall which often precedes a thunderstorm has been used for some spectacular gliding flights, and is also frequented by soaring birds, with swifts conspicuous among them. The lift in this case is produced at the leading edge of an advancing layer of cold air at ground level, just in front of heavy precipitation. Harper and Beimers (1958) have obtained radar pictures of such line squalls rendered visible by the presence of soaring swifts, which have been seen on the radar and also identified by direct visual observation. It is not for nothing that the swift has been termed the 'thunder swallow' in some parts of Europe (Wallington, 1961).

Swifts and gliders at a sea-breeze front
One of the most interesting of these meteorological formations which provides exciting soaring possibilities to bird and glider alike is the sea-breeze front; it is also a dynamic event whose progress can sometimes be followed in detail by a

suitably located radar. Unfortunately, the occurrence of sea-breezes of the required frontal form are not so common that bird or glider can become thoroughly familiar with their structure and practised in their exploitation.

It is the summer months which provide the meteorological circumstances required for the formation of sea-breeze fronts. Peters (1938) found that May and June were the most likely months for the passage of sea-breeze fronts over his meteorological station near Winchester; such passages took place on about nine days in the year. More recently Simpson (1964) has similarly studied the occurrence of sea-breeze fronts in the neighbourhood of the gliding centre at Lasham in Hampshire. Assisted by a network of nine recording stations, he has been able to study the penetration of sea-breezes from the south coast northwards to Lasham and beyond. He has concluded with Peters that the penetration of a sea-breeze front as far as Lasham occurs about eight times a year and that, very occasionally, a distance of 50 miles may be achieved.

The utilization of sea-breeze fronts for the purpose of making long glider flights was shown to be possible by Phillip Wills as early as 1938 during his flights to Cornwall, but it is only with the increasing skill and numbers of glider pilots in recent years that frontal flights of this kind have been more frequently reported. The glider flights and investigations of Simpson (1962 and 1964) into the structure of the sea-breeze front have a special interest for the ornithologist, since this pilot has also made many visual sightings of swifts soaring at the sea-breeze front.

Sea-breeze fronts have occasionally been 'seen' by radar and so a very interesting comparison is now possible between the radar recordings of the passage of a sea-breeze front and the bird observations made by Simpson during the course of his own glider flights. What is a sea-breeze front? How and when does it occur and why is it of such interest to the glider pilot and to the insect-hunting swift of the summer months?

Structure of a sea-breeze front

The sea-breeze front is a meteorological formation which only occurs in this country on some of the sunny, calm days of summer. On such a day, after many hours of sunshine, the temperature of the land is higher than that of the adjacent sea. In response to this temperature differential, a circulation of the air mass across the land/sea boundary is set into motion. At sea level the movement of the air is from the sea to the land while a seawards directed flow occurs at an altitude of approximately 3,000 ft. The cooler air from off the sea may be likened to a solid wedge slowly advancing over the land, causing the warmer inland air to rise above it. This upward surge of warm air at the nose of the advancing wedge of cooler sea air is often strong enough to support the soaring flight of a glider and certainly it is frequented by soaring swifts and gulls. If the inland air is not too dry, then during its ascent some condensation of its moisture content takes place, so that the existence of a sea-breeze front is often evidenced by the presence of a filmy curtain of cloud at the upper interface, as in Fig. 10.3, while the

186

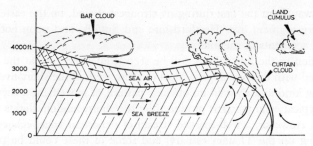

FIG. 10.3. Section of a sea-breeze front (after Simpson, *Sailplane and Gliding*, 1962)

top of the lift region may be capped by small cumulus cloud as shown. On a really dry day in summer, however, there may not be sufficient water in the land air to lead to the formation of these characteristic cloud indicators, and so the sea-breeze front presents no visible discontinuity and often escapes detection, although its passage would be recorded by the usual meteorological instruments supplying temperature, humidity, and wind data.

A radar observation of a sea-breeze front

The succession of events which accompany the formation and development of a sea-breeze front can be reconstructed from a particularly interesting case of such an incident reported by Eastwood and Rider (1961). By a fortunate coincidence, Bushy Hill radar was operating throughout 20 June 1960, and provided a complete record of the development and passage of the front. A selection of pictures from the p.p.i. showing the progress of the front is given in Plate 19.

The radar line echo which marks the position of the front on the p.p.i. first became evident at about 12.00 h along the coast near Felixstowe; it then moved inland increasing in intensity and accelerating gradually until sunset, by which time it had penetrated nearly 50 miles inland and was moving at a speed of 6 knots. It will be seen that a similar line echo developed over Kent and Sussex, and moved inland in an identical fashion. This frontal occurrence was remarkable in that the total length of the north and south segments at the time of maximum development was little short of 120 miles.

The sea-breeze explanation of this remarkable radar echo was inferred from the meteorological evidence. On 20 June 1960 an anti-cyclone covered the country and there was little wind and almost no cloud, so that a comparatively clear radar tube free from meteorological echoes would have been expected. Fig. 10.4 plots the isochrones for this frontal incident and shows the development and movement of the front for comparison with the radar pictures of Plate 19; the changes in wind speed and direction at some well-known weather stations are also indicated on the diagram.

One feature of the radar pictures of the advancing front which is of great interest and significance is the sharpness of the leading edges as compared with the diffuseness of their trailing edges. Scintillating discrete angels could be seen

187

breaking away from the line during its strongest period, on the eastern side of the northern segment over Hertfordshire and Suffolk, and upon both sides of the Sussex segments of the line.

In addition to the line echo it will be seen from Plate 19 that the p.p.i. was well covered with discrete angels. Most of these were of the short-lived, rapidly scintillating kind and showed no obvious pattern of movement – they were, in fact, the typical echo patterns produced by the short, random flights of smaller passerines. However, a well-marked stream of persistent angel echoes could be seen moving up the Thames estuary, and some of these could be tracked for

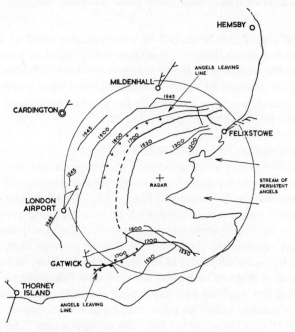

FIG. 10.4. Meteorological development of the sea-breeze front, 20 June 1960. Range ring at 40 n.m.
Surface winds: 12.00 h, short arrow
18.00 h, long arrow
(after Eastwood and Rider, *Nature*, 1961)

considerable distances, occasionally across the line echo itself, but there was no method of identifying the species of birds involved. As the Sussex segment of the front advanced northward, there was a noticeable diminution in the volume of angel activity in its wake, suggesting a tendency of the general bird population to remain grounded after passage of the front; this effect was not repeated in the wake of the northern segment of the front. The fall in temperature as the front passed over was only two or three degrees, and the rise in humidity was small, so it is not apparent what change in the physical conditions produced the comparative dearth of bird activity behind the front.

188

The interesting question now arises as to the nature of the interaction between the radio beam and the sea-breeze front that caused the front to be visible to radar. The day was cloudless and sunny and so cloud can be ruled out as the reflector of radar energy from the front. A greatly magnified picture of a portion of the northern segment of the front is shown in Plate 19 (b). The sharpness of the leading edge and the presence of the rearward moving angels shed from the tracking edge of the advancing front, can be clearly seen. The speed of motion of these echoes was estimated by the time compression film technique and was found to be about 30 knots. This speed may be compared with the velocity of advance of the front itself, which was approximately five knots, and the overland gradient wind of 2–10 knots. These figures clearly suggest that the rearward moving echoes can be attributed to flocks of birds. We are prompted to ask the further questions – have birds been located at a sea-breeze front? If so, can the number of these birds completely explain the visibility of the front to radar, or is some other reflection mechanism also involved?

Radar reflections from swifts at a sea-breeze front

It will be appreciated that the detection of soaring birds at a sea-breeze front would be most difficult for visual bird watchers to achieve. A glance at Fig. 10.3 immediately suggests why this should be so. The altitude scale at the left of the diagram indicates that the turbulent, lift region of the front extends up to 3,000 ft and beyond. The glider flights that have been reported in the literature, for example that of J. K. MacKenzie on 6 July 1956 (MacKenzie, 1956), confirm the possibility of a glider climbing to the 4,000-ft region. On this occasion the front was moving northwards from the south coast at a speed of 5 knots, and the process of its development and movement was in every way similar to the behaviour of the sea-breeze front observed by radar on 20 June 1960. MacKenzie reported that the lift region was confined to a very narrow belt some 100–250 yd wide situated on the leading edge of the front, which is very relevant to the radar observation of the sharpness of the leading edge on the p.p.i., but to exploit this lift, which was in places as high as 1,500 ft/min, it was necessary for the glider to be flown parallel to the front; circling was not possible due to the down-draught on the northward side of the front. On the assumption that birds are operating in the lift region of the front then the majority will be flying at altitudes in excess of 1,000 ft and so will be undetected by a ground observer – but it would be precisely this mode of flying that would put the birds within the cover of the Bushy Hill radar and so permit their detection by radar.

Simpson (1964) has found in his glider flights that birds are not much disturbed by the presence of the glider – in fact, there is often give and take in the discovery and sharing of up-currents in general and sea-breeze fronts in particular, so that the presence of birds has materially assisted his frontal investigations. On 13 May 1961, while operating a glider from Lasham in Hampshire, Simpson found a sea-breeze front at 4 p.m., the existence of the front having been revealed by a hazy curtain of cloud. This flight lasted for 20 min, and during its course he met groups of swifts at an altitude of about 1,500 ft. A similar flight of 55 min was made on 26 May 1963, during which groups of swifts, each numbering three or four birds, were encountered along a line about 3 miles in length. These swifts were mostly flying at a height between 1,800 and 2,400 ft, with a few birds at a higher altitude still. From the frequency of his encounters with the groups of swifts, Simpson was able to assess the density of the birds at the front as approximately 100 birds per mile. If this same density of bird population were assumed to be present along the radar front of June 1960, and if the situation at 17.30 (Plate 19 (a)) corresponding to the stage of maximum intensity of the front be considered, then the amplitude of the signal which would have been received can be calculated and compared with the radar records. The average range of the front from Bushy Hill at this time was 25 miles, so that the radar beam was illuminating a sector of the front about half a mile long at any instant, with the result that approximately 50 swifts would be contributing to the amplitude of the echo received. The calculated signal under these circumstances would be approximately 20 db above the threshold of detection. Such a signal amplitude could certainly produce the records of Plate 19. The fact that the birds would be contained within the narrow frontal region, 250 yd thick according to MacKenzie, means that the leading edge of the echo would possess the sharpness observed, since the range resolution of the Bushy Hill radar is 0·46 miles.

The evidence provided by Simpson's glider flights on the density of swifts at the front, when associated with the system parameters of the Bushy Hill radar, suggest that the visibility of the front to the radar can be convincingly explained by the reflections of the radio energy from the soaring swifts. The resultant echo from such an assemblage of birds would present the continuous line appearance seen on Plate 19 as in the case of the ring angels already shown in Chapter Nine to be due to starlings. The sharp edge seen on the frontal echo is also evident on the starling rings.

Radar reflections from a refractive discontinuity at the front

The significance of Simpson's direct visual observations of the roughly uniform distribution of the swifts along the front will be better appreciated when it is remembered that the radar evidence alone hardly permits a firm choice between the two possible explanations of the visibility of the front to radar, i.e., an attribution to bird scatterers or reflection from a refractive index discontinuity at the front. In the case of the incident reported by Eastwood and Rider (1961), an endeavour was made to calculate the magnitude of the received signal on the simple theory of discontinuity at the front between the moist, cooler air from the sea and the drier, warmer air over land. The frontal region was considered to be formed by a line of thermals rising to 4,000 ft. and in the absence of mixing it was estimated that the rising air would possess a refractive index difference relative to the surrounding air of 40 N units ($N = (n - 1) \times 10^{-6}$; n being the ordinary index of refraction). If this discontinuity takes place within a distance of a few centimetres only, then following Appleton (1946) a reflection coefficient of $\rho = 1.5 \times 10^{-5}$ may be employed, and if assumed to apply over the whole sheet intersected by the radar beam from 4,000 ft to say 1,000 ft at the ground cut-off, then the received signal would be 1 db below the threshold of detection of the radar.

It has been explained earlier, however, that the frontal region cannot be regarded as a mere uniform surface of discontinuity between the sea and land airs, but is a region of great turbulence containing the equivalent of many thermals. Within this turbulent region there will be many interfaces capable of reflecting radio energy back to the radar aerial, so that the resultant signal from the frontal region may be expected to exceed that calculated by the simple method above, with its assumption of a hypothetical plane sheet functioning as a partial reflector or scatterer of radio waves. It seems reasonable to conclude, therefore, that a small contribution to the signal received by the radar from the front may conceivably be produced by the refractive index discontinuity within the turbulent air volume at the frontal surface, but the above discussion suggests the probability that swifts, soaring at the front, provide the bulk of the radar signal. It has been pointed out earlier that sea-breeze fronts in England are phenomena associated with the summer months; radar records of such fronts have been obtained in the months of June and July only, which are the months when the busy swifts are flying and foraging, and so it appears likely that many sea-breeze front penetrations of the early summer are missed by the radar because the swifts, as the tell-tale indicators of the presence of a front, are not yet active over the land.

Plate 19 (c) shows the thinning out of the front as sunset approaches; the radial white line corresponds to radio noise received from the sun and shows that the sun is now at a very low angle of elevation and just about to set. The sea-breeze front on this picture has almost disappeared, from which we conclude that the refractive index discontinuity has likewise almost been obliterated. The turbulence and lift have subsided and so the swifts have departed – but to reappear in strength for their vesper flights.

Vesper flights of swifts

At first sight it seems a fortunate coincidence that a sequence of radar pictures which record so vividly the movement of a sea-breeze front and its retinue of foraging swifts should also supply a spectacular affirmative to the age-long question – do swifts spend the night on the wing? Yet the film for 20 June 1960 provides just this information. But other Bushy films, recorded on certain warm afternoons and evenings in high summer, provide pictures of a similar succession of events. Probably this association is not a coincidence after all, but a pointer to the conclusion that meteorological states in the south of England which favour sea-breeze front formation during the day are likely to be followed by warm summer evenings ideal for the night operations of the swift.

After the setting of the sun at 20.20 h the general angel activity shown in

Plate 19 continued to decrease, but at 21.15 h this trend was sharply reversed and the face of the p.p.i. rapidly increased in brightness due to the diffused light produced by a sudden upsurge of widespread angels. The dramatic nature of this change is shown in Plate 20 in which the upper p.p.i. picture corresponds to 21.00 h of 22 June 1959, while the lower record was made at 22.20 h. Of particular interest in this figure is the concentration of echoes which can be seen at points corresponding to large towns, such as Norwich, Eastbourne, Calais, and Boulogne. It will also be noted that the boundaries of the angel swarms at this time were parallel to the coast-lines of France, Essex, Kent, and Sussex, but drifted out to sea as if in response to the off-shore breeze which takes place at dusk (Eastwood, 1962, 1963). These off-shore boundaries became more diffuse as the night advanced, but not before the overlap in the Straits of Dover of the French and English contingents was complete. The angel density was maintained until 02.00 h and then decayed rapidly to leave the tube face clear for the starling ring display at sunrise.

What is the explanation of this spectacular form of night display of angels? These displays have been recorded at Bushy Hill on a number of occasions, but always the nights have been fine and warm and have occurred only in June and July. Days in high summer which have yielded radar pictures of a sea-breeze front penetration have tended to be followed by the night display of angels just described, which differs sharply from the heavy night displays of the spring and autumn in that the 'angelic hosts' are virtually static, no progress is made in any direction other than the seaward drift already mentioned. The nights of these displays have been calm and clear with neither clouds nor rain visible on the radar. No meteorological scatterers seem to be possible sources of the echoes, and the conclusion appears inevitable that the radar is recording a night ascent of birds to altitudes of 2,000 to 5,000 ft, which, thereafter, continue airborne, the flocks engaging in circling or hovering flight.

Radar records show that general migration is very small at this time of the year so that the familiar night migrants cannot be responsible for the summer night displays. But the swift, the 'dragon of the night' as Shakespeare refers to it, has long been known to make night ascents after sunset and many detailed descriptions have been written of the mysterious vesper flight of this remarkable bird. There can be little doubt that, with the aid of radar, we are witnessing the vesper flights of innumerable swifts. What is more, we are seeing that this night ascent is no mere short duration excursion but lasts many hours for the majority of the birds – they are spending the greater portion of the night on the wing. This curious behaviour of the swift had long been suspected; it was for long a subject of major debate between ornithologists, but only the advent of radar has permitted a complete demonstration of these night flights.

A very precise description of the night soaring of swifts was given by Masson (1930). He was investigating the reliability of the belief that male swifts 'spend one or two nights in the height of summer at a very high altitude. It must be set fair with the further outlook favourable also.' His best observations were made on 14 July 1926, and were made with the aid of glasses of moderate power but with large lenses to assist in seeing the birds in failing light – a good combined rest for head, body, and arm was also essential! The day had been fine and warm and by 21.00 h the swifts were flying in large numbers at low altitudes; by 21.25 all had disappeared to their nests. Activity recommenced at 21.35 with rapid ascents to 2,000 ft, followed by immediate descents. Using the technique of following a single bird through its gyrations Masson found at 21.41 that he was led into a mass of ascending birds at an altitude of about 2,500 ft, in which the birds were hovering but maintained a wing vibration which was very rapid. By 21.45 the birds appeared to have reached an estimated altitude of $1-1\frac{1}{2}$ miles, when they became lost to view. Masson was uncertain whether the birds remained airborne, but he was confident that the swifts did not re-enter their nests even if they descended, and finally he permitted himself the prophetic utterance, 'Do the birds come down and roost in the open? The only way to prove conclusively that they do not is to go up in an aeroplane and find them soaring in their "aerial park" – to cruise round the flock and, with the aid of a searchlight, get details of how the birds maintain their height in the park all night.' True, this method of finding swifts would not be as easy as it sounds and that is why it was a test which was not performed until 30 years later – when radar made it possible.

Other watchers at this time were less certain that the birds spent all the night on the wing. Cash (1930) thought that some swifts do come down at nightfall and enter their nests in the dark. Booth (1930) was certain that the birds return to their nests in the dark; he was equally convinced, however, that evenings of vesper flights were always followed by very dark nights, but this is certainly not the case, for some of the best radar records of ascended swifts have been made within a night or two of full moon, e.g. 22 June 1959.

In his delightful book *Swifts in a Tower*, David Lack (1956) discusses all aspects of the life and behaviour of this fascinating bird. He has created a classic of bird literature which is everywhere illumined by the results of the elegant observational techniques developed and applied by his wife and himself. In particular, he considers the behaviour of the swifts at night and describes the ascending screaming parties, birds bunched together and climbing with rapidly beating wings until they disappear from sight. Lack reviews the evidence for a return of the swifts to their nests during the hours of darkness, and concludes that this almost certainly does not occur. Conclusive evidence on this question of the non-return to the nest during darkness was finally obtained by Weitnauer (1952, 1954), who fitted a signalling device to the nesting boxes with which he was studying the habits of the swift. No swifts entered the boxes during darkness, even on those occasions when vesper flights took place. This observation does not, of course, prove that the swifts had spent the night on the wing, but this point was finally established by Weitnauer himself during the summer of 1955 – and radar was able to play a vital part in these tests.

Weitnauer was invited by the engineer in charge of the Kloten (Zürich) radar,

Mr Donau, to observe the angel echoes which, at that time, were thought to be attributable in some measure to birds, although this had yet to be proved by Sutter, who used the same radar in his later studies. On the evening of 7 July 1955 a number of fluctuating echoes suddenly appeared on the screen at 21.00 h, being well distributed over the p.p.i., i.e. to 10 miles range, and appeared to be moving in random directions with various speeds. The nature of the motions invited comparison with bird flights and their identification with Weitnauer's ascended swifts seemed inescapable 'for what else was it which was flying at this time of the year and in the night and which was, indeed, estimated as having come from the cities of Zürich, Winterthur, and Baden–Wettingen' (Weitnauer, 1956).

The 11th July was a warm day, cloudy, but with bright periods. A heavy storm occurred in the afternoon but was followed by further bright periods and Weitnauer noted that the 'unencumbered' swifts ascended in the evening, i.e. the non-breeding yearling birds. At Kloten the ground temperature was 17° C and there was 2/8 cloud at 2,000 ft. Radar echoes were observed on the p.p.i. after 21.00 h which, it was considered, must have been produced by birds. At 22.14 h a light aircraft took off from Kloten with Weitnauer as passenger-observer and was vectored on to the supposed swifts by Mr Donau, who used the Kloten radar for normal ground control. At 22.40 h Mr Donau was able to inform the pilot that the aircraft was directly on the track of a flock of birds at an altitude of about 3,000 ft – so at this moment a searchlight on the aircraft was switched on and six swifts were clearly seen in the cone of light. Masson's prophesy of 1926 had been fulfilled! The radar observations on 18 July showed that the swifts were reduced in number after 01.00 h, but a time plot of the density of the echoes was not possible, neither was Weitnauer able to measure with any certainty their speeds of movement. Nevertheless, his radar-controlled flight had finally shown that vesper flights of swifts do not end in a quick return, but that many swifts do indeed spend on the wing long hours of favourable summer nights.

It is this night display of swift echoes which is shown in Plate 20 (b). On this occasion the night ascent as seen by the radar commenced at 21.30 h and reached a maximum at 23.00 h. Progressive reduction in the number of echoes visible then took place but numbers were still visible at 02.00 h when the minimum occurred. The number of angels commenced to increase at 03.00 h, but the echoes were not of the swift type. This increase continued until the starling dispersals at 04.20 h followed by sunrise at 4.43 h (B.S.T.). Concentration of the echoes over towns has already been mentioned, and is clearly visible on Plate 20 (b); this is in accordance with the well-known tendency of the swift to find nesting places in plenty under the tiles and eaves of houses. This remarkable concentration of swifts over towns was made apparent to the author in no uncertain way during a May-time visit to Rome. Every evening the sky was thick with screaming swifts at sunset, and to watch from an hotel bedroom in the neighbourhood of the Spanish Steps masses of these birds flying with unerring precision into their nests beneath the pantiles that cover many of the old buildings in that neighbourhood was quite breathtaking. The Rome circus of swifts would have provided a marvellous radar display. One other useful piece of information is provided by Plate 20 (*b*), for it will be noticed that the haze of swift echoes ceases near the coast of France at a range of about 80 miles. It will be shown in Chapter Eleven that this cut-off indicates a radio horizon corresponding to an altitude of 4,000 ft which must have been the level at which the swifts were operating on this occasion.

Little purposeful, directed flying could be detected during the echo display of Plate 20 so that the drift of the swifts over the sea must have been a consequence of the off-shore wind at night. Lack reports observing swifts on a number of occasions flying out to sea in the failing light of late evening. These seaward flights were made at a height of about 200 ft; they were made in all kinds of weather and Lack concluded that they had no relation to the screaming, circling vesper flights which took place only on fine warm still evenings.

It is inevitable that this question of the night behaviour of the swift which radar has substantially assisted in answering should prompt two further questions. Can the swift sleep on the wing? Also, why does it choose to waste energy by staying in the air all night when it would be quite safe in the roost, which it apparently occupies quite happily on most other nights? Lack (1956) has pointed out that the swift's wings are adapted for high speed flight and not for gliding or slow speed soaring. For the swift to stay at an altitude of 2,000–4,000 ft will require frequent wing flapping in order to counteract the rapid loss of altitude in the glide. Even so, Lack believes that the swift would gain enough sleep in these short gliding periods. On the second question Lack supports Weitnauer (1955) in his suggestion that the night ascent phenomenon probably derives from the circumstance that the swift on its long migrating flights will have difficulty in finding roosting holes suited to its needs. The swift is not built for normal tree perching. Since roost holes in unknown regions might be difficult for the birds to find there is obviously great value in an adaptation that permits the swift to spend the night on the wing and yet to secure some intermittent sleep. Lack (1956) considers that the evening seaward flights of swifts which he has observed were probably made by birds strange to the region and so made use of their age-long capacity to sleep on the wing. They chose to do so over the sea, free from any possible obstructions. Perhaps radar will also help to solve this interesting behaviour problem of the swift.

It is interesting to note that Schaefer (1966) by the signature analysis method, has found the wing-beat frequency of the swift to be seven per second when performing its leisurely summer night flights; the normal daytime flight of the swift corresponds to ten wing beats per second.

CHAPTER ELEVEN

The altitudes of migratory flights

The altitude control problem is an intriguing one. Why do migrating birds so frequently climb to altitudes of many thousands of feet, when such high altitudes would appear to be unrelated to the needs of the journey to be made? It has been argued that the migrating bird flies at an altitude that will avoid any risk of meeting high ground; it has also been suggested that the choice of high altitudes during nocturnal migration is to avoid the mist which may be encountered at lower levels. It is when we find birds climbing to an altitude of a few thousand feet in order to cross the North Sea or the plains of the middle west in the United States, locations where there is clearly no question of the presence of high ground likely to impede their progress, that it would appear necessary to look for some other explanation. Does the bird indeed 'choose' an altitude, and, if so, how? Could it be that the flight level adopted is optimum from the energy consumption point of view? Closely linked with these questions is the equally significant one of the means by which the bird is apparently able to keep altitude during an extended night flight over the sea. The circumstances which prompt changes in altitude are also of interest. Lack, for example, has shown how birds will descend to lower levels when a rain shower is encountered at night (Lack, 1963a).

It will be seen that a study of the heights at which birds fly raises some very important questions concerning their flight behaviour. Although the need for altitude studies has long been recognized, investigation was hardly possible when visual measuring techniques only were available. It is true that useful general observations of the behaviour of birds in flight can be made through field glasses, but only a comparatively small proportion of the birds airborne at any time may be observed in this way, while the nocturnal flights of birds are almost completely inaccessible to the visual observer. The moon watching experiments of Lowery (1951) and his school are a notable exception, but this type of observation is too laborious to allow the collection of a large volume of data. Moreover, with ground-based visual techniques it is difficult to make accurate measurement of the altitudes of birds in flight.

Perhaps the most informative summaries of visual observations on the altitudes of birds are those by Meinertzhagen (1955) and Mitchell (1955, 1957, 1964). Many of the former's records and all the latter involved sightings of birds of identified species from aircraft. The most spectacular of such direct sightings of birds from aircraft was surely that of the swift by Weitnauer which was described in the last chapter. The frequency of such aeroplane sightings, however, is too low to yield a body of information on altitude that can form the basis of an adequate statistical analysis. Ir was, in fact, the limitation of the direct visual method of assessing the heights of migrating birds that permitted the erroneous conclusion to be drawn by Meinertzhagen that the majority of migratory flights by smaller passerines take place at altitudes less than 200 ft. Visual work on birds is indispensable, but as Sutter (1950) clearly pointed out, even the daylight operation of such precision optical equipment as that used by the military would not provide the data required for a thorough analysis of the altitude behaviour of birds.

The application of radar methods of bird observation to the height-finding problem during the last few years has changed the situation greatly. A modern height-finding radar can measure the altitudes of aircraft, angels, or birds with fair accuracy at long range and with high accuracy at short range. It becomes possible to study changes in altitude during an extended flight and to make observations by night as well as by day; the heights of birds above, or even within cloud can also be measured.

Measuring height by radar

The first radars measured only the range and bearing of the aircraft they had detected. Useful as this information was it would not have provided an adequate Fighter and Anti-Aircraft Gun defence system if it had not proved possible to measure also the altitude of enemy aircraft while they were still at long range. To estimate the height of an aircraft by radar requires the measurement of the slant range of the target from the observer and also the angle of elevation above the horizontal plane. In the early C.H., G.C.I., and G.L. radars this measurement of angle depended upon the comparison of the amplitude of the signals received in two aerials at different heights above the reflecting plane. With the introduction of microwaves it became possible to build aerials of reasonable size that would form sharp beams capable of measuring the angle of elevation of an aircraft directly, as with the optical searchlight of Fig. 1.4.

A nodding-beam height finder is shown in Plate 2 (b); this is usually described as a 'beaver tail' radar in America because of the shape of the aerial. This is a high-powered 10-cm radar which produces a fan beam of radiation whose width is 1° in the vertical plane and 4° in the horizontal plane. This beam is caused to swing up and down in the vertical plane by the mechanical nodding of the aerial and so the beam may be swept over any airborne object, be it cloud, aircraft, or bird. The radar echo produced is displayed at the appropriate range and altitude on a cathode ray rube termed the 'Range Height Display' as in Plate 21.

Electronic azication

In order to observe an aircraft by the height-finding radar it is necessary to adjust the bearing of the equipment so that the plane of sweep of the radio beam contains the target whose altitude is to be measured. The process of measurement is illustrated in Fig. 11.1 in which the radar p.p.i. is shown on the left and the height-finding display on the right. All objects in the airspace seen by the surveillance radar are shown on the p.p.i. in their correct map positions relative to the radar station. The arrow indicates a small illuminated circle or 'strobe' which can be superimposed upon any target of interest by the manipulation of a small joy-stick. This electronic device controls the azimuth of the height radar and the act of strobing a target on the p.p.i. causes the height radar to take up the bearing of the target, a process which is termed 'electronic azication'. The

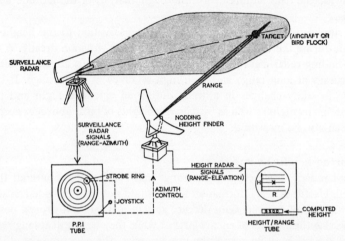

FIG. 11.1. Measuring height by radar, using Electronic 'Azication' to control the bearing of the height-finder (after Eastwood and Rider, *British Birds*, 1965)

radar echoes from all targets swept by the beam are now displayed upon the range/height tube, but the target of interest on this display is identified by the small arrow head which is electronically coupled to the strobe of the p.p.i.

In the illustration shown in Plate 21 the bird flock identified by the ring strobe on the p.p.i. is at a range of 51 miles; the arrow on the R/H tube identifies the target and when adjusted to the centre of the echo measures the angle of elevation. A small electronic computer is associated with the display and performs the calculation for altitude from the range and angle of elevation almost instantaneously; the appropriate corrections for earth curvature and refraction by the atmosphere are also inserted and, in this illustration, an altitude of 10,000 ft resulted.

Accuracy of height measurement

The width of the beam in the vertical plane of the height radar is about 1° which means that an aircraft at a range of 60 miles produces an echo on the H/R tube that extends over about 5,000 ft. However, the cursor on the height display can be placed on the centre of the echo with very little error, so that the angle of elevation can be measured to better than 1/10°, i.e. a height error not exceeding 500 ft in this example. The difference in altitude of two near aircraft can be

measured much more accurately and so the system is adequate in military interception work, also for manoeuvring one aircraft in the presence of another in the
civil case.

The large pulse volume associated with a radar of this type is a major disadvantage when it is used to measure the altitudes of birds. Because such radars
were designed to measure heights of distant targets they are usually operated
with fairly long pulse lengths, viz. 2–5 μs, since a long pulse in association with a
narrow band receiver increases the sensitivity of the equipment. In other words,
resolution in range was sacrificed in order to obtain higher sensitivity and detection at greater distances. It is this fact, coupled with the large values of θr and
ϕr at large values of the range r which makes the pulse volume large, even though
the beam widths θ and ϕ in the vertical and horizontal planes respectively are
quite small. This is clear from the expression for the pulse volume – $\frac{1}{2} c \tau \theta \phi r^2$
where c is the velocity of light and τ is the pulse length. For the S-band nodder τ
is 2 μs, θ is $1°$ and ϕ is $4°$, so that the pulse volume at a range r ft becomes $1.2r^2$
ft³. In consequence, the spatial resolving power of the S-band nodding radar is
fairly low at long range and it is the average altitude of the birds contained within
a pulse-volume, or within a single angel, which is measured rather than the
altitudes of the individual birds.

Height measurement of angels using a steerable aerial
A nodding height finder controlled by electronic azication is an ideal arrangement
when the altitudes of a number of civil aircraft are being monitored, or when it is
desired to effect interception between military aircraft. If masses of migrating
birds are being observed, however, this method of measuring the altitudes of
individual angels is rather slow; it is also necessary to exercise care in order to
avoid the possibility of statistical bias in the selection of targets by the operator.
A statistical study of angel heights during the progress of a major movement is
best made by photographing the Height/Range display simultaneously with the
p.p.i. and selection of targets is then avoided.

Many of the height measurements at Bushy Hill were made with the aid of the
steerable tracker radar shown in the Plate 1 (a). As explained in Chapter 1 this
equipment consists of a circular paraboloid of 30-ft aperture which can be tilted
about a horizontal axis and so causes a $1.8°$ beam of 23-cm radiation to be swept
up and down in a vertical plane. The echoes resulting from such a scan were
displayed upon a cathode ray tube and photographed. Large numbers of such
records were measured by optical projection of the echoes on to the height chart
of Fig. 11.2, on which curves of constant altitude are plotted, the axes being
angle of elevation as ordinate and range in nautical miles as abscissa. As Plate 1
clearly shows, the radar-tracker was located close to the surveillance radar and
so both radars were operated from the same site at a height of 250 ft above sea
level. These two radars shared the same transmitter so that the circumstances
of the radar observations on the two equipments were strictly comparable.
The radar was equipped with the M.T.I. facility, so that the bird targets below

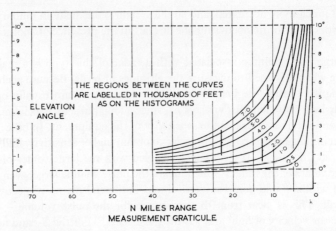

FIG. II.2. Constant height curves on a range – elevation angel graticule to measure the altitudes of angels 'seen' by the L-band tracker (after Eastwood and Rider, *British Birds*, 1965)

1,000 ft, which are normally obscured by the ground clutter, could also be observed and their altitudes estimated.

Although this L-band equipment was useful for gathering a statistically significant sample of angel altitudes within the range interval 10–35 miles, it suffered from the disadvantages of large pulse volume and lack of vertical resolving power at long range and low angles of elevation which characterized the S-band radar. The great advantage of the L-band tracker was that an angel could be held in the radar's searchlight beam and variations in its signal amplitude, range, and altitude measured and averaged over many minutes.

Height measurement of birds using short-range, high-resolution radars

Clearly, the way to overcome the defects of the S- and L-band height finders described above is to reduce the pulse volume by shortening the pulse length and reducing the beam width. If the measurements are confined to short range the pulse volume may then be kept small because r is small. Altitude measurement at short range means that the angles of elevation of targets are high and vertical beam width effects then become of less importance. One method of improving the nodding radar is to use a wavelength of 3 cm, for it is then possible to sharpen the radar beam considerably which makes for improved accuracy in angle measurement. A 3-cm magnetron will also cope with a short pulse length of 1–0·1 μs. Nodding height finders operating at a wavelength of 3 cm were produced to meet the need for Blind Landing equipment at civil airports where long range is not a requirement. Such Precision Approach Radar equipments are capable of supplying precise altitude information not only on aircraft but also on the echoes from individual birds as was shown by Sutter (1957b).

The vertical beam method

An operational difficulty associated with a narrow beam radar is that of pointing it on to a particular target. This difficulty can be avoided when studying bird altitudes by pointing the beam vertically upwards and simply measuring the ranges of the birds that happen to fly through the beam as in Fig. 11.3. Recording of the altitude, which, for a vertical beam, is the same as the range, can be conveniently made by photographing on moving film the time base of a Z-modulated display as in Fig. 2.3. This record provides the time distribution of the bird transits as well as the altitudes.

An unavoidable shortcoming of the vertical incidence method is the minimum altitude of measurement which is imposed by the finite pulse length. Obviously

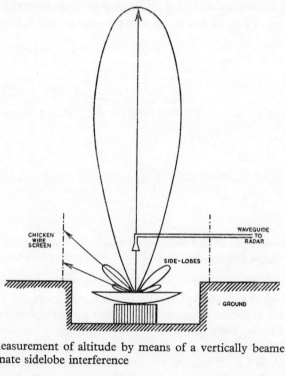

FIG. 11.3. Measurement of altitude by means of a vertically beamed radar. The screens eliminate sidelobe interference

an echo cannot be received and its range measured until the transmit pulse has finished. Thus, the minimum range which can be measured is $\frac{1}{2} c \tau$, identical to the minimum separation of two targets if they are to be resolved; this corresponds to 491 ft for a 1-μs pulse.

A further disadvantage of the vertical beam method is that for a beam width of 1° or less the rate of passage of birds through the beam is quite small. If the beam is broadened by reducing the aerial aperture the number of echoes can be increased, provided that the transmitter power is raised. But this will cause the

sidelobes to be enhanced; it then becomes necessary to prevent clutter interference from nearby ground by providing low-angle screening of the aerial.
Screens may be made of chicken wire, or by bales of damp hay or straw. Sinking
the aerial in the ground as in Fig. 11.3 is also effective.

Height measurement by conical scanning

A way of retaining the advantages of the vertical incidence method of studying
bird altitudes while securing increased sampling rate of birds, together with an
indication of flight direction from a normal p.p.i. display, was employed by
Bellrose and Graber (1963) in their study of the altitude of nocturnal migrants
over the state of Illinois, U.S.A. Their apparatus was an airborne type of radar
operating on a wavelength of 3 cm. This radar produced a 3° beam which was
caused to scan around the vertical at an angle of 60° so as to produce an annular
cone of cover as in Fig. 11.4. The overflying birds intersected this cone at two

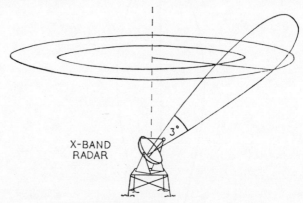

X-BAND
RADAR

FIG. 11.4. Measurement of bird altitudes by means of a conically scanning X-band
radar (after Bellrose and Graber, *Proc. XIIIth Int. Ornith. Congress,* 1963)

points and so the directions of flight of the birds as well as their altitudes could
be deduced from the photographic records which were taken.

Another form of conical scanning for use near the vertical was employed by
Eastwood and Rider (1966) in a 3-cm radar study of height distribution of birds
over Bushy Hill. The transmitter of the X-band radar supplied pulse lengths of
1 μs or 0·3 μs which corresponded to minimum altitudes (and linear resolutions
in range) of 491 ft and 147 ft respectively. The aerial took the form of a slotted
linear array contained in a horn which produced a fan beam 0·7° wide. This
fan beam was rotated at 18 r.p.m. around a vertical axis. Since the beam was
tilted upwards so as to cover elevation angles 90° to 70°, a solid cone of cover was
established as in Fig. 11.5. The signals were applied to an ordinary p.p.i. and
produced echoes whose ranges corresponded very closely to the altitudes of the
targets; this form of display may be termed a Height Azimuth Indicator or H.A.I.
As in the case of Bellrose and Graber it was possible to count the total number of
transits of birds through the beam, also their altitudes and directions of flight.

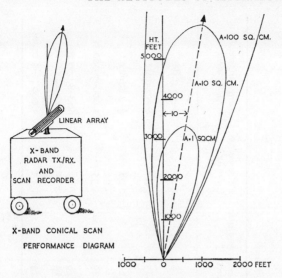

FIG. 11.5. Measurement of bird altitudes by means of a fan beam rotated about the vertical; the performance diagram of the radar is shown on the right

It is important to notice that these high-angle, short-range observations with high resolution X-band equipments 'see' individual birds and not groups of birds. This is because the pulse volume is small and the average separation of birds is considerably greater than the spatial resolution cell.

Height measurement with an S-band tracking radar

A fire-control radar was employed by Schaefer (1966) to measure the altitudes of birds over Leicestershire. A wavelength of 10 cm was employed and the paraboloidal reflector of about 5-ft aperture produced a beam whose angular width was 5°. The aerial dish could be moved in elevation and in azimuth and so was usable in the tracker mode as well as for conical scanning. This equipment was operated in a shallow depression in the ground in order to eliminate permanent echoes and measurements were made only at angles of elevation above 2°. In consequence, the ranges observed were comparatively short and since the pulse length was $\frac{1}{2}$ μs the pulse volume was sufficiently small to ensure that single bird echoes were usually being observed. The great advantage of this kind of equipment is the use of 'split', or rotation of the aerial beam about the dish axis, which permits angles of elevation to be measured with great accuracy by signal balancing. A similar equipment was used by Harper (1958) to demonstrate the bird content of angels seen on the p.p.i. of his surveillance radar.

Choice of radar for measuring the heights of angels or birds

A rather bewildering collection of height-measuring radars has now been described and so it is probably appropriate to summarize the factors which govern the choice of a radar best suited to a particular research. Table 11.1 compares the

203

TABLE II.I *Pulse volumes of some radars used to measure the heights of angels and birds*

Radar	Wavelength (cm)	Pulse length (μS)	Beam widths Horizontal θ	Vertical φ	Range resolution ½cτ ft	Pulse volume (approx.) ½cτθφr² ft³	Range interval for measurement
Long-range S-nodding Height Radar	10	2	4°	1°	982	1·2 r²	8–50 miles
Long-range L-band Tracker	23	5	1·8°	1·8°	2,455	2·4 r²	8–50 miles
Precision Approach Radar (P.A.R.)	3	0·5	1·8°	0·6°	246	0·08 r²	½–2 miles
Short-range X-band Aircraft Equipment	3	1	3°	3°	491	1·35 r²	1,000–7,000 ft
Short-range X-band Vertical Incidence	3	{ 1, 0·3	0·7°	10°	491, 147	1·05 r², 0·31 r²	600–8,000 ft, 300–2,000 ft
Medium/Short-range S-band Fire Control	10	0·5	4·8°	4·8°	246	1·7 r²	3,000 ft–4 miles

system parameters of the various radars and the pulse volumes which result from them.

It will be seen that the factor which chiefly determines the magnitude of the pulse volume is the range r at which the measurements are made. In the case of the high powered S- and L-band equipments the design objective was to measure the altitudes of aircraft at long range for this was an important tactical requirement in the military application. It was for this reason that aerials of high gain, powerful transmitters, and long pulse lengths coupled with narrow band width receivers, were employed. The large pulse volume at large values of r was no disadvantage for the controlled fighter interception operations that were required.

Height measurement at ranges much less than 10 miles is not possible with these equipments due to the long pulse length and to the ground clutter produced by sidelobes in the absence of a low-angle screen. When the equipment is used against bird targets this long range results in a large pulse volume so that the display is usually recording angel echoes produced by groups of birds contained within the pulse volume. Nevertheless, this form of equipment has been a valuable means of measuring the heights of angels at long range, which corresponds to birds performing migratory flights over the sea. The question of whether such an 'angelic' assemblage of birds is to be treated as a true group in the sense that the association between them possesses social significance, or whether the 'group' merely arises from an interaction between the parameters of the radar and a random distribution of birds, is examined in the next chapter.

Clearly the way to ensure that the altitudes of individual birds are being measured is to make altitude measurements at short range only, for then the pulse volume is small. Table 11.1 shows that the beam widths in the vertical plane of the short-range equipments are actually greater than for the high-power radars, but relative errors in elevation measurements are smaller because the measurements are made at large elevations, i.e. $10°$–$90°$, whereas the elevations of angels measured by the long range radars usually lie between $\frac{1}{2}°$ and $7°$, since bird altitudes rarely exceed 10,000 ft.

This comparison of radar height finders shows that a comprehensive survey of the altitudes of migratory flights over an extended region, including sea crossings, requires a high-powered equipment; it is then the altitudes of angels or groups of birds within the pulse volume that is measured. In order to study the altitudes of single birds a short pulse radar must be used that will permit measurements at short range and high angles of elevation.

Altitudes of birds and angels in the U.S.A.
The height of nocturnal migration over Cape Cod, Massachusetts, was studied by Nisbet (1963b) using a high-powered, S-band height finder. This radar was located at South Truro and height observations were made of the birds involved in the migratory movements reviewed in Chapter Seven. Photographic records were taken of the height/range tube on 37 nights during the spring and autumn

and 22,000 echoes were examined. Ground returns prevented the measurement of the altitude of echoes below 600 ft but, from general observation, Nisbet concluded that on average only about 10–20 per cent were below this altitude and that these referred in the main to non-migrating birds such as shorebirds and seabirds. Most of the measurements were made on targets within 12 miles of the radar station and these echoes were of the angel type, i.e. they comprised a flock or loose group of birds contained within the pulse volume. Usually the measurements were made about three to four hours after sunset when the most frequent height was found to lie between 1,500 ft and 2,500 ft above sea level, while 90 per cent of the angels were below 5,000 ft. On a few of the nights it was found that a majority of the echoes were below 2,500 ft, but usually angels were present up to 6,000 ft or even 8,000 ft.

Observations were made at 20.00 h and 22.00 h and suggested that the average height at the earlier hour was about 10 per cent lower than at the later time. It

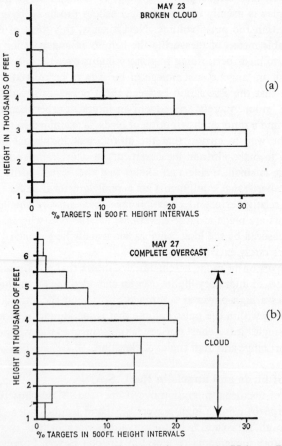

FIG. 11.6. The altitude distribution of night migrants over Urbana, Illinois (after Bellrose and Graber, *Proc. XIIIth Int. Ornith. Congress*, 1963)

appeared that the maximum altitude occurred about 22.00 h, since films taken at midnight on a number of nights showed that the altitude had then decreased from its value at 22.00 h. The altitude continued to decrease until 04.00 h when it had fallen to 75 per cent of its peak value; a sharp increase took place at dawn but not of an amount comparable to Myres' observations described in Chapter Six.

Nisbet considered that a substantial portion of his observations related to small passerines and suggested that these birds tend to migrate higher than most larger species. Usually, very few angels were observed above 10,000 ft although in the autumn of 1961 a few angels were seen as high as 20,000 ft; from their appearance on the p.p.i. he attributed these echoes to shore birds migrating directly across the Atlantic to eastern South America and the Lesser Antilles.

The altitude measurements of Bellrose and Graber (1963) were made at Urbana, Illinois, with a 3-cm radar. It was found that a typical altitude distribution for a night with broken cloud took the form shown in Fig. 11.6 (a). In this histogram the successive horizontal rectangles correspond to the percentage of the migrants which lay in the 500-ft height interval plotted as ordinate. Thus, on 23 May, 32 per cent of all the migrants were contained in the height level 2,500–3,000 ft. In a histogram for 16 October, taken with a clear sky, the most frequently occurring altitude band was 3,000–3,500 ft which was occupied by 30 per cent of the migrants. Altitude distributions were secured on a number of nights during the spring and autumn of 1960 so that it was possible to detect a tendency for migration to occur at a slightly higher average altitude in the autumn than in the spring. The distribution showed quite marked variations from night to night; nevertheless, there was still a tendency for the most frequent altitude in the spring to be about 2,500–3,000 ft. The cut-off below 1,500 ft was due to the characteristic of the TR switch employed.

Altitudes of angels and birds in Europe

Measurements of the daytime altitudes of birds in the vicinity of Kloten airport were made by Sutter in 1956. The Precision Approach Radar equipment was employed for this purpose, the height-finding component of which was a nodding 3-cm radar covering 6° of elevation only. Measurements were made out to a distance of 5 miles and up to 3,000 ft above the ground. A range-height plot of the observations which were made on four days during October 1956 are shown in Fig. 11.7. Range is shown as abscissa and altitude as ordinate; it should be noted that heights were measured above the airport level, which was itself at an altitude of 1,380 ft above sea level, as the height plots in Fig. 11.7 make clear.

It will be seen that the majority of the targets were situated between 100–600 m (330–1,970 ft) above ground level but the form of the altitude distribution was found to change quite rapidly.

Only limited observations on nocturnal flights of birds were possible but Sutter (1957a and b) showed that there was a tendency for these birds to fly below 1,000 ft above ground level. On one night in October 1956, for example,

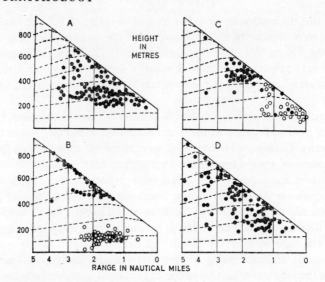

FIG. 11.7. Altitude distribution of birds on the display of the P.A.R. at Kloten, Zürich. Site height 420 m (after Sutter, *Orn. Beob.* 1957b)
A. 13 October 1956, 08.00
    Upper limit of mist 180 m
B. 16 October 1956
    Circles 06.50; Points 08.00
    Mist layer from 200 m to 400 m
C. 20 October 1956
    Circles 10.30; Points 08.10
    Thick mist in two layers produced a thick covering until 09.00 when it began to disperse.
    The lower layer was 180–280 m, the upper 880–1180 m
D. 21 October 1956 12.15. Weather fine

the majority of the birds were found to be located below 600 ft. Some interesting observations upon the altitude behaviour of birds in the presence of mist and cloud were made with the P.A.R. equipment by Sutter and also by Gehring (1963), and are considered later.

Using the surveillance radar equipment at Kloten for plotting the movements of night ascended swifts, Weitnauer (1956) was able to gain visual contact with a flock at an altitude of 3,300 ft, the measurement being made from the aircraft's altimeter. Similarly, Hofmann (1956) was able to make a daylight interception of a large flock of lapwing by means of radar control from Kloten, and showed that the altitude was 7,500 ft above sea level, the birds being at a height of approximately 1,000 ft above the upper limit of the cloud layer.

The radar equipment installed at the Meteorological Office Research Station at East Hill, Bedfordshire, included a medium-powered 10-cm nodding height-finding radar which was used by Harper (1958) to show that the most probable height for bird migration flights in that region of England was between 2,000 ft and 3,000 ft. The spread in height of the birds was quite wide and radar heights up to 5,000 ft were of frequent occurrence. Altitudes between 5,000 ft and 10,000 ft were much less frequent and only a few observations were made of birds above 10,000 ft, although the maximum height which he recorded was at 16,000 ft. The maximum height observed by Houghton and Coultas (1958) for a spring movement of birds in the region of Great Malvern was 9,500 ft; they also noted that most of the birds were located at altitudes below 4,000 ft.

Throughout his extended study of bird migration across the southern North Sea, Lack (1959) made a number of measurements of angel altitudes using an S-band height finder similar to that shown in Plate 2 *b*. Observations during the spring of 1958 showed that most of the echoes were located between 2,000–5,000 ft during the first part of the night, with several echoes also spread between 6,000–9,000 ft. Next morning 2,000–4,000 ft was the most favoured altitude band, with a number of echoes scattered between 5,000–7,000 ft and a few only between 8,000–10,000 ft.

Observations were made on a number of spring mornings in 1959 during the hours 06.00–07.00 when it was found that the most frequent height for bird echoes was 2,000 ft or below (three mornings), 2,000–3,000 ft (one morning), 3,000 ft (one morning), 4,000 ft (two mornings), and 5,000 ft (one morning). About 700 individual echo heights were secured on these mornings and of them 70 per cent were below 4,500 ft. Lack considered that the true proportion of lower heights was even greater than this figure suggests since the echoes at low elevations tended to merge with each other and with the ground echoes. The altitude pattern showed marked variation from day to day but appeared to be roughly the same over land and sea. The highest daytime altitude recorded was 12,000 ft, but this was exceeded by one of 14,000 ft taken at night. During the night the altitude pattern was very variable with the most frequent height being as low as 2,000 ft and as high as 4,000–8,000 ft. Some interesting observations were made by Lack on starlings migrating out to sea; these birds could be readily identified by the form of the echo (Chapter Nine). Most of the flocks were between 2,000–3,000 ft but some were at 4,000 ft, 7,000 ft, and even 8,000 ft.

Although no systematic height measuring programme throughout the year was attempted by Lack (1960) he was able to show that there was a tendency for the autumnal flight of winter visitors into England to be made at lower altitudes than the spring emigration movements of the same species. Similarly, a tendency to fly higher by night than by day was also noted. Particularly interesting were Lack's observations at sunrise in September 1959 and 1960 of the arrival off Norfolk of small waders such as Dunlin that had left Scandinavia the night before. These echoes were usually below 6,000 ft but a few echoes were scattered up to 15,000 ft, and on two mornings the peak altitude was as much as 21,000 ft!

Height measurement made by Lack on lapwings suggested that many wader movements occurred between 3,000 ft and 6,000 ft, such movements taking place within a fairly narrow height bracket of 2,000 ft in contrast to the rather broad spread of height which he found to be the pattern of passerine migration.

The mean heights of the lapwing movements differed significantly from day to day and a higher proportion of high flying birds was present in June–July compared to the movements of the same species in the autumn. It appeared that the autumn lapwing migrants were able to regulate their heights above the sea more precisely than the same species performing its summer movements (Lack, 1963b).

Changes in altitude during the night were observed by Lack (1963a) on departures south-south-east over land during October 1960, when thrushes and lapwing were involved; a change of the highest birds from 7,500 ft to 6,000 ft took place in less than an hour. An altitude change was also recorded for Scandinavian thrushes on 11 November 1958, when the dawn ascent phenomenon of Myres was shown to be accompanied on this occasion by an increase of the highest birds from 7,000 ft to 8,000 ft.

These various observations made with a height radar prompted Lack to ask how migrating birds maintain their height above the sea and whether they depend on visual height estimation only or possess some special adaptation. Lack was greatly impressed by the fact that even small birds appear to be capable of operating at quite high altitudes where oxygen lack and low temperature would appear to be prejudicial to the bird's flight operations – do birds possess special adaptations that permit them to cope with these effects?

Altitude distribution of angels: day and night effects

An extended study of angel altitudes was made by Eastwood and Rider (1965) at the Bushy Hill station during 1962–3. Both the S-band nodding height finder and the L-band tracker described above were employed in this investigation

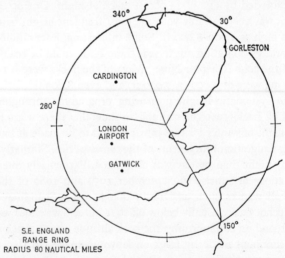

FIG. 11.8. Outline map of south-east England showing Bushy Hill, and the sectors in which altitude measurements were taken. The meteorological stations mentioned in the text are included

and some 20,000 measurements of angel altitudes were taken; observations were made by night as well as by day. Correlation of the paints upon the Height/Range tube with the echoes upon the p.p.i. was at all times possible so that the heights measured referred to discrete angels and not to agglomerations of angels. As discussed above, such a single angel may correspond to a single bird; more likely it refers to a flock or group of birds contained within the pulse volume. The number of individuals within the angel may change with the species, the season, the time of the day and also with the range since the magnitude of the pulse-volume depends upon the range.

The height measurements were made along azimuths selected at 10° intervals. It will be seen from Fig. 11.8 that the sightings of angels made to the east of the station referred in general to bird movements over the sea, i.e. to migrants moving between Britain and the Continent. The daytime measurements overland included the random flights of resident birds as well as the migrants, but the night-time results involved only true migrants.

The analyses of the bird altitude distributions which were derived from all the measurements made during the year are shown in Fig. 11.9. In this figure, day and night altitude measurements have been separated, but no distinction has been made between overland or oversea effects. In the histograms the length of the rectangles are the percentages of the total number of measurements which fall in the corresponding height intervals. Thus the envelope of the rectangles approximates to the altitude distribution function. The M.T.I. facility allowed birds at altitudes below 1,000 ft to be seen, but the estimates of such low heights

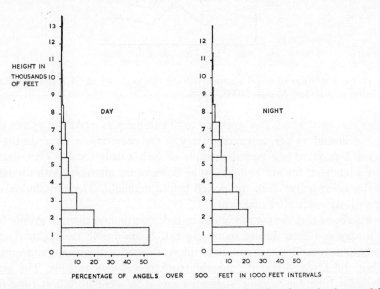

FIG. 11.9. Average altitude distributions by day and night of angels observed from Bushy Hill, 1962–3. Equal weighting by months (after Eastwood and Rider, *British Birds*, 1965)

could only be approximate and for this reason the distribution is shown from 500 ft upwards. All heights quoted refer to the height of the aerial which was itself 250 ft above sea level.

It will be seen that the centre of gravity of the night histogram occurs at a higher altitude than that corresponding to the daytime histogram and so demonstrates a tendency for the birds to fly higher by night than by day. Otherwise expressed, 80 per cent of the birds at night fly below 5,000 ft, but during the day 80 per cent of the birds fly below 3,500 ft, so that the day to night altitude effect is a significant one. On the other hand, the maximum night altitude recorded was 11,000 ft as compared to the maximum daytime figure of 14,000 ft.

Diurnal and monthly variations of angel heights (Bushy Hill)

In order to study the change in altitude throughout the twenty-four hours, distributions were compiled for consecutive 6-h time intervals and the three

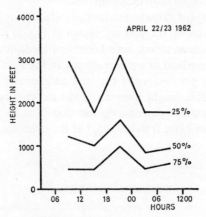

FIG. 11.10. Variation of angel altitude during the night of 22/23 April 1963 (after Eastwood and Rider, *British Birds*, 1965)

heights extracted which corresponded to the altitudes exceeded by 75 per cent, 50 per cent and 25 per cent respectively of the observations taken during the interval. Fig. 11.10 is a typical example of such a daily record. This diagram shows a tendency for low altitudes to be flown in the afternoon with maximum altitudes being achieved in the period before midnight. The altitude becomes progressively lower after midnight.

It was found that the pattern of the altitude distribution changed greatly from day to day and even during successive half hours during the night. Average distributions compiled each month of the year introduced a measure of smoothing but still revealed that the monthly pattern was very variable. The height analysis for June, for example, suggested a most frequent altitude of 1,000 ft by day and 2,000 ft by night. In November, on the other hand, the most frequent altitude was approximately 1,000 ft for both the day and the night distributions.

Comparison of angel altitudes for the spring and autumn (Bushy Hill)
The large scatter in the monthly pattern tended to obscure the persistent seasonal differences. Doubtless this was caused by the wide variations in weather conditions which prevailed on the randomly selected observational days. Nevertheless, it is of interest to compare the altitude distributions for the periods corresponding to the arrival of the winter visitors from the Continent, i.e. the westerly movements of October and November, with the distribution for February

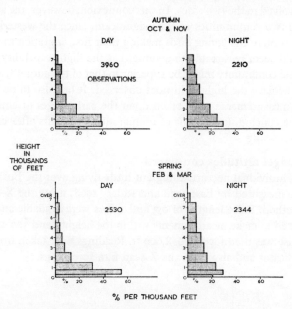

FIG. 11.11. Comparison of angel altitudes during the spring and autumn (after Eastwood and Rider, *British Birds*, 1965)

and March when these same winter visitors fly eastwards to their continental breeding grounds. The resulting autumn and spring distributions are shown in Fig. 11.11. The day and night effect is once more apparent and holds for both the autumn and spring movements as shown in Table 11.2.

TABLE 11.2 *Percentage of angel altitudes above 2,500 ft (Bushy Hill)*

	Day	Night
Autumn	25	30
Spring	31	52

Table 11.2 shows very clearly that while the daytime altitude for the spring movements is significantly higher than for the reversed direction of flow in the autumn, the night altitude in the spring is substantially higher than the night

altitude in the autumn. In contrast, Bellrose and Graber (1963) showed that the altitudes of their south-bound migrants of the autumn were slightly greater than those flown by the north-bound migrants of the spring.

One reason for this seasonal change in the altitude of migrants might be due to species differences. A contribution from this cause to the night/day effect is undoubtedly present, but its influence ought to be small when a comparison is made of the spring/autumn altitudes for the east–west movements across the North Sea, since it is highly probable that roughly the same communities of birds are involved in the two cases. In this connexion, however, the age difference between the two communities may be significant, since the westerly streams of the autumn contain the young birds making their first migration to winter quarters. It would seem reasonable to assume that the flight capability of the more mature spring community might be superior to that of the autumn, and so would be likely to achieve the higher altitudes observed. It has also to be remembered that height measurements were taken upon the early stages of emigrant flights but upon the concluding portions of immigrant movements after completion of a tiring sea-crossing.

Bird and angel altitudes compared

Altitudes of individual nocturnal migrant birds flying over the Bushy Hill radar station were measured by Eastwood and Rider (1966) using the X-band conical scanning method. Pulse lengths of 0·3 and 1·0 μs were available and the shorter pulse was used to make measurements within the height band 300–2,000 ft while the long pulse was used for 1,000–8,000 ft. Readings were taken from the height azimuth indicator and also from the Z-scan film recordings.

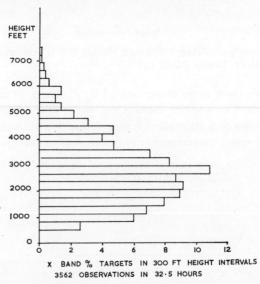

FIG. II.I2. Altitude distribution of nocturnal bird migrants over Bushy Hill, spring, 1966 (after Eastwood and Rider, *Nature*, 1966)

The distribution pattern derived from measurements made during the spring of 1966 is shown in Fig. 11.12 in which 300-ft steps are plotted. The most frequently occurring altitude band was 2,700–3,000 ft; the relative scarcity of bird echoes below 1,000 ft will be noted, probably due in some measure to the recovery time of the TR cell.

In Fig. 11.13 the histogram has been replotted in 1,000-ft intervals for direct comparison with the springtime night distribution of angels taken on the L-band tracker in 1963. The angel distribution refers to echoes observed at distances between 8 and 35 miles, mainly over the sea, and shows that the percentage of

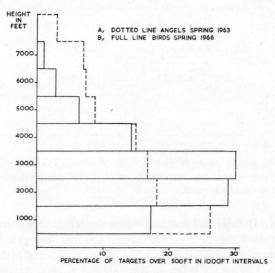

FIG. 11.13. Comparison of nocturnal altitude distributions of (a) angels, spring, 1963 (b) birds, spring 1966

low angels was greater than the proportion of low birds flying over the X-band radar at a point distant 12 miles from the coast. It is hardly profitable to compare too closely distributions which were not determined on the same migrant flights, but it is worth noting that the median altitude of the bird diagram was 1,800 ft while that of the angels was 1,700 ft. Remembering the probable errors associated with the L-band angel altitude measurements this difference is hardly significant, which might suggest that there is no correlation between the number of birds in an angel and the altitude of that angel.

During the course of these vertical incidence observations, it was found that the altitude pattern could change rapidly from hour to hour in response to the local weather, and also from night to night. These effects are illustrated in Fig. 11.14. Rain tended to suppress bird activity while the maximum rate of passage of birds occurred on warmer, moonlight nights with little wind.

It is of interest to compare the X-band histogram of Fig. 11.12 with the corresponding diagram established by Bellrose and Graber (1963) and shown

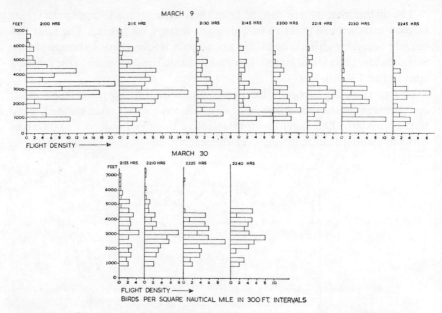

FIG. 11.14. Changes in altitude distribution of birds over Bushy Hill (9 and 30 March 1966) as measured by the number of birds per square nautical mile during successive quarter-hour intervals

in Fig. 11.6 (a). In this latter diagram, which also relates to nocturnal migrants, a most frequent altitude between 2,500 ft and 3,000 ft is clearly indicated. The site height of Urbana had little relevance as the radar was situated in the middle of an extended plain; but the site height of Bushy Hill is 250 ft and should be added to the altitudes in Fig. 11.12, making the most frequent altitude 2,950–3,250 ft.

The influence of wind speed and direction on angel altitudes

The direction and speed of the wind were obvious factors that might have contributed to the altitude differences revealed in the autumn and spring comparison of Fig. 11.11. To test for wind effects Eastwood and Rider (1965) derived the altitude distributions for a number of days when clearly defined migrant streams were identifiable on the p.p.i. The median height and the percentage of heights above 2,500 ft were extracted for correlation with the wind direction. In order that the analysis should be as free as possible from any ambiguity of interpretation, the observations were limited to the easterly and westerly streams of the spring and autumn respectively and involved only heights measured over the sea.

The analysis revealed a rather surprising and unexpected lack of correlation between the wind direction and the median altitude. The spring results showed no correlation at all, while the autumn figures suggested only a slight tendency for marginally lower altitudes to be assumed in the face of headwinds.

The effect of wind speed was also investigated, but again, no correlation could be detected between the median height and the resolved component of wind velocity along the flight path of the angels. In this work the wind speed and direction at 900 m as given by the Hemsby Meteorological Station were employed, as this station was reasonably close to the measurement area. These results suggested that birds migrating over the North Sea at night did not adjust their altitudes by any significant amount in response to the speed of the wind or its direction.

This result is not necessarily at variance with the common observation that birds overland tend to fly low into an opposing wind, nor with the report by Gruys-Casimir (1965) that the highest altitudes of migrants over Holland occur with following winds. Similarly, birds flying out to sea in the face of an opposing sea breeze are commonly observed to fly close to the water surface. The migrant bird, airborne at night over the sea at an altitude of 2,500 ft, however, can have little cognizance of the wind state as a factor affecting its altitude, provided that it is not disturbed by air turbulence. It was suggested by Eastwood and Rider that it is hardly reasonable to expect altitude adjustment by nocturnal migrants in response to the variations in wind speed and direction encountered during an extended flight over the sea, nor would it be effective in improving ground speed unless the altitude were reduced to a dangerously low level. It is recognized that upper air turbulence increases as wind speed rises and this may well limit the height flown by birds under these conditions.

It is interesting to note that Bellrose and Graber (1963) also reported that the altitudinal distribution of their overland, nocturnal migrants was substantially the same regardless of whether winds were opposed or following. On the other hand Nisbet (1963b) found that, on average, migration tended to take place at lower heights with crosswinds than with following winds. Gehring (1963) also reported very low heights of migrants over Switzerland in the presence of head-winds. In view of these differences between the various experimental results it is obviously desirable for further studies to be made of the altitude/wind effect. Such investigations will demand the accumulation of a considerable volume of data on individual birds and angels by day and by night over both sea and land, with wind parameters accurately determined at the time of observation and not inferred retrospectively from synoptic weather charts.

The influence of cloud cover upon the altitude distribution

One of the advantages of the X-band radar method of study employed by Bell-rose and Graber was that it permitted them to detect the presence of cloud and to measure the height band which it covered. In this way it was found that the birds had a tendency to migrate at higher altitudes when the skies were overcast than when they were clear. The evidence suggested that the migrants apparently attempted to fly above an extended region of overcast unless the clouds were too high for them to overfly. Even more surprising was the conclusion that on many occasions migrants were to be found not only below and above the cloud layer but also within it (see Fig. 11.6 (*b*)). Single birds were also observed within rain cloud at night by Eastwood and Rider (1966).

Nisbet's altitude measurements from Cape Cod suggested that the birds he was observing remained below cloud and did not climb through them although the presence of some shorebirds above cloud was recorded on one occasion.

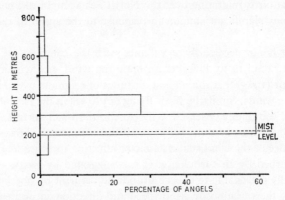

FIG. 11.15. Altitude of birds above the Kloten airfield. The dotted line indicates the upper limit of the mist (after Gehring, *Orn. Beob.*, 1963)

The behaviour of birds by day in the presence of mist was observed by Sutter (1957b) using the P.A.R. equipment at Zürich. A clear tendency for the birds to avoid a layer of mist by overflying is shown in Fig. 11.7 (*a*), while both overflying and underflying are indicated on Fig. 11.7 (*b*). Using the same equipment Gehring (1963) also observed the birds concentrated immediately above a mist layer, as Fig. 11.15 makes clear; this diagram also shows a small percentage of birds within the mist.

The effect of cloud cover upon the heights of angels was also investigated by Eastwood and Rider (1965) using Bushy Hill measurements made on those days and nights when overcast prevailed over a large area. The criterion adopted for

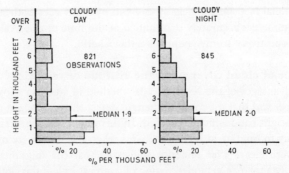

FIG. 11.16. The influence of cloud cover upon the altitude of angels: 8/8 cloud reported at Gatwick, Gorleston, and Cardington (after Eastwood and Rider, *British Birds*, 1965)

218

the presence of widespread overcast was the simultaneous registering of 8/8 cloud at Gatwick, Gorleston, and Cardington. The altitude patterns which resulted are shown in Fig. 11.16. For comparison, Fig. 11.17 shows the histograms derived from the measurements made on days and nights when the cloud cover records at the same three stations were 4/8 cloud or less. It was presumed that under these conditions all birds airborne would have a reasonable opportunity for clear viewing of the ground. The diagrams clearly indicate a tendency for

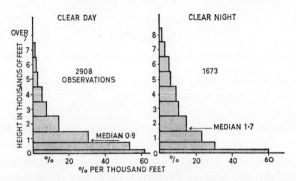

FIG. 11.17. The influence of cloud cover upon the altitude of angels: 4/8 cloud or less and no precipitation reported at Gatwick, Gorleston, and Cardington, i.e. the birds could see the ground (after Eastwood and Rider, *British Birds*, 1965)

higher mean altitudes to be flown in the presence of complete cloud cover than under a clear sky. This effect is brought out very well in Table 11.3.

TABLE 11.3 *Percentage of angel altitudes greater than 3,500 ft (Bushy Hill)*

	Day	Night
Clear	13	25
Cloudy	33	35

The day and night effect already discussed is seen to be present in the case of the clear sky results, but it is interesting to note that the presence of cloud causes the daytime distribution to approximate more closely to that of the night.

It would appear reasonable to interpret these results in terms of the birds seeking to overfly the overcast and so cruising at higher mean altitudes. It should be noted that the lower flight levels are not wholly abandoned, neither is there zero population above the cloud base; the birds are, in fact, more uniformly distributed in altitude. By means of the tracker and with the aid of the discrimination provided by the M.T.I. facility, birds have been observed and measured within the cloud layer itself. The histogram shown in Fig. 11.18 for 23 October 1962 (afternoon) is particularly interesting in that the distribution, although continuous through the levels reported for the cloud base at Gatwick and Gorleston respectively, shows a marked change at this level with a reduced density of

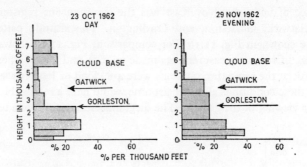

FIG. 11.18. Altitude distribution of angels in the presence of low cloud
(a) afternoon, 23 October 1962
(b) evening, 29 November, 1962
(after Eastwood and Rider, *British Birds*, 1965)

distribution above the cloud base. A night histogram is given in Fig. 11.18 and is also continuous through the cloud-base level, but a significant percentage of birds above this level is seen to be present. Unfortunately, no information was available from the meteorological office on the height of the upper limit of the cloud layer on this occasion but it was likely to have exceeded 7,000 ft. The conclusion seems to be inevitable that approximately 35 per cent of the birds were flying within the cloud layer itself.

Evidence of altitude differences over land and sea

It was shown by Bergman and Donner (1964) that the common scoter and long-tailed duck fly at higher altitudes over the land portion of their migratory routes than over the sea. Altitudes between 1,600 and 5,000 ft were flown over land, with 3,400 ft as the average. The heights measured on birds migrating over the sea ranged between 300 and 1,000 ft. It is hardly to be expected that passerine migrants over the North Sea would make an altitude change of this amount

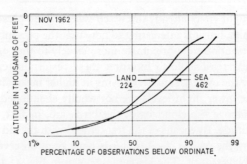

FIG. 11.19. Height change of passerine migrants on passing from sea to land. Cumulative distributions are shown for November 1962, for the height of angels contained in westerly movements in the sectors 30° to 150° over sea and 280° to 340° over land (after Eastwood and Rider, *British Birds*, 1965)

when passing from sea to land, but to test the point the height measurements made from Bushy Hill during November 1962 were analysed for Fig. 11.19. The heights included in the analysis were those corresponding to westerly flights only, taken with a following wind; the land and sea curves are based upon measurements made in the sectors 280°–340° and 30°–150° respectively as indicated in Fig. 11.8.

The land and sea cumulative distribution curves of Fig. 11.19 are sensibly identical up to the 1,200-ft level but diverge thereafter with the 'land' curve climbing above the 'sea' curve. The median altitude of the 'overland' distribution is 2,200 ft and is significantly greater than the median altitude of 1,700 ft derived from the 'oversea' distribution.

The autumn migration of the chaffinch has been studied intensively in Holland over a number of years and, since this bird is an important member of the immigration movements into East Anglia covered by the above analysis, it is of great interest to compare the two groups of observations. It has been shown by Deelder and Tinbergen (1947) and by Deelder (1949) that there is a relation between the flying height of the migrant chaffinch over Holland and the form of the landscape. Broadfront migration over the forests usually takes place below 700 ft, but bare landscapes induce the birds to fly at greater heights. Birds flying along the coast do so at lower heights than those flying out to sea. It was found by Klomp (1956) and Gruys-Casimir (1965) that chaffinches commencing the crossing to England rise steeply at the coast or even some distance from it. On days suitable for migration, for example, with north-easterly to easterly winds, some of the birds proceeding from forest areas at low heights commence to climb when they reach the bare polders and continue the climb over the coast. Many flocks cross the coast at heights up to 4,900 ft.

This behaviour at the coast of Holland refers specifically to chaffinches migrating in the daytime. The East Anglian coastal crossings were observed by radar at night; they contained many chaffinches but included other species as well. Both coastal crossings were made with roughly following winds, but perhaps the other circumstances differed too much for comparison of the results to be meaningful. More altitude measurements at the coast are required, but if this land/sea altitude effect in the course of the same migratory movement proves to be real, it becomes of great interest to discover the cause. If the bird measures its altitude by visual observation it would be expected that the physical features of the ground would permit more accurate height estimation over land than over sea, particularly at night, and so a lower altitude over the land would seem more probable.

The ear of a bird is undoubtedly capable of functioning as an aneroid barometer type of altimeter – just as the human ear is sensitive to sudden pressure changes accompanying descent in an aircraft, passage of a locomotive into a tunnel, or even by rapid descent of a hill in a car. The bird's altimeter would be capable of responding to changes in altitude, but it is more difficult to understand how the bird could measure absolute altitude with the unaided ear. Such a measurement would require that the bird should 'remember' the sea level pressure, just as the pilot finds his altitude in the neighbourhood of his destination by setting the zero of his altimeter to local ground pressure. The migrant bird's en route flight behaviour has all the appearance of being servo controlled in altitude, but the nature of the loop still remains obscure, perhaps pressure, temperature, and humidity all have a part to play. The remarkable visual acuity which a bird possesses may prove to be sufficient explanation of the various altitude effects even at night, although this appears unlikely.

A 'ceiling' effect attributable to temperature

Wide variations in the altitude distribution pattern of birds are common as shown in Fig. 11.14; a particularly interesting example of this kind was recorded at Bushy Hill on 12 March 1959. Radar observations on that morning commenced at 07.00 h and showed that a heavy eastward migration was in progress, the intensity of which gradually reduced until 14.00 h. The weather was fine and clear and a westerly wind of 5 knots produced ideal conditions for the heavy easterly movement of chaffinches, thrushes, and starlings which took place in accordance with the characteristic pattern of March migratory movements for East Anglia.

Vertical sections of the angel formation were taken at azimuthal intervals of 45° by the S-band height-finding radar and showed a remarkable constancy in altitude of the birds. The height/range measurements are summarized in Fig. 11.20. Although this dense angel formation covered an area greater than 7,000 sq miles, the birds were clearly concentrated in a comparatively thin layer whose

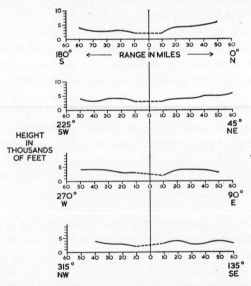

FIG. 11.20. Altitude/range relation for a dense angel formation 11.10 h on 12 March 1959 (after Eastwood and Rider, *British Birds*, 1965)

altitude was approximately 4,000 ft. The meteorological station at Hemsby gave the noon height of the freezing level as 4,500 ft.

It appears difficult to avoid the conclusion that the migrating birds were climbing to a height just below the freezing level, but were deterred from penetrating this layer, whether by the presence of ice crystals or simply because of the low temperature, is not clear. Nevertheless, the presence of the freezing layer appeared to impose a 'ceiling' upon the birds and did so much more effectively than the presence of a cloud layer. This observation suggests that temperature is a factor of some importance in determining the form of the altitude distribution function. This possibility is all the more interesting in view of Lack's demonstration that temperature at ground level plays a very secondary role in the initiation or suppression of migration.

Altitude estimation from the vertical cover diagram

Plate 13 (a and b) shows the initial and final phases respectively of the two temporary winter movements of lapwings. The fact that the limiting range to which the birds were observed was approximately 90 n.m. in both cases, suggests that the lapwings were flying in a comparatively thin layer and the problem was to estimate the common altitude at which the movements took place.

The vertical cover diagram of the Bushy Hill radar given in Fig. 11.21 shows the relation between the range and altitude of a standard target at the limit of visibility; if the extinction range of a target of known echoing area can be measured then the altitude at this point can be read off from curve. Altitude estimation from the vertical cover diagram is, of course, only approximate but can

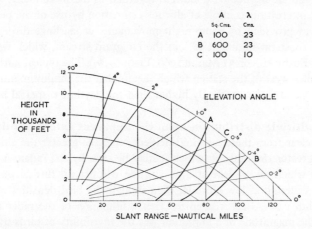

FIG. 11.21. Vertical cover diagram relating range and height for 50 per cent probability of observing a target of echoing area A
Curve A: Bushy Hill surveillance radar, wavelength 23 cm, A = 100 cm²
Curve B: Bushy Hill surveillance radar, wavelength 23 cm A = 600 cm²
Curve C: Bard Hill surveillance radar, wavelength 10 cm A = 100 cm²
(after Eastwood and Rider, British Birds, 1965)

supply useful information and this method has been used by a number of workers, including Gehring in Switzerland (1963).

Special interest attaches to the radio horizon at 0° elevation, for targets below this horizon are invisible to the radar. Curve A of Fig. 11.21 intersects the 0° elevation line at a range of 51 miles and an altitude of approximately 1,600 ft. A bird flock of equivalent echoing area 100 cm² approaching the station at an altitude of 1,600 ft would remain invisible below the horizon until the range was reduced to 50 miles, when it would fly into the beam and become visible to the radar. Similarly, from curve B, a target of cross-section 600 cm² at an altitude of 4,500 ft would be invisible at all ranges greater than 80 miles. When a bird flock rises above the horizon at ranges well within the limiting range contour corresponding to its echoing area, then the echo will be quickly strong and does not pass through the flickering uncertain period typical of crossing the cover curve at high altitudes. This applied to the lapwing echoes.

Now the extinction range of the two lapwing movements was 90 miles. If the visibilities of these movements are assumed to be horizon limited then the altitude at extinction is seen to be $\sim$ 5,700 ft and the average echoing area of the flocks must have been approximately 1,000 cm². Assuming an echoing area for a single lapwing of 40 cm² then the average flock size would be approximately 25 birds, which is not an unreasonable figure. If a lapwing flock were assumed to possess a cross-section of 600 cm², corresponding to 15 birds of 40 cm², then curve B would apply and extinction at 90 miles would imply an altitude of 7,000 ft, which is markedly different from that yielded by the former assumptions. In the present instance the sharpness of the range cut off suggests horizon limitation and an altitude of 5,700 ft is regarded as the more likely.

Another interesting example of altitude estimation by use of the performance diagram was provided by some night movements of starlings dispersing from temporary roosts at midnight to join the emigrant stream, which were photographed at Bushy Hill on 31 March 1966 (Plate 18 (b)). The typical starling echoes were 63 miles west of the station which means that the minimum altitude must have been 3,000 ft, i.e. markedly higher than the daytime dispersal height.

Effect of altitude distribution upon the apparent extent of migration

It will be clear from these lapwing incidents that the greater the altitude of an angel the greater the range at which it may be seen by the radar. A migratory movement which takes place at high altitude will extend further on the p.p.i. than one occurring at low altitude, even though the bird densities may be the same in both cases. Lack recognized that a limitation of the radar method of assessing the magnitude of a migration was the invisibility of birds flying below the radar beam, which meant that the apparent density might be an underestimate if a greater proportion of the birds than usual were flying at low altitude. Lack (1962a) stated, 'With the information and techniques at present available, it does not seem possible to make any proper allowance for the influence of height of flights on apparent density, so the reader must keep in mind that what is here recorded is the volume of migration above the radar horizon, and not the whole volume.'

Since the general form of the altitude distribution of North Sea migrants has been established by the investigations described above, it is of interest to examine briefly how this pattern interacts with the vertical cover diagram of the radar to affect the apparent migration density. We know that the majority of angel altitudes lie between 0–8,000 ft and so we expect that angel displays will very rarely extend beyond 110 n.m., no matter what echoing areas the angels possess, because this is the distance to the radio horizon for an altitude of 8,000 ft as Fig. 11.21 shows.

Reference to curve A of Fig. 11.21 shows that an angel of echoing area 100 cm^2 and altitude 4,000 ft will be seen to a range of 61 miles by the L-band radar. Increasing the altitude to 6,000 ft would extend the limiting range to 67 miles. The parameters of the S-band radar used by Lack yield curve C for the same target, which would be seen to limiting ranges of 70 and 78 miles for altitudes of 4,000 and 6,000 ft respectively. If an angel of echoing area 600 cm^2 were observed by the L-band set at the same altitudes of 6,000 ft then the limiting range would be 85 miles, but at the lower altitude of 4,000 ft the angel would be visible at all ranges up to the radio horizon at 75 miles.

These examples show that height has an influence upon the apparent extent of a migration, but the relation is not a sensitive one in the case of the Bushy Hill radar, nor in the 10-cm version of it as used by Lack. The fact that the median altitude for North Sea migrants is about 2,000 ft with the majority of birds below 5,000 ft suggests that the limiting or extinction range to which an extended migratory movement is visible is set by the radio horizon. The simple geometry of this situation then shows that the fractional change in extinction range is half the fractional change in altitude producing it (i.e. 20 per cent change in altitude at the radio horizon would yield 10 per cent change in extinction range).

CHAPTER TWELVE

Counting birds by radar

The Battle of Britain was fought over the south-east corner of England, where the C.H. and C.H.L. stations were most densely grouped. These long-wave radars provided alerting information which included range, bearing, and height of the attacking formations. This meant that standing fighter patrols were rendered unnecessary – a vital alleviation in view of the limited aircraft and pilot strength of the R.A.F.

Equally important with initial detection and location, however, was the indication which radar was able to give to the defence of the probable numbers of enemy aircraft in every attacking formation. This ability to estimate the numbers of the attacking force with some certainty was vital to the success of the whole defence operation, for it meant that from the very limited forces of the R.A.F. at any time it was necessary only to commit the minimum number of fighters required to achieve interception and break up the attack. How was this counting of aircraft carried out?

Counting aircraft by radar

A-scope displays were used in the C.H. stations and all aircraft within the cover of the radar were displayed simultaneously as range echoes upon the A-scope trace. Single aircraft appeared as steady 'blips' and could be counted directly. Two aircraft flying close together produced only a single blip but this combined echo showed a rhythmic fluctuation in amplitude. This fading and subsequent regrowth of the echo occurred because of the interference between the radio waves scattered from the two targets. A change of path length of one quarter of a wavelength only was required in one wavetrain with respect to the other in order to pass from the reinforcing condition to the cancelling state. Since the wavelength employed for the Home Chain stations was about 12 m a change in relative path length of 3 m was required, so that the rate of change of the resultant signal occurred sufficiently slowly to be followed readily by the eye.

The radar operators soon learned to recognize the beating signal which was characteristic of a pair of aircraft. Similarly, after some experience, the fluctuating signal pattern typical of the composite echoes from 3, 4, or 5 aircraft at the same range could be recognized. In those days very close formation flying of large numbers of combat aircraft was not practised, so that the range differences between the aircraft composing a large formation were usually sufficient to produce a spread echo on the A-tube trace, and counting of the beats of the several portions of this echo served to indicate the total number of aircraft in the attacking group. The operators were, in fact, performing a simple form of signature analysis.

Years after the war the author was engaged in discussion with an officer of the German Luftwaffe who had been engaged in these sorties and who was most curious to discover what kind of device had been used by the R.A.F. that had helped them to assess so accurately the strength of the German strikes. 'British girls could count blips' was the truthful but hardly convincing reply – but, so it was, for the W.A.A.F. operators became very skilful at the counting game as applied to echoes on a C.H. radar trace.

The signal fluctuation effect can still be observed on the older type of television set, for the sound of an aircraft in the distance is often accompanied by a rapid fading of the pictures on the tube, produced in this case by interference in the receiver between the direct wave from the transmitting station and the radio wave reflected from the aircraft to the receiver aerial.

Counting echoes on the p.p.i.

With the introduction of the p.p.i. counting of aircraft was greatly improved, and still more improvement was obtained when microwave radars with their narrow fan beams were introduced. Nowadays, with beams of angular width of $1°$ or less, very little overlapping of aircraft echoes occurs, and then only momentarily at the point where the tracks of two aircraft at different altitudes intersect; the counting of aircraft then reduces simply to the counting of paints upon the p.p.i.

Unfortunately, the counting of birds by radar is not so easy a process for the simple reason that whereas a true, aeroplane-type echo almost invariably corresponds to a single aircraft, signature analysis has shown that an angel seldom corresponds to a single bird and so counting angels does not lead immediately or directly to an estimate of the number of birds involved. It is important to find a method of translating angel events into numbers of birds for radar would appear to be the obvious and only way in which the masses of birds comprising a migratory flight can be counted. Success in radar bird counting could well lead to reliable estimates of the total flow of birds both into and out of a region like the British Isles, and such statistics would clearly be of great value in bird population studies.

Any angel distribution is made up of a vast assortment of targets whose individual echoing areas cover a wide range of values, from 1 cm^2 up to 1 m^2 and for every echoing area there is a different fading range. Moreover, these target cross-sections change with time and produce fluctuating signals at the radar. A single angel may be produced by a mass of small targets contained within a single pulse volume. On the other hand, an angel may be formed by the resultant signal from a few closely grouped birds comprising a true flock. The changing relative positions of the birds within such a flock cause the secondary waves scattered from them to vary in phase with respect to each other and so produce a resultant signal which shows a rapid fading characteristic. When a truly steady

227

angel is observed it may with confidence be attributed either to a single large bird or, more likely, to twenty or more birds of medium size which are producing a signal-to-noise ratio substantially above the limit level of the display.

Clearly, two factors of importance in determining the magnitude of the angel signal which will be received from a group of birds are firstly, the number of birds contributing to the signal and, secondly, the echoing areas of the individual birds. The spacing of the birds will also influence the instantaneous amplitude of the signal, but since these relative positions will be changing rapidly it is possible to consider only the average amplitude of the signal and to say that this corresponds to the average total power received. Total power is equal to the sum of the powers of the signal scattered from the individual birds. In other words, it is assumed that the reflections from a random flock of birds occur incoherently and so we make no attempt to calculate the relative phases of the various individual wavetrains in order to deduce the resultant amplitude. Instead, we simply sum the powers scattered by the birds individually. This means that for a flock of birds whose extent is less than the pulse volume the effective echoing area of the flock is the sum of the echoing areas of all the birds within the flock.

How many birds make an angel?

One swallow does not make a summer, neither does it make an angel. In fact, all radar ornithologists have come to recognize that an angel echo results from radar scattering by an assembly of birds contained within a pulse volume and too closely grouped to be resolved. Such a group of birds may or may not be a true flock in the sense of the birds being linked by some form of social association, temporary or otherwise. The problem has been to determine the average number of birds comprised within an angel, and to know whether this number changes significantly as between nocturnal and diurnal angels, or between spring and autumn angels; or whether there is an angel structure characteristic of any particular species. If the answers to these questions were known then it ought to be possible to translate angel counts into numbers of birds.

The difficulty has been that an estimate of birds per angel requires precise correlation between a particular radar angel and a flight of birds observed visually, in which species and numbers of birds can be accurately determined. In his studies of the equivalence of birds and angels, Sutter (1957b) noted on one of his observational days, when the angel frequency of occurrence correlated well with the flight frequency, that the flocks of migrants observed visually consisted of finches, larks, and thrushes in the usual sized groups of around 10–50 birds. He concluded that the radar was seeing most of the flocks of these small birds; it appeared to be certain that flocks of 20–40 thrushes or finches gave weak but significant echoes within 10 miles range of his radar. But Sutter cautiously added, 'Whether the minimum bird content can be gauged from a radar echo must remain an open question.'

Upon the question of whether a night-angel differs from a day-angel Sutter (1957a) was more emphatic. He considered that daytime angels were sharp and precise, whether composed of large flights of pigeons or crows or made up of numbers of small birds. In contrast, his night-angels were much weaker and more variable; they were also larger in total number and more separated from each other. He concluded that only loose formations of birds fly by night as compared to the tight flocks of the daytime and that night-flying birds are fairly homogeneously distributed in the air space. Bergman and Donner (1964), on the other hand, considered that their migrant ducks were grouped into flocks by night as well as by day; a flock consisted of about 150 birds.

Visual inspection of a flock of lapwings from an aircraft was made by Hofmann (1956) when actual counting showed that 120 birds were contained within a particularly strong and persistent angel which was observed and tracked for an hour and a half by the Kloten radar. Such a strong multiple-bird echo represents an angel intermediary between the weak, fluctuating echoes typical of warblers on night migration and the massive echoes from flocking starlings which were discussed in Chapter Nine. Visual estimates of the numbers of birds contained within a single angel tracked by his wind-finding radar were also made by Harper (1958), the counting being made through a telescope. He found that the flock size appeared to vary from 5 to 30 small birds, but, of course, this result would not necessarily apply to a night-angel.

Lack (1960b) also recognized that nocturnal displays of angels were not only commonly denser than daytime displays but were also composed of weaker echoes. He agreed with Sutter that a possible explanation of these facts was that airborne birds were more numerous by night than by day and that small passerine night migrants might usually fly singly. Although this manner of night flying had been believed to be true, Lack (1963b) clearly pointed out that 'one cannot assume that each radar echo corresponds to only one bird since the equipment does not separate echoes from birds which are very close in range and bearing'. Lack's studies did not include an estimate of the number of birds that go to make an angel.

Reference has already been made to the 'misty light' type of p.p.i. display which is characteristic of small warblers on migration. A similar diffuse appearance is provided by night ascended swifts as in Plate 20. There would appear to be little doubt that these forms of p.p.i. display are a consequence of a random and wide distribution of the birds in space, so that the individual echo paints are pulse-volume effects whose fluctuations are a measure of the changing number and positions of birds within the volume. In this case signal/noise ratios are low and the rate of fluctuation is then understandably high. Measurement of these diffuse echoes is difficult and so it is more profitable to investigate the bird content of strong, individual angels whose amplitudes may be readily measured and studied.

Counting birds by the measurement of angel signal strengths
In Chapter One it was shown that the signal power received from a target was dependent upon its echoing area and range, also upon various parameters of the

particular radar equipment employed, as well as upon the angle of elevation of the target within the radar beam. A simplified form of the radar equation which expresses this dependence may be written:

$$P = K \frac{G^2 A}{r^4}$$

Where P is the available power in watts received by the antenna

A is the echoing area or target cross-section in square metres

r is the range in nautical miles

G is the aerial gain for the angle of elevation concerned

K is a constant for the system which may be determined by calibration using a standard target of known echoing area.

The limit of performance of a radar system is set by the minimum signal power which can be detected. In the case of Bushy Hill the power level corresponding to this minimum is 5×10^{-15} W. One form of graphical representation of this equation is the Vertical Performance Diagram shown in Fig. 1.8. This figure gives the limiting range of visibility in the vertical plane of a target having a radar cross-section of 100 cm^2 for various altitudes and angles of elevation. An alternative form of presentation which is more convenient for quantitive work is that of Fig. 12.1. This figure gives the ranges at which targets of various radar cross-sections, and which lie on the axis of maximum sensitivity, can be detected. Thus the minimum cross-section of a target which can just be seen at a range

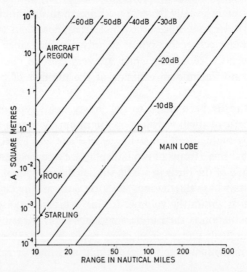

FIG. 12.1. Maximum range of detection with the Bushy Hill surveillance radar for targets of different echoing area A. The lower line 'main lobe' refers to targets in the main lobe of the aerial beam. For other target positions, or when the system sensitivity is reduced in some other way, by the number of decibels indicated, then the other lines refer

of 70 miles is 10^{-2} m^2 (100 cm^2). If a stronger angel signal is received at this same range and which requires the insertion of 10 db of attenuation in the receiver line to reduce it to the receiver noise level, then the target cross-section is the ordinate corresponding to the point D, i.e. 10^{-1} m^2 or $1,000$ cm^2. Measurement of the target cross-section of a particular angel does not necessarily lead to an accurate value of the number of birds that contribute to this angel since birds of a number of different species may be involved; also the positions of the birds within the pulse volume are unknown as are their angles of elevation in the case of a fan-beam radar. Nevertheless, knowledge of the effective echoing area of an assembly of birds can sometimes lead to a useful figure for the number of birds involved when the birds are at roughly the same range, possess a common angle of elevation, and are known to be of the same species. Such a situation is presented by the masses of starlings which erupt from a roost at sunrise.

It will be clear that if birds-per-angel estimates of this kind could be made in sufficiently large numbers, and for angels selected from migratory movements that could be associated with definite species, then it would be possible to arrive at a distribution function of angel echoing areas and ultimately a good value for the average bird content of an angel could be obtained. Such a series of measurements were made at Bushy Hill with the aid of the steerable, tracker aerial shown in the frontispiece (Eastwood and Rider, 1966). By means of this apparatus it is possible to select an angel and then align the aerial dish so that the signal is maximized, which means that the angel lies on the axis of the aerial. In this way

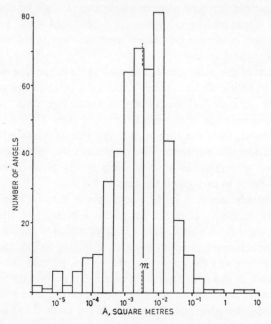

FIG. 12.2. Histogram showing how the frequency of occurrence of angels depends upon the echoing area A (after Eastwood and Rider, *Nature*, 1966)

no correction is necessary for off-axis location of a target and the signal power can immediately be measured as so many decibels above the noise power by means of the adjustable attenuator. The effective echoing area of the angel can then be quickly calculated from the Radar Equation and the frequency of occurrence of angels of various cross-sections gradually established.

The echoing area distributing histogram which was obtained for both day and night angels during July 1962 is shown in Fig. 12.2. This diagram shows that angels having cross-sections of 500 cm^2 or greater are markedly more rare than those having echoes less than this. If we take from Fig. 12.2 the most probable value of the echoing area to be about 70 cm^2 then it is possible to make a rough estimate of the number of birds per angel as between 5 and 35, on the assumption that the average echoing area of the most likely birds to be airborne at the time of the measurements was between 14 and 2 cm^2. It was also found that there was no significant difference between the magnitudes of the echoing areas of angels observed by night and by day during the month of July. If this result is confirmed by further work then it will lead to the very interesting conclusion that for the south-east region of England and the North Sea at least, there is no significant difference between the day and night composition of a passerine angel.

Counting starlings

Chapter Nine has presented a full description of the starling flocking and dispersal phenomena as seen by radar. Since the Bushy Hill radar recorded all the starling dispersals that took place in a land area of 5,000 sq miles, it was possible to use the signal measurement technique described above to make an estimate of the minimum starling population contained within this area (Eastwood, Isted, and Rider, 1962).

The amplitude of the radar signal produced by an expanding ring of starlings was estimated in terms of the receiver noise level by the calibrated attenuator method already described. Introduction of successive steps of attenuation showed that the amplitude of the signal returned from different positions of a ring, and, of course, from the ring at different moments during its expansion, could show considerable variation. The rings from the Matching Green roost, which is located at a range of 20 n.m. from Bushy Hill, required 60 db of attenuation in order to extinguish the radar echo.

As previously mentioned, it is the power which is to be summed from the many randomly situated targets in the pulse volume, and since the power reflected to the radar from a single target is proportional to the echoing area (A), we may treat the echoing area additively also. Applying to Fig. 12.1 the range of the roost in question and the measured attenuation, permits the effective value of A to be read off. If the echoing area for one bird is known, the total number of birds in a pulse volume follows. An estimate of the ring and roost populations may now be made, though certain limitations in the method must be mentioned. The chief of these arises from the aerial scanning rate of 4 r.p.m. The multiple target provided by a flock of birds produces a fluctuating signal, and to obtain a reliable measurement of mean power a number of measurements should be averaged. This is quite impossible here, since the number of birds in the pulse volume is constantly falling as they fly radially from the roost.

The method of measurement employed is to commence a pre-determined series of attenuation settings when the first eruption is seen. Subsequent examination of the film records indicates the setting which has just caused the extinction of the echo, and the radius of the starling ring at this time. The latter figure leads to the proportion of the ring enclosed in the pulse volume.

A further complication is caused by the need to take account of the para-meters of the M.T.I. system and the vertical distribution of field strength at the roost, the birds being more strongly illuminated than the ground.

The following example illustrates the approach:

date of attenuation measurements	= 22 February 1961
radar range to Mountnessing roost	= 12·5 n.m.
radius of ring at time of extinction	= 4·0 n.m.
attenuation required to extinguish ring (using M.T.I.)	= 25 db
attenuation required to extinguish ground echo (no M.T.I.)	= 40 db

Figure 12.1 is now entered with the values 12·5 n.m. and 40 db giving:

Ground echoing area in pulse volume $= 8 \times 10^{-2} \text{ m}^2$

The 'sub-clutter visibility' is taken to be -10 db, i.e. a moving target, in a certain pulse volume, can just be detected in the presence of a stationary target of ten times its effective echoing area. Then echoing area of birds in one volume to be just detected at ground level $= 8 \times 10^{-3} \text{ m}^2$.

However, the starlings were flying in a stronger radar field than that illuminat-ing the ground. The height gain calculated is 12 db; a power ratio of 16. A further 25 db attenuation (power ratio 300) was needed to extinguish the ring.

Thus: echoing area of starlings in pulse volume
$$= 8 \times \frac{10^{-3}}{16} \times 300$$
$$= 0 \cdot 15 \text{ m}^2$$

echoing area of one receding starling $= 0 \cdot 00025 \text{ m}^2$

Hence, number of starlings in pulse volume
(0·15/0·00025) $= 600$
number of pulse volume in ring $= 178$
number of rings emitted from roost $= 5$
roost population $= 500,000$ birds

It may be objected that this figure of half a million birds derived for the Mountnessing roost depends upon the value assumed for the cross-section of a starling, viz. 2·5 cm^2 and that this value is too low in view of the discussions in Chapter Three. However, the values measured by Edwards and Houghton (1959) for the broad-side and tail aspects respectively, were 20 cm^2 and 1·3 cm^2. In the case of Mountnessing the direction of dispersal was such that many of the birds

233

were observed near to tail aspect and so it seemed preferable to take a value for the average echoing near to the minimum.

The calculated bird population of half a million for this roost was in substantial agreement with an estimate made by a number of observers from the Ministry of Agriculture, Fisheries, and Food who also kept visual watch on this particular morning of 22 February 1961. The same method of estimation was applied to all the other dispersals observed and led to an estimate of the starling population within the radar cover of 3×10^6 birds, i.e. an average population density of one starling per acre on 22 February 1961. The seasonal variation in the number of roosts observed by radar was plotted in Fig. 9.2 and suggests that the maximum starling population may be two or three times this figure, or even more, since only large roosts have been assessed in this way.

The figures obtained by radar fit well with the estimate of Roebuck (1934) that the density of starlings in his study area was at least one bird per acre and at most three birds per acre. Detailed visual methods of assessing the population of a number of starling roosts in Shropshire were described by Symonds (1961) who concluded that winter roosts could number between 500,000 and 1·5 million starlings due to the reinforcements from continental winter visitors. In view of these figures the population established by radar for roosts in Essex appears to be in no way excessive.

The fading of angel signals; the need for a statistical approach

Angel signals are subject to quite rapid fading which means that successive frames of the film used to record the angels 'seen' by the radar on consecutive rotations or scans of the aerial fan beam, may differ markedly from each other, not so much in the average density of angels over the frame as in the lack of continuity in tracking individual angels. When the film is projected at the usual speed of 24 frames per second these frame to frame discontinuities are smoothed out and the eye sees a remarkably steady progress of angels across the screen. Nevertheless, since individual frames are commonly used for the measurement of angel densities it is desirable to investigate the implications of this fluctuation phenomenon rather carefully.

Some years ago the author and his colleagues at Bushy Hill endeavoured to establish the form of the angel echoing area distribution function by means of film records of a B-scope displaying signals from the surveillance radar. In this study use was made of a klystron amplifier transmitter in which the radar power output could be rapidly increased in steps. The procedure adopted was to record the radar microscope display which covered a 15 mile × 15-mile region of the p.p.i., first at the initial power level of $\frac{1}{4}$ MW and thereafter to increase the power in steps for each successive sweep of the aerial up to the maximum power of 4 MW. In this way a sequence of frames of film was obtained which recorded the build up of angel density as smaller and smaller angels became visible due to the progressive increase of the transmitter power. It had been assumed that only the strongest angels would be recorded on the first frame and

234

that these angels would continue throughout the sequence of pictures as the weaker angels were added. This would have permitted the distribution function of the angels with respect to echoing area to be readily calculated. In the event this was not possible, due to the variation of the angel pattern between successive frames, even when the power output was kept constant. Signature analysis has now shown why this should be so. The sequence of frames corresponding to power levels of $\frac{1}{4}$ MW, $\frac{1}{2}$ MW, 1 MW, 2 MW, 3 MW, and 4 MW, respectively, are reproduced in Plate 22 and cover a time interval of 7 min only; nevertheless, the lack of continuity in the form of the angel pattern is clearly apparent. It follows that counts of angels on a single frame would possess little significance – many frames must be assessed and the results treated statistically.

The factors which determine the power level of the signal scattered from an assembly of birds which either form a discrete angel or which are contained within a pulse volume and so contribute to a single echo point on the p.p.i. have already been reviewed. These contributory effects can never be known precisely and so the target cross-section of an angel can only be defined in statistical terms. The result is that for an angel with average cross-section A, there is only a probability that it will be seen by a surveillance radar during a single transit of the aerial and this probability varies with range and altitude. The radar cover diagram of Fig. 1.8 has, therefore, to be interpreted statistically, in that the curve expresses the range/altitude relation for a target having a time average cross-section of 100 cm^2 which will give a recognizable radar echo for half the scans of the radar beam across it, i.e. the curve has been plotted to correspond to a 50 per cent probability of detection. If it were plotted for a 90 per cent probability of detection the ranges would be substantially reduced.

The steerable tracker radar permits one signal to be examined continuously and a good time average cross-section can be derived; the process of signature analysis can also be applied. A scanning surveillance radar, on the other hand, allows many angels to be examined simultaneously, but the results have to be interpreted statistically, since the precise scattering details of each individual angel is then unknowable. This does not mean that such statistical results have no value for radar ornithology. On the contrary, surveillance radar studies are indispensable to further progress in the understanding of migratory flight processes, but interpretation of the radar observations has to take due note of the limitations of the statistical method – this is particularly true in bird counting via angels.

Correlation of angel densities with bird counts in Massachusetts

Before radar became available as a means of observing and recording the nocturnal flights of birds the only method that could be employed to study the flights of birds at night, and to estimate the numbers airborne was the technique of 'moon-watching' which was developed by Lowery (1951). It is well known that the disc of the moon subtends an angle of 29' (1/120 rad) at the earth as in Fig. 12.3. If an observer, armed with suitable binoculars and fortified with much

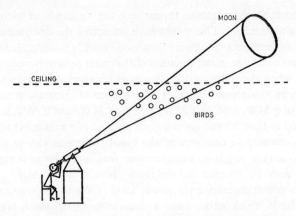

FIG. 12.3. Measuring the density of nocturnal bird migrants by the 'moon-watching' method

patience, maintains a steady watch on the moon's surface throughout the night then he will be rewarded from time to time by the sight of a transit of a bird across the moon. The bird appears as a black silhouette against the bright disc of the moon. An alert observer may even note the apparent angle of traverse of the bird across the moon and Nisbet (1959) has shown how such observations can yield the approximate direction of flight of the bird in the horizontal plane.

What is especially significant from the point of view of migration studies is that a time record of the observed transits during the course of the night can lead to an estimate of the number of birds airborne at any time. In this classic work of Lowery (1951) it was necessary to assume that the population density of the birds with height was uniform up to a ceiling of 5,280 ft and zero thereafter, in order to calculate the flight density, i.e. the number of birds crossing a mile front in an hour, the front lying normal to the direction of travel of the birds.

The method suffers from various limitations apart from the physical strain of making the observations, such as the fact that it is not really applicable for angles of elevation of the moon of less than 20°, or that observations should be limited to the five or six nights around full moon. Nevertheless, the moon-watching method has contributed substantially to our knowledge of the night flights of birds. But its importance from the point of view of the present chapter is that it is a method of determining the density of birds airborne at night. By comparison of this figure with a radar count of angel densities taken simultaneously, it is possible to arrive at an estimate of the number of birds that go to make an angel. This is the basis of the method used by Nisbet (1963a) to study quantitatively the night migration of passerines recorded by his radar on Cape Cod, Massachusetts.

Nisbet employed the moon-watching method for bird counting as outlined above. He improved on the simplifying assumption made by Lowery as to the form of the height distribution of the birds by using radar measurements of angel heights he had made from Cape Cod (Nisbet, 1963b). It is true that these height measurements were not made simultaneously with the radar angel count nor with the moon watch, but at least a substantial part of the inaccuracy introduced by the assumption of a uniform height distribution was removed. In addition, field trials were conducted to establish by means of bird models more realistic distances at which various birds could be seen through binoculars, since this was also a figure which influenced greatly the bird densities finally calculated. Nisbet concluded that with the techniques and methods of data reduction employed the resulting estimate of migration density was not likely to be in error by more than a factor of two, which is by no means excessive for work of this kind.

In order to determine the angel density Nisbet made a systematic study of the thinning effect with range as observed upon the South Truro 23-cm radar. Recognizing that the apparent reduction in angel density with range is a consequence of all the factors which govern the visibility of a group of birds to radar which have been considered above, Nisbet concluded that it was virtually

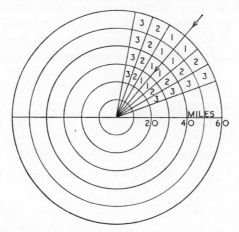

FIG. 12.4. Estimating the densities of angels by counting targets in 10 miles × 10-degree sections grouped symmetrically about the flight direction

impossible to separate them. He decided that the most profitable method of analysis was to measure directly the fluctuations in the rate of thinning from night to night and so arrive at an empirical law which would permit him to determine the absolute angel density from the angel density measured at a known range.

Counts of angels were made from films secured on 24 nights, mostly over the sea and in areas north and east of South Truro. A convenient method of assessing the variation of angel density with range was to count the angels contained within the squares formed by a 10 mile/10° grid on the p.p.i. screen, as in Fig. 12.4. By counting in six squares within each 10-mile annulus, so that the squares were grouped about the main direction of migration, it was possible to eliminate any

237

azimuthal thinning effect since the angel movements were then mainly radial. After the elimination of various errors and applications of corrections for time variations of angel density, it was found that an approximately straight line was obtained when the logarithm of the angel density was plotted against the range as in Fig. 12.5. In other words, the angel density decreased roughly exponentially with range and was, in fact, halved for every 8 miles increase in range.

It was found that the rate of thinning was substantially independent of the angel density prevailing at any time and so by extrapolation of the curve backward to meet the zero range ordinate at *P* it was possible to estimate the absolute density of the angel targets. The argument employed to justify this conclusion was that calculations based on the Radar Equation showed that the South Truro radar was capable of seeing a single bird, the size of the majority of passerines under consideration, within a limiting range of 15 miles. Thus *all* angels, whether single bird or multi-bird, were visible within the 0–10 mile region, and this is the required figure for the absolute angel density which is achieved by extrapolating the curve backwards. The smoothness of the curve showed that the counts within the 0–10, 10–20 range intervals were continuous with those at longer ranges where only the larger angels of the multi-bird variety would be visible. This suggests that Nisbet's basic assumption was justified, viz., that the graph of Fig. 12.5 could be used to determine the absolute density of angels of all echoing

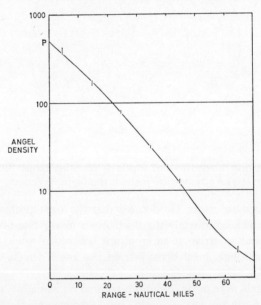

FIG. 12.5. Average rate of thinning of angel density at South Truro, Massachusetts. The horizontal scale gives the range in nautical miles; the vertical scale (plotted logarithmically) is proportional to the average density of angels in 29 series of counts. The vertical lines give twice the standard errors of the means, based on the fluctuations in the counts within each series (after Nisbet, *Ibis*, 1963)

areas from the measured density of angels at ranges where the counts could be accurately performed.

Nisbet's analysis assumes a uniform target density in the horizontal plane, and such distributions appear to occur in the massive migrant streams that pass over New England and the sea adjacent. Such streams are also characterized by parallel flow lines as was discussed in Chapter Seven. In the North Sea region, on the other hand, convergent and divergent streams appear to be the rule and such flow patterns do not result in uniform horizontal distributions. It was, in fact, stressed by Nisbet that the quantitative results established by his research could not be applied immediately to other radar stations nor to other locations. Perhaps it is a coincidence that application of Nisbet's thinning factor to the angel densities quoted for various workers in Chapter Five shows general agreement between them and Nisbet's own high density figure of 0·4–1·0 angels per sq mile at a range of 20–30 miles, and 0·05–0·2 as low density.

Nisbet's radar and moon-watching observations were made during the spring and autumn of 1959 and 1960 and resulted in 50 h of observation time that permitted direct comparison of angel densities measured by radar with bird densities established from moon watching. It was found that all the estimates of the number of birds per angel lay between 2·3 and 12·7. Nisbet concluded that many birds were performing their night migrational flights in well-defined groups. This view should be compared to that which many ornithologists in North America had held earlier (for example, Lowery and Newman, 1955) who considered that most passerines did not normally migrate in groups at night.

A double radar method of counting birds in an angel

The Lowery 'moon-watching technique' was an ingenious approach to the study of the nocturnal flight behaviour of birds before suitable radars had become available for such research. The method possessed the great advantage that the counts of moon transits referred to individual birds and not to groups or flocks of birds. On the other hand, the observations were not easy to make and operator fatigue could seriously prejudice the accuracy of the counts. Final estimate of flight frequency was also dependent upon the height distribution of the birds which was assumed in the analysis. It would clearly be advantageous if the 'moon-watch' operator could be replaced by an automatic recording device and if some apparatus could be introduced that would measure the altitude of each bird at the moment of passage across the moon's disc. Modern photoelectric detectors and recorders are exceedingly efficient so that it would undoubtedly be possible to automate Lowery's moon-watching system. Instead of pursuing this method at Bushy Hill, however, an alternative approach to the problem of counting birds in an angel was employed by Eastwood and Rider (1966) which makes use of two radars working in association. By these means optical devices are removed from the system and heights are measured simultaneously; dependence upon the moon is also avoided so that observations are possible on any night.

The essential feature of Lowery's experiment was the presence of a narrow cone of visibility provided by the moon, the position of which was known accurately in azimuth and elevation. In the Bushy Hill method the cone of optical visibility was replaced by a radio beam provided by a 3-cm radar. Any bird flying through this vertically directed beam produced a signal in the radar receiver, and so the rate of passage of birds overhead could be counted and their altitudes measured.

An X-band Transmitter/Receiver was housed in a mobile trailer on the top of which was mounted a fixed aerial which projected the beam vertically upward. The output from the receiver was applied to a cathode ray tube displaying an intensity modulated trace, which was photographed according to the scheme shown in Fig. 2.3. This radar telescope was located on Saling airfield at a point distant 15·3 miles from Bushy Hill radar. Simultaneous photographic recordings of the angel density in the Saling region, as seen by the Bushy Hill surveillance radar, were made from a B-scope display, adjusted to present an area of 15 × 15 sq n.m. centred on the spot occupied by the X-band radar (Fig. 12.6).

It was found that the time variation of angel activity derived from the B-scope counts showed general correlation with the frequency of bird transits through the X-band beam. As a means of establishing an accurate, quantitive relationship between angel density and bird density, however, the method left much to be desired, mainly due to the small volume of space overhead sampled by the X-

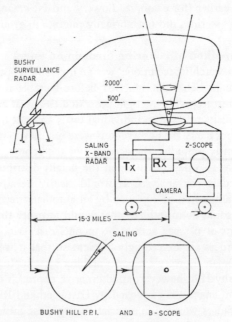

FIG. 12.6. Method of estimating the average number of birds per angel using:
(1) L-band radar and B-scope to measure *angel* density
(2) X-band radar and Z-scope to measure *bird* density

band beam. To overcome this defect and to provide frequency counts of bird transits which were statistically significant the fixed aerial was replaced by a scanning linear array as shown in Fig. 11.5. This aerial provided a horizontal beam width of 0·7°. The Vertical Performance Diagram of this radar is shown in Fig. 11.5; the aerial was mounted so that the axis of the beam was inclined at an angle of 10° to the vertical. The aerial was scanned at 18 r.p.m. When setting up this system it was considered that calibration against a standard target was desirable and so arrangements were made for observing the magnitudes of the signals received from metallized balloons of known echoing area. This proved to be unnecessary, for confidence in the apparatus was soon gained by some fortunate observations, first on a mounting skylark and second on a Canberra aircraft of known echoing area flying through the beam at an altitude of 40,000 ft. These observations confirmed that single bird targets could be detected in accordance with Fig. 11.5.

The main advantage of this second system was that much greater areas of sky could be kept under continuous surveillance than with the fixed aerial, with the result that many more bird transits could be recorded. This enhanced frequency of occurrence of echoes permitted comparison between bird and angel densities during periods of fluctuation such as were impossible by the first method, and comparisons could also be made at much lower angel densities. The use of a Height Azimuth Indicator type of display was also an advantage, since the directions of flight of the birds could then be deduced; information which was denied to the vertical beam method. It is true that the beam width in the vertical plane caused the height measurements to change systematically as the bird flew through the beam. This will be apparent from Plate 23 which shows the Z-scan film records obtained with the two types of aerials. Multiple paints were obtained with the scanning aerial. It was also necessary to make proper correction for the effect of altitude upon the area swept by the radar beam.

The height investigations described in the last chapter showed that 90 per cent of nocturnal spring migrants cross the Essex coast at an altitude below 4,500 ft. Using this range in association with the beam width of the aerial indicates that the minimum separation in the horizontal plane between two birds for complete resolution by the radar is only 55 ft, with proportionately smaller separations at lower altitudes. It was concluded that echo counts on the X-band equipment may confidently be equated to the number of individual birds traversing the beam, which permits bird densities to be derived for comparison with the angel densities supplied by the surveillance radar. Nocturnal counts of angels and birds during the spring of 1966 indicated that for the South of England the birds/angel ratio is usually less than 25, and greater than 4, with 10 as the average value.

Estimates of bird flow

There can be little doubt that the most accurate method of assessing the rate of passage of migrants over any station is to use a high resolution radar with its beam directed vertically. Unfortunately, this technique provides only the local

241

bird flight activity and many radars would be needed to probe the density of migration over a broad front; also, the method could not be used to measure the densities of movement over the sea.

Surveillance radars cover a very wide area, and, provided a good average value for the bird content of an angel is known, then it is possible to make an estimate of the number of birds comprising a major migratory movement. The Bushy Hill radar covers a front which extends from the Wash in the north to the French coast in the south. On a favourable night in the spring, migration to the Continent from the south-eastern region of England may easily extend over 120 miles with the bulk of the movement passing over the coast in about 6 h at an average speed of about 30 knots. Using figures for bird and angel densities suggested by the X- and L-band radar work leads to an estimate of the bird exodus on one medium-busy night as 7×10^5. Lack (1959) has studied the variation of this migratory movement throughout the spring, and if it is assumed that the bulk of the spring departure from this region is represented by about 40 such nights, then the total bird movement appears as 30 million. Obviously, the figures can only be rough at this stage but more observational work will introduce precision into the calculation. Integration of results from a number of overlapping radars will then ultimately permit the major migration of birds into and out of the country during the year to be assessed.

An estimate of the number of birds contained in one dense spring movement was made by Harper (1958). He assumed that birds were distributed so as to provide one flock of 20 birds per pulse volume at a range of 10 miles, and finally arrived at a figure of 3×10^6 birds crossing a front of 60 miles in a period of 2 h at a recorded ground speed of 43 knots. Nisbet also estimated that a few million birds crossed a 100-mile front during one of the busy nights of the autumn migration in the Cape Cod region. It will be seen that these various attempts to count the number of passerine birds in a major movement at least agree in order of magnitude. Bergman and Donner (1964) in their radar studies in the Gulf of Finland, estimated the spring passage of the common scoter to be about $1\frac{1}{2}$ million birds.

The grouping of nocturnal migrants

The radar evidence relating to the distribution of nocturnal migrants during flight has been reviewed by Eastwood and Rider (1966). Many of the pictures in this book have illustrated the fact that discrete angels may be seen on the p.p.i., both by day and night, but in the daytime it is well known that many species, such as the chaffinch or starling, migrate in large flocks in which the birds move together as a coherent group by reason of their mutual sight of each other. The aerial manoeuvres of a starling flock in the vicinity of its roost are clear evidence of the precision which this visual mode of control permits. Films of nocturnal angels on the p.p.i., also show that many of the stronger echoes persist over long distances and can be tracked in spite of the fading effects which have been discussed above. There is a strong temptation to conclude from these facts that these nocturnal angels, like their daytime counterparts, also correspond to groups of birds and that the association between the birds of a group may derive from some form of social relationship between them.

On the other hand, the displays of warblers and swifts, which were considered in earlier chapters, did not present an assembly of discrete angels but approximated to a hazy continuum in which were embedded transient echoes of low intensity. It seemed certain that this appearance was explicable in terms of the number of randomly dispersed birds contained within the pulse volume changing continuously, and there was no necessity to assume any form of group relationship between the birds.

Signature analysis tests performed with the L-band equipments have clearly shown that discrete angels are multi-bird targets, whether they are observed by night or by day. These results, in association with the tracker measurements of echoing areas, have suggested that an average passerine angel contains a number of birds – in the order of ten. The question is whether these birds which are contributing to the angel signal on the p.p.i. are a true group or whether they are merely the fortuitous occupants of a pulse volume. If it is the latter, then all angels are to be regarded as resulting from an interaction between the polar diagram of the aerial, the parameters of the radar and a random distribution of migrants.

The application of a mixed radar and optical technique by Nisbet (1963a) showed that the average number of birds per angel which he was observing in the region of Cape Cod was usually between 2 and 12. After a careful review of the evidence, particularly the fact that the average composition of an angel increased only very slowly with the migration density, Nisbet concluded that many birds were migrating in well-defined groups.

The double radar method described above has also suggested a birds-per-angel figure not significantly different from that of Nisbet's but this does not fully prove the group nature of the angels observed in the two regions. One method of testing the objective existence of angel groups would be to record and compare the angels occurring in a particular region by means of two radars having different pulse volumes at the ranges in question. Real groups of birds should then be seen as such on both radars. In fact, this experiment was performed when angels observed on the L-band surveillance radar were also examined by the S-band height finder, as Fig. 11.1 showed. Similarly, this is what the X- and L-band radars were also examining, in that the former sees single birds while the latter sees angel groups. These X-band measurements showed that the rate of passage of individual birds over Bushy Hill was far from uniform. In taking the observations it was particularly noticeable, not only that the number of transits during a series of successive quarter hour intervals changed greatly but that the rate of passage varied from minute to minute. In other words, the spatial distribution of the birds was very granular and areas of concentration were present among the general spread of birds; the separations between the members of such closely grouped sections were well within the pulse volume of the L-band radar.

243

According to this evidence it would appear probable that the L- or S-band angels are primarily pulse-volume effects, but this would seem hard to reconcile with the long life which many angels often appear to possess on the speeded film method of viewing, and with the fact that the same angel may be examined by two dissimilar radars. There is also to be taken into consideration the fact that the fission of angels on the B-scope is not a common event; this is surprising if angels were only a pulse-volume effect.

The films showing the night ascent of the swift and the departure of warblers during the autumn migration show that, although these echoes probably arise from a pulse-volume effect, there is a continuity to the geometrical pattern or geographical distribution of the birds at take-off which takes a surprisingly long time to disperse. This effect is even more marked in the case of the night-waves of starlings which was described in Chapter Nine, also the dispersals of the starlings from their roosts to join the migrant stream. These examples suggest that some form of station-keeping is practised by the birds which can supplement the migration-direction programme with which all the birds are endowed and so ensures the continuity of the initial distribution pattern over quite long periods.

All the evidence suggests that while some of the nocturnal angels which give good echoes at long range are probably true groups analogous to those observed by day, others, and perhaps the majority, are pseudo-groups which are a consequence of the pulse volume effect. Even the 'true groups' may only be groups in the sense that the birds composing them have taken off from a common locality or a common roost, the group form being roughly maintained because the birds fly at the 'same' speed and in the 'same' direction. Nevertheless, the well known visual acuity of the birds may serve to bind the birds into some approximation to a unified group; acoustic calling on the wing, which is well known, would also help to the same end. If this is indeed the explanation of nocturnal angels it means that the appearance of discrete angels only differs from the appearance of warblers by reason of the echoing areas of the birds involved and the closeness of the distribution. As with so many other problems in radar ornithology, more evidence is needed before final answers to these questions can be given.

CHAPTER THIRTEEN

The influence of radio waves upon birds

In the preceding chapters an account has been given of how the behaviour of birds in flight can be observed and studied by means of radio waves reflected from them. The tacit assumption has been made throughout this work that the birds were unaware of the fact that they were being 'looked-at' by radio. Clearly, a relevant question and one which must be answered if the radar method of conducting ornithological research is to be free from doubt is – are birds affected by radio waves? In these days of television and broadcasting we know that our bodies are bathed in a flood of man-made radio waves, not to mention the radiation that comes to us from the sun and from the giant radio-stars located in deep space. Our health does not seem to be impaired by this electromagnetic deluge, neither does human conduct appear to be influenced, and so it would appear reasonable to conclude that birds are similarly unaffected. Nevertheless, the question is so important to radar ornithology that it is worth reviewing certain aspects of the matter in more detail, including an account of some 'radio and birds' rumours and of the experiments that have been conducted to test them.

Radio waves as carriers of energy
It is not quite true to say that human beings are unaffected by radio waves, as anyone who has visited a hospital for radiotherapy treatment well knows. The human body can absorb energy from a radio field and becomes heated accordingly. Similarly, forms of radio transmitters are used to supply energy in various industrial processes, such as the fabrication of semiconductor devices, or the welding together of plastics by dielectric heating. It is true that in these cases the transmitter produces high-frequency oscillatory currents which are applied, not to an aerial for radiation, but to an arrangement of coils or parallel plate condensers surrounding the material to be heated, with the result that energy is transferred from the oscillating electric and magnetic fields to the material. True radiation is involved in microwave cooking when the output from a magnetron is passed through a waveguide containing the meat to be cooked.

It was shown in Chapter One that if a high-frequency alternating current is fed into a vertical wire or aerial then a succession of radio waves are produced which spread outwards like the ripples on a pond. Such an electrical disturbance is called an 'electromagnetic wave' and consists of travelling electric and magnetic fields which oscillate with the same frequency as the current in the aerial emitting the radiation.

Figure 13.1 shows that at a point remote from the transmitter there exists an

R

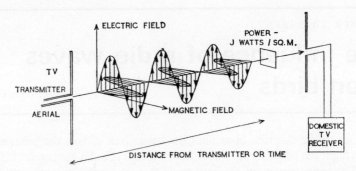

FIG. 13.1. An electromagnetic wave. This perspective view of a solid graph shows the waxing and waning of magnetic and electric field vectors, either at different distances at an instant of time, or at successive instants at one point. The flow of energy outwards from the transmitter is measured as $\mathcal{J}$ W/m²

oscillating electric field, with a magnetic field at right angles to it oscillating in sympathy. It is these fields which interact with the receiver aerial to produce a small, alternating electric current which can subsequently be amplified so as to yield the sound or vision signal required to operate the loud-speaker or television display tube respectively.

It will be clear that in order to operate the receiving equipment, energy must be collected by the aerial; this energy must have flowed from the transmitter, becoming weaker in intensity as the distance from the transmitter is increased – since the same quantity of energy is spread over greater and greater areas. We measure the strength of the received signal either by the electric field which produces it (E V/m), or in terms of the energy flow ($\mathcal{J}$ W/m²).

Typical values of radiation flux and field strength may be given for certain well-known stations, for example, at a distance of 20 miles from the Crystal Palace Television Transmitter the field strength available to operate a domestic television set is about 10^{-2} V/m, or 0.265×10^{-6} W/m². Since all electromagnetic radiation ultimately degrades into heat energy we may simply regard this figure as defining the quantity of heat energy passing through 1 m² at a distance 20 miles from the transmitter. It will probably help to fix orders of magnitude if we remember that the quantity of heat energy from an ordinary 100-W electric light bulb passing through 1 m² placed at a distance of 100 m is 8×10^{-4} W/m², while the sun itself produces a radiation flux or energy flow at the earth's surface of 1.7 kW/m².

Radio waves vary greatly in wavelength according to the operational purpose which they serve; some examples are gathered together in Table 13.1. These stations employ transmitters which deliver power appropriate to their function, and this may range from a few watts to hundreds of kilowatts, but all contribute to the radio flux in which we live.

In radio broadcasting the energy is generally radiated in all directions equally, but for many purposes it is desirable to concentrate all the energy into a narrow

TABLE 13.1 *Comparative frequencies, wavelengths, and purposes of some radio stations in England*

Station	Frequency	Wavelength	Purpose
Rugby	16 kc/s	18,700 m	Round the world communications
London Region	908 kc/s	330 m	Sound broadcasting
Air Traffic Control (Birdlip) Communications	4·5 Mc/s	67 m	Communications to aircraft over the North Atlantic
Crystal Palace (B.B.C.) Channel 1	45 Mc/s	6·7 m	Television
Croydon (I.T.A.) Channel 9	195 Mc/s	1·5 m	Television
Air Traffic Control Communications	150 Mc/s	2 m	Short-range V.H.F. communications to aircraft
London Airport Radar	600 Mc/s	50 cm	Air traffic control radar
Bushy Hill Radar	1,305 Mc/s	23 cm	Experimental radar for A.T.C. and defence
Missile Control Radar	10,000 Mc/s	3 cm	For anti-aircraft defence

beam and so produce a greater intensity in one direction. This same principle of beaming is used in the optical lens system of a lighthouse, or in the reflector of an automobile headlamp, in order that the light shall be able to penetrate to greater distances. Thus, at a distance of 100 m from a 10-W car headlamp the radiation flux at a point on the axis of the beam is approximately 0·3 W/m^2 compared with 8×10^{-5} W/m^2 in the unfocused case. An identical arrangement is used in radar; it was explained in Chapter One how a reflector having an aperture many feet wide is used to concentrate the energy into a very narrow beam in order that aircraft at much greater ranges can be detected.

The steerable tracker shown on the left of Plate 1 (*a*) produces a symmetrical beam which is 1·8° wide between the half-power points. At a point on the axis of the dish and 10 miles away from the aerial, the radiation intensity is $7·6 \times 10^{-3}$ W/m^2; this flux corresponds to a peak electric field strength of 48 V/m and a peak magnetic field of $1·3 \times 10^{-4}$ oersteds. The radiation is vertically polarized, i.e. the electric field in the beam is vertical and the magnetic field is horizontal.

The electric fire type of reflector which is used in the surveillance radar on the right of Plate 1 (*a*), produces a vertical fan beam in which the electric field is horizontally polarized. The radiation intensity at a point on the axis 10 miles away from the aerial is 14×10^{-3} W/m^2, corresponding to a peak electric field strength of 65 V/m (or $1·7 \times 10^{-4}$ oersteds).

'Reports' of radio interactions with birds

The energy fluxes quoted above are obviously quite small if only the heating effect of the radiation absorbed by a bird or human is to be considered, but it is possible that even a feeble electromagnetic field produced by a distant transmitter may affect the sensory mechanisms of a bird in some other and more subtle way.

It is a curious fact that reports of a direct interaction between radio waves and the flight behaviour of birds did not appear before the advent of radar. Powerful radio stations have existed for many years but no untoward behaviour of birds in the vicinity have been reported, not even at the moment of switch-on. With the introduction of directive aerials into radar there have been a number of reports that pointing of the radar beam at a flock of birds produced dispersal of the birds. One report from a former member of a British Naval team said that on one occasion he noted a skein of geese scattered by pointing the radar beam. On removal of the beam the birds reformed only to be dispersed once more by repositioning of the beam. Similarly, Drost (1949) claimed that birds reacted to radiations emitted by certain radar stations located near an ornithological station at Heligoland. Rooks, geese, gulls, and some songbirds appeared to be affected by the radiations, but other birds showed no such reactions.

On the other hand, Kramer (1951) could detect no sensitivity of birds to radio, neither was Sutter (1957b) able to observe any birds behave in a peculiar manner in the vicinity of his radar. It is, of course, impossible to confirm or refute many so-called eye-witness reports, often made many years after the event. Dorst (1962) has briefly reviewed the rather sketchy and conflicting evidence in connexion with this subject and concludes, 'the question cannot be settled, but it is worth more detailed study, as these perceptions are important'.

There can be no dissent from this conclusion that the interaction of radio with birds merits detailed experimental study, since the detection of bird perceptions of this type could greatly affect our understanding of the sensory apparatus of birds. It was for this reason that a series of observations was undertaken at Bushy Hill in order to discover whether positive effects could be detected, when radar equipments of much higher power than any that have been used hitherto were employed. Detailed examination of radar microscope recordings of the tracks of flying birds, however, have failed to disclose any directional changes or flock scattering effects due to the passage of the birds through these radio beams. These experiments are described later and compared to other observations which have been reported.

It is possible that the birds of the various reports were merely frightened by the proximity of the rotating aerial, since it is fairly clear that the observations were made at visual range. If track changes indeed took place and were not caused by fear, then, presumably, it was because the bird's directional or orientational sense was influenced by the radio waves. So mysterious is the bird's ability to perform long migratory journeys over the earth's surface that it must not be assumed too readily that radio waves would have no possible influence upon

248

whatever senses are involved in the associated navigation process. Many theories of bird navigation have been advanced which have been reviewed in detail by Matthews (1955) and Dorst (1962). In particular, the possibility that the earth's magnetic field might provide one fixing co-ordinate of a bi-co-ordinate system of navigation by some interaction with a magnetically sensitive element within the bird has been considered, but the difficulties confronting such a theory have been shown to be formidable. The horizontal and vertical components of the earth's magnetic field are typically 0·18 and 0·3 oersteds respectively; these field strengths are small as magnetic fields go but it is pertinent to point out, however, that a modern land-mine detector is capable of detecting a field gradient of only 10^{-5} oersteds/ft, so perhaps the lack of a magnetic detector of the required sensitivity in the bird must not be inferred too readily.

This caution is necessary when we remember that it has been shown that a magnetic field can influence the form of growth of the roots of certain plants and, what is more relevant, that the influence of the earth's field upon the movements of certain species of snails and flagellates is also well established (F. A. Brown 1963; J. D. Palmer, 1963). Not the least serious of the objections to the theory that the earth's magnetic field might provide one co-ordinate in the navigation process practised by birds, is the experimental fact that many flights have now been made by homing pigeons to whose wings have been attached small permanent magnets, but the homing performance of the birds does not appear to have been affected by this additional magnetic field which greatly exceeds the magnitude of the earth's field itself (Matthews, 1955). On the other hand it was reported by Dost (1962) that migrating geese behaved peculiarly when flying over the buildings housing the powerful cycloctron magnet of the Californian Institute of Technology, Pasadena.

If such careful thought should have been justifiably applied to a possible interaction between a bird's 'navigation instruments' and the earth's magnetic field, it is equally desirable to look for any influence exerted by radio waves.

Observations on spring migrants

The general principle governing the observations of radiation effects which were made at Bushy Hill by Eastwood and Rider (1964) during the spring migrations of 1961 and 1962 was to employ the large surveillance radar for recording the tracks of the moving birds, while other radar beams were maintained in fixed positions so as to irradiate the portions of space through which the birds were moving. The 'perturbing' radar could be switched on and off and this provided control periods during which the paths of the birds in the absence of radiation could be established. Recording was maintained throughout the half-hour of each radiation period; this corresponded to a film running time of 5 s during subsequent projection, which was sufficient to reveal the directions of motion of birds near the coasts of Essex and Suffolk.

The method of observation finally adopted was to locate the perturbing radar well outside the permanent echo region of the Bushy Hill station so that the bird tracks could be clearly seen. The perturbing beam was then pointed north and south during successive half-hour intervals, in this way bird movements in two separate areas could be simultaneously observed and any path deflexion effects would have been immediately apparent. No such effects were observed; both day and night recordings of the spring migration were made.

Distance of irradiated areas from perturbing radar   = 3 miles
Wavelength of perturbing radar   = 23 cm
Mean Flux from perturbing radar   = 8×10^{-2} W/m^2

Observations on starling roosts

The movements of starlings in the vicinity of their roosts had been studied at Bushy Hill for some years as described in Chapter Nine, so that the technique of observation was well established. It so happened in 1962 that a large roost existed in the proximity of Rivenhall Airfield where the Marconi organization maintained a second radar test site on which a number of high power radars were undergoing tests. These radars operated at wavelengths of 10 and 50 cm and were located so that their radiations could be beamed upon the Rivenhall roost. It was hoped that any effect of the combined radiations upon the starlings might show itself as anomalous behaviour in the manner of assembly to, or dispersal from, the roosts as recorded at the Bushy Hill station. No such effects were observed; the perturbing field strengths are given below:

10-cm radar A—0·41 W/m^2
10-cm radar B—0·65 W/m^2
50-cm radar   —0·01 W/m^2

It will be seen that the mean total flux in the vicinity of the roost was in the order of 1 W/m^2.

Tracker observations on approaching bird flocks

It will be appreciated that a radar used for recording the movement of birds is itself irradiating the birds just as did the perturbing radars used in the above observations. The recording radar, however, is scanning continuously and so the birds are only momentarily in its beam; the mean radiation energy is, therefore, small and any perturbing effect upon the birds would be likely to be very slight. It was for this reason that the surveillance radar was used for recording only. It was considered to be of interest, however, to use the L-band tracker radar in the azimuthal scanning mode so that a scan frequency of 20 c/m could be obtained over an angle of 10° in order to see if any perturbing effect could be observed upon flocks of birds approaching the station radially, the radar acting as both perturber and recorder. This test was of particular interest since the reports of radiation effects upon birds that have appeared in the literature, all refer to the dispersive effect of a radio beam when directed at an approaching flock of birds, the deflexion of the birds being observed visually. The film records did not reveal any perturbing effect upon the flight of the birds.

Discussion of the radar/radio evidence
The observations described above (and later in this chapter) show that no perturbing effects upon the flights of birds were observed for radio flux levels in the range from 0·1–1,000 W/m². Various species of birds were involved, mainly passerines and waders, but including also some sea birds. The radio wavelengths were in the band 3 to 50 cm, i.e. frequencies 10,000–600 Mc/s.

These negative results do not prove, of course, that positive interactions might occur at higher field strengths or at other radio frequencies. It should be noted, however, that the radio flux incident upon the birds in these tests was clearly sufficient to give radar echoes, so that the electromagnetic field was undoubtedly interacting with the bird's body to give surface or volume scattering of the radar energy in amounts sufficient to be easily detected by the radar receiver. We can at least conclude that electromagnetic fluxes of intensity less than 1,000 W/m² show no interaction with that portion of the bird's sensory equipment concerned with orientation.

During the past ten years the increase in power of radar stations and tropo-spheric scatter communication stations has prompted careful investigation of the effects of radio frequency fields upon both humans and animals. It is true that such experiments have been directed to the study of possible tissue damage produced by intense beams of radiation rather than seeking to detect subtle interactions with the sensory equipment of the animal. Thermal damage has been readily observed and in the case of humans a statutory 'safe' level of radia-tion flux has been arbitrarily fixed as not to exceed $10 \, \text{mW/cm}^2$, i.e. $100 \, \text{W/m}^2$. This figure arises, however, from the simple consideration that it is the level of heat loss per sq cm from the skin of a healthy human being. This flux level does not apply to the eye, the cornea of which is rather imperfectly cooled, and one case has occurred in the Marconi laboratories of temporary conjuctivitis induced by looking down a waveguide carrying 10 W of radiation of wavelength 8 mm, i.e. about $5 \times 10^4 \, \text{W/m}^2$. Extreme tissue damage was also reported by the same laboratories in the case of a blackbird killed by radiation of about the same density carried by a waveguide that the bird had inadvertently penetrated in the hopes of making a nest. This occurred in 1950 and is an early example of micro-wave cooking!

No case has yet been recorded of other than thermal effects being produced in human cells by radio-frequency radiation. At the Marconi laboratory, where radiation effects have been investigated for many years, there has been one record of an engineer who claimed he could detect the instant of passage over him of a scanning radar beam, a sensation in the roots of the hairs at the back of the head being experienced. It is possible, also, for acoustic effects to be produced attribut-able to the fact that radar transmissions are pulsed at audio frequencies, i.e. in the range 50–1,000 c/s.

Knorr (1954) reported visible panic reactions of certain birds to a beam of 10-cm radiation, but the powers he employed were much less than those used in the Bushy Hill tests, in fact, only about one-fiftieth. Since his observations of effects were made visually the range was presumably about 1 mile and the evolutions of his birds in the beam suggest that the beam width was comparatively wide, which means that the flux at the birds was small. In visual observations of this type it is difficult to be sure that the rotating structure of a large radar is not itself a perturbing influence. If the birds are near enough to be observed then they are fully aware of the mass of rotating metal looming in front of them. Such observations should be conducted on a statistical basis, with and without radiation, if they are to be convincing. It is for this reason that it is preferable to make observations at night by means of photographic recordings of the tracks so that the birds are substantially oblivious of the proximity of the rotating aerial. One report from the U.S.A. speaks of some troops operating a metric radar and 'playing the game' of pointing the beam at approaching bird flocks so causing them to split up. The author has operated $1\frac{1}{2}$ m radars possessing very large apertures so that with 500 kW of pulse power the mean flux level at a range of 1 mile was 4×10^{-3} W/m²; but no dispersal effects on bird flocks have ever been observed.

Proceeding to still lower frequencies, i.e. in the 2–30-Mc communication band of Table 13.1, effects on birds have been repeatedly looked for but with no positive results. One of the most detailed reports comes from Mr A. E. J. Symonds (1962) formerly an engineer at a large radio communication station in Shropshire. Mr Symonds, an experienced bird watcher, made systematic observations upon the behaviour of starlings for a number of years in the vicinity of the transmitter aerials in regions where the field strength was in the order of 2 W/m². He reported no untoward behaviour of the birds at any time. It should also be borne in mind that there have been observations extending over a number of years upon the behaviour of birds in the proximity of broadcast aerials carrying powers of hundreds of kilowatts. Similarly, sea birds perching upon the aerial of a ship is a common sight, even when the ship's radio is transmitting but no reports have been made of any peculiar behaviour of the birds. It is also relevant to point out that many species of birds make a habit of perching on power lines and telegraph lines – the assemblies of swallows at migration time are too familiar to require comment. Yet these power cables are carrying heavy currents so that the birds may be subjected to magnetic fields in the order of 0·1–40 oersteds which are alternating at 50 c/s. The magnetic field in the case of telegraph wires may be in the order of 10^{-7} oersteds and oscillate at frequencies in the region of 4,000 c to 20 kc/s for carrier lines. No ill effects appear to be experienced by the birds which frequent these convenient perches and the birds are manifestly oblivious of the oscillating magnetic fields which envelop them. In like manner sparrows and other birds perch with impunity upon the radars shown in Plate 1 (a) even when rotating and radiating full power!

Angel fission
There is little doubt that the photographic technique of recording and viewing the flight paths of birds would have been sufficiently delicate to detect any radar

beam effects upon the direction of flight of the birds if such effects has been present. Similarly, any scattering of a bird flock would also have been apparent. During the course of night observations at Bushy Hill on bird migration the splitting or fission of angel echoes corresponding to flock division is occasionally seen upon the films. A good example is shown in Plate 24. It would be expected that the number of such splittings would be greatly multiplied in the case of the passage of birds through a radar beam if an interaction of the radio waves with the birds were taking place. No such effects have been observed.

Pigeons and the B.M.E.W.'s station

Although a number of reports have been made of the perturbing effect of radar beams upon the flights of birds, no record of a carefully controlled series of observations was available until the Bushy Hill observations were published. Similarly, a statistical approach to the behaviour of the birds in the radar inter-action cases that have been claimed to have occurred, has been lacking, so it is difficult to assess the probability of a radio explanation of these effects.

A particularly outstanding case was the one which occurred in one of the national daily newspapers in May 1963; a report was published which indicated that six racing pigeons had been released in the vicinity of the Ballistic Missile Early Warning radar station on Fylingdales Moor in Yorkshire. It was stated that the birds had been affected by the beams of this station so that their return home had been greatly delayed. Investigation of this incident through official channels revealed that no semblance of a test had been arranged; it was not even certain that the radar station had been operational at the time of the release of the birds! An approach to the Editor of the daily paper concerned disclosed only that the correspondent's contact with the source of his information had been lost!

This case was discussed with Mr S. W. E. Bishop, Editor of *Pigeon Racing*, in the hope that perhaps one of his readers might have reported this very interest-ing and important incident. No report had been made, but Mr Bishop's com-ments on this occurrence as an expert in pigeon racing were very pertinent. He pointed out that it is a common occurrence for losses of birds to occur when releases are made in an unknown area. He further emphasized that unless the birds are carefully trained by gradually extending the range of their flights, then it is useless to pretend that they will be able to home from an unfamiliar location, radio beams or no radio beams.

Some observations with 3-cm waves

Mention has already been made of the hazard which flocking birds in the vicinity of airports provide for jet aircraft at the time of take-off or landing. This problem has been closely studied by the Canadian National Research Council; in parti-cular, examination has been made of the possibility of using radio signals to scare the birds away from the vicinity of airfield runways. In the course of this work Tanner (1966) has found that ordinary domestic chickens, also pigeons, can show a physical reaction to the switching on of a microwave beam. The birds were contained in a small cage located immediately beneath a J-band radar aerial of the usual horn type. Ciné films were made of the birds, which appeared to behave quite normally until the radar transmitter was switched on; at this moment the birds showed a tendency to droop a wing or flex one leg, or to crouch on the bottom of the cage. Switching the radar off restored the birds to normality.

In this experiment the birds were subject to a radiation flux between 10 and 30 mW/cm². Nevertheless, it was considered that the reactions of the birds were so immediate that the cause could hardly be attributed to an ordinary heating effect. Dr Tanner suggested that some interaction was taking place between the electromagnetic field and the bird's nervous system; he is continuing research to elucidate the effect in more detail.

It is of interest to report here some observations made by Mr John Stewart (1963) of the Ferranti Electronic Systems Division. He has been concerned with the testing of 3-cm radars used for missile control. During the tests of these equipments it was noted that birds repeatedly flew into the beam of the radar at distances well within the Rayleigh range. The power flux was in the order of 1 kW/m². No dispersal of the flocks of birds was observed, nor was any perturbing action upon the flight direction of the birds detected. It would appear, therefore, that even in the case of a 3-cm radar which produces very sharp beams of very high intensity, no effects upon the flight of birds have been noted.

Three-cm radiation has also been employed by scientists of the Royal Radar Establishment to investigate whether various birds at the Wildfowl Trust, Slimbridge, could be influenced in any way by radio fields, but the reactions have been wholly negative (Lack, 1966; Houghton and Laird, 1967).

Is radar bird watching valid?

It will be seen that even the most recent research work into the influence of radio waves upon birds is still providing conflicting evidence. Although Tanner's experimental arrangement bears little relationship to the habitat in which a bird normally operates, and he also used fields considerably in excess of those which a bird experiences in flight, the fact that he obtained a positive reaction by the bird to the presence of the field is of great importance. It remains to prove whether the interaction was purely thermal or whether some more subtle relationship exists. The outcome of further research will be awaited with interest.

When the experiments of the present chapter are considered in association with other observations, such as the behaviour of birds in the proximity of power cables, telegraph wires, broadcast aerials, communication aerials, radar aerials of all kinds and, finally, ships' aerials, it seems difficult to avoid the conclusion that any interaction between alternating electro-magnetic fields and the bird's sensory organs can be second order only, if it exists at all. We may conclude that radar is, indeed, a legitimate tool to use in ornithological research and does not perturb the birds whose presence it detects.

CHAPTER FOURTEEN

The future of radar
in ornithological research

The contribution which radar is best fitted to make to ornithological research is information about the behaviour of birds in flight. Birds are fascinating creatures in many ways, but probably it is their mastery of the air which most excites our interest, and to understand the birds' way of life requires that we gain as much information as possible about their behaviour when airborne. Many aspects of flight behaviour can only be studied by means of radar, and so it would appear to be a truism that the future of radar in ornithological research is assured. But before we consider what this future role of radar might be, it would be helpful to pause for a moment and take a quick look at the radar contribution to ornithology since Lack and Varley wrote their letter to *Nature* in 1945 about the new method of bird watching.

First and most important was the proof supplied by radar that nocturnal migration occurs on a far greater scale than had ever been thought likely. It is true that the performance of night flights by birds had long been inferred from morning observations of 'new arrivals' which were interpreted as falls of migrants en route; the presence of birds airborne at night had also been detected from their calls to each other while on the wing. But neither of these methods of observation suggested the presence of the vast hordes of birds at altitudes of a few thousand feet now revealed by radar which, on nights of favourable weather, wing their way to northern breeding grounds in the spring, or make the return journey to winter quarters in the autumn.

The radar method of tracking the flight paths of birds has confirmed many patterns of migration which have long been known or half suspected, although they had never been directly observed. The understanding of many of these migrations has been enlarged by the use of radar and many new movements have been discovered.

Bird watching over the sea is difficult – but not to radar, and the fact of long sea crossings for which radar has provided objective proof, came as a surprise to many ornithologists as also did the frequency with which such flights occur in a region like the North Sea. Similarly, radar has shown that flights of many hundreds of miles in length are commonplace with many species of birds. By this work radar has provided evidence in support of arguments based on thermo-chemistry that long non-stop flights are well within the fuel capacity or fat reserves of the birds. In consequence of this work, it now appears likely that step-by-step or short-hop migration may not be the dominant method of progress it was once thought to be.

Radar monitoring of birds in flight has permitted the influence to be assessed of various meteorological factors such as clouds, rain, temperature, wind state, and even the pressure changes at weather fronts. The effect of light as a factor initiating morning departure, also the reduction in intensity of daylight at sunset, prompting both the termination of some local flights as well as triggering the departure of migrants, have been correlated with bird movements observed on the p.p.i.

While the detection and tracking of the broad front movements that dominate the migration pattern of both Europe and North America has proved to be a major triumph of the radar method of investigation, the flexibility of the new technique when applied to detailed study of small regions is shown by the studies of the starling and the swift, also the movements of birds through the Swiss valleys, which have been described in earlier chapters of this book. The unique value of the radar tool is also shown to great advantage in its ability to supply accurate measurements of the heights at which birds fly, and researches in this field have revealed that the altitude behaviour of birds engaged on long migratory journeys is a subject of great complexity.

Radar has shown that birds on migration fly straight tracks over land and sea, and that at the point of transition between day and night, the tracks are both continuous and free from deviation. These are remarkable discoveries, but what light do they throw on bird navigation? When birds migrate they have to find their way over distances of thousands of miles and they need to do this in a fashion that will ensure the maximum probability of survival of their species. It is, perhaps, a rhetorical question to ask, 'How do birds navigate?' since it is far from certain that birds navigate at all in the sense of having the ability to determine their present position on the earth's surface and then to determine what track to fly from this point in order to achieve a desired future position in the presence of variable and unknown winds. Be this as it may, the bird has certainly to select a heading at every moment of its flight, and the ability to orient itself is just as fascinating a problem for study as the related, but even more problematic capability for navigation. Terrestrial experiments on orientation have suggested that the bird can make use of the stars by night and the sun by day in order to orient itself, but radar has shown that denial of these celestial aids to birds in flight does not necessarily result in disorientation. In fact, the disoriented state occurs very rarely and appears to be a consequence of the simultaneous presence of total cloud or overcast, wind and rain. If radar has not resolved the navigation problem it has certainly shown that other means of orientation are apparently available to the bird in addition to the celestial aids that were thought capable of supplying the whole answer a few years ago. Perhaps radar has confused the situation by supplying more facts about what birds do in flight, as distinct from their behaviour in the highly artificial environment of a cage – essential and suggestive though this laboratory work is.

P.p.i. displays of birds on migration are mostly granular, these bright points being the composite echoes from assemblies of birds. Some species of birds produce angel displays in the form of hazy regions of light with various brighter points set in them like stars in a nebula; warblers and night-ascended swifts are typical examples. Such an appearance probably arises from a random distribution of birds in space, the variation of intensity of the echo signal over the face of the p.p.i. being a consequence of the random fluctuation of the number of birds contained within the pulse volume. The displays of discrete angels typical of the nocturnal migrations of larger passerines, such as the thrush or starling, or of movement of waders, show close resemblance to the diurnal angels provided by the same species, which it is known fly in flocks by day. Analysis of the pulse-to-pulse amplitude variations of the echo signals given by both diurnal and nocturnal angels of these species shows that they are mostly multi-bird angels and contain about ten scattering centres. It is tempting to conclude from these results that many migrant birds of these species do indeed make their nocturnal flights in groups. It will be necessary, however, to study in more detail the variation in constitution of a single angel during an extended night flight in order to decide whether such a nocturnal angel group is composed of a fortuitous association of a few birds which is imposed by the radar geometry, or, less likely, whether there is some social significance to the group. If the birds of an angel are indeed a social group then it is an intriguing question to ask how the birds communicate in order to maintain the group in existence during a night flight – presumably only acoustic and visual means are available to them.

The future

This brief review of radar in ornithology shows that it has already contributed valuable new facts and has helped to better understanding of many bird phenomena, so that there seems little reason to doubt that it has an equally significant part to play in the future. Clearly, many investigations being performed with the aid of radar at the present time are far from complete and part of radar's future contribution must inevitably be an extension of some of the work described in this book. But new fields of research will also be helped and illumined by the application of more recent radar techniques such as the study of target characteristics as derived from signature analysis. Bird counting by radar has already provided much interesting information and refinement of the measurement procedures will ultimately permit detailed quantitative studies to be made of the movements of bird populations.

Emphasis in the future will need to be laid on radar studies of individual angels, and particularly single-bird angels. In this way we may hope gradually to build up information on the orientational behaviour of individuals beneath overcast at night, and even between layers of cloud so that sight of both ground and stars is simultaneously denied to the migrants. Such methods of study will also ensure that accurate altitudes are simultaneously measured; this information could lead to knowledge of the rate of climb of a bird, a performance figure which could, in turn, be related to the metabolic processes in the bird itself and to the wind state, temperature, relative humidity, and the presence or otherwise of vertical air currents. The ability of the bird to maintain altitude over long intervals of time when large distances are covered and different ground pressures experienced could then be examined, and information derived on how birds sense altitude both absolutely and differentially.

Similarly, the structures and motions of clouds in proximity to the migrant will be capable of extraction by use of tracker radar techniques. We have seen that the vexed question of whether birds do, or do not, correct for drift will only be satisfactorily settled when the wind speed and direction are known at the altitude and location of the migrant bird in flight. There is a strong hope that radar will be able to provide this information, but orientational studies on individual birds would also be greatly assisted by the use of small radio beacons which modern micro-electronic techniques now make feasible. The use of a VHF or UHF beacon in association with radar would aid both direction finding and identification; this technique would be invaluable as a means of studying the flight of a beacon-fitted bird released from a light aircraft at a range of 15 miles say, and an altitude of 5,000 ft.

Identification still remains a limitation of the radar method of observing targets in the air space, and only the use of beacons or secondary radar transceivers appears likely to overcome this defect in the case of aircraft. Such a system would be much too heavy and complex to use for a solution of the bird identification problem, but recent advances in biotelemetry suggest that simple active beacons for use with birds will definitely be produced in the not too distant future. When bird ringing was introduced it permitted the movements of a few individual birds to be determined precisely as opposed to the general impressions of movements of masses of birds on migration gleaned by the field observer. Similarly, radio labelling of a few birds in flight would allow precise information to be obtained on the progress of a movement; such information would be most helpful in guiding the interpretation of the mass of radar data that describes a major migratory movement in which the labelled birds might be 'embedded'. It is possible that echo modulation due to wingbeat may also assist identification, but the method is hardly likely to be effective at long range where the large pulse volume precludes the observation of single birds.

There is a real need to establish long tracks of some hours duration on selected individual angels which modern computer controlled precision radars will be capable of fulfilling. Such information would include altitude, angel composition (from echoing area), and accurate directional information on the track, particularly through the day/night transition. It is only by methods such as this that data of the required accuracy will be accumulated on the orientational performance of birds in flight under a variety of weather conditions that will adequately complement experiments on caged birds.

Although the mechanics and aerodynamics of bird flight have been studied theoretically, there is need for many more studies of these subjects in the light of detailed performance data which radar can supply. Bird flight close to the sea's surface should receive attention and also in rising thermals.

Radar observation of birds engaged upon aerial feeding has been touched upon in this book but much remains to be done on the radar detection of insects in thermals and the flight behaviour of the birds which feed upon them. This information should be accessible to modern, high-power tracker radars, many of which possess very narrow beams with high Doppler detection capability deriving from the continuous wave system employed. This type of radar will also facilitate the detection of the wingbeat effect and the identification which stems from it.

Precision altitude measurements on birds simultaneously with observations of meteorological angels will help to show whether any correlation exists between bird altitude and humidity effects. Any aeroplane traveller is familiar with the presence of clouds in stratified layers – do bird altitudes show any such layering effects consequent upon the interaction between heat and water output of the bird's 'engine' and the temperature and humidity profiles present in the atmosphere through which it is flying? Performance data on bird flights at altitudes in the range 10,000 to 20,000 ft, when supported by theoretical studies, should lead to some very interesting results, particularly as the density of the air and the resistance it offers to flight are then substantially reduced.

The organization of radar research in ornithology

Valuable as the results of the radar method of research have already been it has to be remembered that the use of radar in ornithological research has been largely accidental. Perhaps 'opportunist' would be a more appropriate word, for enthusiastic 'radar ornithologists' have had to make the best use they could of military and air traffic control equipments to which they might be allowed access. These radars were sited in locations best suited to the operational functions they were designed to fulfil; certainly, the solution of the complex routing problems of migrant birds was not one of the original objectives.

If radar is to make the contribution to ornithological research of which it is capable, then more thought will have to be given to the planned use of available equipments. Co-operative programmes of research will have to be organized between adjacent radars having suitable overlapping regions of cover, so that continuous tracking of migrant birds might be possible over distances of many hundreds of miles. Military and Airport authorities have co-operated excellently in the past and doubtless they will continue to do so in the future, particularly if ornithologists submit well-considered observational programmes that are within the station's capability to discharge.

When one surveys the map of the Americas and reflects upon the vast, complex pattern of bird migration which must exist over this enormous region it will be apparent that the radar studies which have been presented in this book can only be regarded as an introduction to the radar researches which must surely appear during the next decade. Similarly, when we consider the broad sweep of springtime migratory movements from Central and Southern Africa into Europe it will be apparent that the number of radar stations which have so far helped to plot them have been pitifully few. Powerful air traffic control radars are becoming standard equipment at most of the world's major airports and air route staging posts; military radars are also much less emphatically barred to scientists than formerly, so that circumstances are favouring a significant surge forward by ornithologists into research by radar methods. Although it will be some years before networks of powerful radars exist of capability equal to those described in this book, nevertheless, there is already a great harvest of information waiting to be reaped from the stations already in existence and which could be acquired by the use of photographic recordings taken from standby p.p.i.'s.

There are many very interesting regions of the earth from the bird migration point of view that are not covered by any radars, nor are ever likely to be. It will, therefore, be necessary to secure the loan of suitable mobile radars from the Military in order to obtain records of migration in specially significant geographic regions, such as offshore islands or the entrance to mountain passes. Fortunately, much of the tracking of migrants can be accomplished with simple surveillance radars whose design is well established. Certainly, it will not be necessary to design a special ornithological radar. Ordinary L- and S-band pulse radars have made a great contribution in the past and are likely to do so in the future and mobile equipment of this type would be very helpful in many of these places since they are thoroughly proven, reliable and economic to operate. Small X-band sets used in the vertical incidence mode can also be usefully employed at small expense. It is also probable that much useful information would be gained by the use of the high-power C.W. radars which are now available and which are perfectly adapted to the study of individual birds in flight, but equipment of this type would have to be operated by the military units which use them.

Probably the first major research aimed at following the movements of birds into a large region by the use of a co-ordinated group of radar stations was that initiated in Canada in 1964 and was prompted by the very practical problem of bird strikes on aircraft. The presence of huge breeding communities of birds in northern Canada results in heavy concentrations of birds around airfields in this region and flocking birds are a major hazard to aircraft during take-off and landing. The ingestion of birds into jet engines is one risk; impacting of birds upon the pilot's windscreen is another and both have resulted in serious accidents. Methods of controlling the birds are being actively studied but it also seemed desirable to the authorities that more information should be gained of the flow of the birds into northern Canada during the spring migration. A method of gaining this information was conveniently to hand in the chains of radar stations which stretch across Canada. These stations form a continuous radar-fence which would give immediate warning of the penetration of any hostile aeroplane that might seek to come by the polar route into Canada and North America. A number of these radars were used in 1964/65 to record the passage of migrants into the region and this study, when published, will provide valuable information on the course of migration into Canada.

A similar effort at collaborative radar research in North Europe was also attempted in 1965 and made use of a number of N.A.T.O. stations. It is obvious that valuable progress would be made in this way and such combined radar station studies are likely to be of great importance in the future. It would be one very happy outcome of military electronics if 'swords were beaten into plough-shares' in this way. I am sure Isaiah would have been pleased at this twentieth-century example of the fulfilment of his prophecy – particularly as he, too, was obviously well versed in the ways of birds.

Wind drift effects

When radar is employed for studying the migratory movements of birds, the data obtained are the bearings of the angel tracks, also the ground speeds and altitudes of the birds. But migrants are seldom flying in still air and the track which the radar records is the resultant of the wind vector and the bird's velocity vector. In order to study the orientation and heading of the birds, it is necessary to 'take out the wind' by means of the Triangle of Velocities, the assumption being that the wind at the location of the birds is accurately known – which is usually far from being the case. Many authors have found that, after such derivation of bird headings from radar track measurements, the spread of headings is greater than the spread of tracks. This result has suggested the apparently reasonable conclusion that active wind drift correction is commonly applied by migrant birds. Is this reasoning valid?

The geometrical relationships between the various velocity vectors involved were examined by Eastwood and Rider (1967) as in the accompanying diagrams.

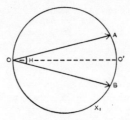

FIG. I. $\overline{OA}$ and $\overline{OB}$ are vectors representing the extreme headings of the birds in a migratory movement
Scatter of headings $= A\hat{O}B = \hat{H}$
$\overline{OA} = \overline{OB} =$ still-air speed of 25 knots (say) X_1 is the circum-circle through points O, O^1, A and B
$O\,O^1$ is the mean heading

It will be seen from Fig. 2 that when the point C, which defines the wind vector, lies outside the circle X_1, then the angle $\hat{H}$, which is the spread of the headings, is greater than the angle $\hat{T}$ which is the spread of the tracks. Fig. 3 shows that when C lies within the X_1 circle then $\hat{H} < \hat{T}$.

In these examples the wind speed has been shown as less than the still air speed of the bird but the relationships can be readily generalized so as to cover all wind states as in Fig. 4. For winds containing a 'following' component, i.e. for wind states defined by points C lying to the left of ZOZ', then Fig. 2 always

262

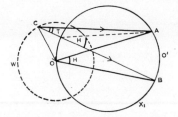 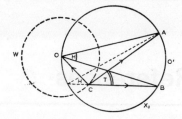

FIGS. 2 AND 3. Select any point C on the wind circle W (for this example the radius of W has been drawn for a wind speed of 10 knots)

$\overline{CO}$ is the wind vector

$\overline{CA}$ and $\overline{CB}$ are the track vectors

The angular spread of tracks is $A\hat{C}B = \hat{T}$

Mean track is the bisector of $A\hat{C}B$

When C lies outside the X_1 circle as in Fig. 2 $\hat{H}$ is greater than $\hat{T}$ (using the equality of angles in the same segment)

When C lies within the X_1 circle as in Fig. 3 $\hat{H}$ is less than $\hat{T}$

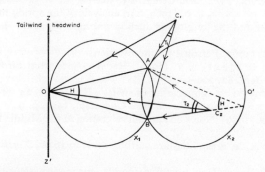

FIG. 4. X_2 is a circle through AB and $X_2 = X_1$

If C_1, the point defining the wind vector, lies outside the circles X_1 and X_2 then $\hat{H}$ is greater than $\hat{T}_1$

If the wind vector point C_2 lies within the circles X_1 and X_2 then $\hat{H}$ is less than $\hat{T}_2$

applies and the spread of headings exceeds the spread of tracks. In the 'headwind' region, i.e. for wind states defined by points C lying to the right of ZOZ', the spread of headings again exceeds the spread of tracks except when C lies within the region enclosed by the two circles, X_1 and X_2. In such a case, for example the point C_2, the spread of headings is less than the spread of tracks.

That the spread of headings should exceed the spread of tracks in a particular migratory movement may thus be a consequence of the simple geometry of the situation and does not necessarily imply that the birds have applied active correction for wind drift. In fact, some authors have provided additional analysis of the interaction between track and wind vectors which has rendered the existence of a measure of drift correction more than likely in the cases they have studied.

References

ADAMS, D. W. H. (1962) 'Radar observations of bird migration in Cyprus', *Ibis*, **104**, 133–46.

BAGNALL-OAKELEY, R. P. (1956) 'The Egmere starling roost', *Norfolk Bird Rep.*, 1955, 17–23.

BAGNALL-OAKELEY, R. P. (1959) 'The Egmere starling roost', *Norfolk Bird Rep.*, 1958, 22–4.

BARLOW, J. S. (1964) 'Inertial navigation as a basis for animal navigation', *Jour. Theoret. Biol.*, **6**, 76–117.

BELLROSE, F. C. & GRABER, R. R. (1963) 'A radar study of the flight directions of nocturnal migrants', *Int. Orn. Congr.*, **13**, 362–89.

BERGMAN, G. & DONNER, K. O. (1964) 'An analysis of the spring migration of the common scoter and the long-tailed duck in southern Finland', *Acta Zool. Fenn.*, **105**, 3–59.

BISHOP, S. W. E. (1963) Personal communication.

BONHAM, L. L. & BLAKE, L. V. (1956) 'Radar echoes from birds and insects', *Scientific Monthly*, **82**, 204–9.

BOOTH, H. B. (1930–1) 'Night soaring of swifts', *Brit. Birds*, **24**, 111.

BOURNE, W. R. P. (ed.) (1951) *Camb. Bird Club Rep.*, 1950, p. 9

BOURNE, W. R. P. (1959) 'Notes on autumn migration in the Middle East', *Ibis*, **101**, 170–6.

BOYD, A. W. (1932) 'A great Cheshire starling roost in 1930', *North Wales Nat.*, **7**, 10–18.

BROWN, F. A., JR. (1963) 'How animals respond to magnetism', *Discovery*, **24**, 18–22.

BROWN, F. J. (1946) 'A Cheshire starling roost, 1944–45', *J. Anim. Ecol.*, **15**, 75–81.

CASEMENT, M. B. (1966) 'Migration across the Mediterranean observed by Radar', *Ibis*, **108**, 461–91.

CASH, J. C. (1930–1) 'Night soaring of swifts', *Brit. Birds*, **24**, 88.

CRAMP, S., PARRINDER, E. R. & RICHARDS, B. A. (1957) *The Birds of the London Area since 1900*, p. 106, Lond. Collins.

CRAWFORD, A. B. (1949) 'Radar reflections in the lower atmosphere', *Proc. Inst. Radio Eng.*, **37**, 404–5.

DEELDER, C. L. (1949) 'On the autumn migration of the Scandinavian chaffinch (*Fingilla C. coelebs L.*)', *Ardea*, **37**, 1–88.

DEELDER, C. L. & TINBERGEN, L. (1947) 'Waarnemingen over de vlieghoogte van trekkende Vinken (*Fringilla coelebs L.*) en Spreeuwen (*Sturnus vulgaris L.*)', *Ardea*, **35**, 45–78.

DOBBEN, W. H. VAN (1953) 'Bird migration in the Netherlands', *Ibis*, **95**, 212–34.

DORST, J. *The Migrations of Birds*, London, Heinemann.

DOST, H. E. (1964) 'Behaviour of geese over a cyclotron', *Newsletter of the Cornell Lab. of Ornith.* No. 3.

DROST, R. (1949) 'Migrant birds sensing ultra short waves', *Vogelwarte*, **15**, 57–9.

DRURY, W. H. & KEITH, J. A. (1962) 'Radar studies of songbird migration in coastal New England', *Ibis*, **104**(4), 449–89.

DRURY, W. H., JR., NISBET, I. C. T. & RICHARDSON, R. E. (1961) 'The migration of "angels" ', *Nat. Hist.*, **70**(8), 10–17.

DRURY, W. H., JR. & NISBETT, I. C. T. (1964) 'Radar studies of orientation of songbird migrants in south-eastern New England', *Bird-Banding*, **35**, 69–119.

DRURY, W. H., JR., & NISBET, I. C. T. (1967) 'Orientation of Spring Migrants studied by Radar', *Bird-Banding* (in press).

EASTWOOD, E. (1962) 'Radar observations of bird movements', *Proc. Roy. Instn.*, **39**, No. 176, 101–17.

EASTWOOD, E. (1963) 'Radar observations of bird migrations in the south-east of England', *Proc. XIIIth Int. Ornith. Congr.*, 390–5.

EASTWOOD, E., BELL, J. D. & PHELP, N. R. (1959) 'Ring angels over south-east England', *Nature*, Lond., **183**, 1759.

EASTWOOD, E., ISTED, G. A. & RIDER, G. C. (1960) 'Radar ring angels and the roosting movements of starlings', *Nature*, Lond., **186**, 112.

EASTWOOD, E. & RIDER, G. C. (1961) 'A radar observation of the sea-breeze front', *Nature*, Lond., **189**, 978.

EASTWOOD, E., ISTED, G. A. & RIDER, G. C. (1962) 'Radar ring angels and the roosting behaviour of starlings', *Proc. Roy. Soc. B.*, **156**, 242–67.

EASTWOOD, E. & RIDER, G. C. (1964) 'The influence of radio waves upon birds', *Brit. Birds*, **57**, 445–58.

EASTWOOD, E. & RIDER, G. C. (1965) 'Some radar measurements of the altitude of bird flight', *Brit. Birds*, **58**, 393–426.

EASTWOOD, E. & RIDER, G. C. (1966) 'The grouping of nocturnal migrants', *Nature*, Lond., **211**, 1143–6.

EASTWOOD, E. & RIDER, G. C. (1967) 'The interpretation of radar evidence relating to wind drift correction by bird migrants' (in press).

EDWARDS, J. & HOUGHTON, E. W. (1959) 'Radar echoing area polar diagrams of birds', *Nature*, **184**, 1059.

ELDER, F. C. (1957) 'Some persistent ring echoes on high powered radar', *Proc. Sixth Weather Radar Conference*, Camb. Mass, p. 281–6.

EVANS, P. R. (1966) 'Migration and orientation of passerine night migrants in Northern England', *Journal of Zoology*, London **150**, 319–69.

GEHRING, W. (1963) 'Radar- und Feldbeobachtungen über den Verlauf des Vogelzuges im Schweizerischen Mittelland: Der Tagzug im Herbst', *Orn. Beob.*, **60**, 35–68.

GERSTER, G. (1960) 'Passport control for migrant birds', *Swiss Air Gazette*, Jan. 1960, 14–16.

GRUYS-CASSIMIR, E. M. (1965) 'On the influence of environmental factors on the autumn migration of chaffinch and starling: a field study'. Thesis, Rijksuniversiteit te Groningen.

HARPER, W. G. (1957) ' "Angels" on centimetric radar caused by birds', *Nature*, **180** (4591), 847–9.

HARPER, W. G. (1958) 'Detection of bird migration by centrimetric radar – a cause of radar "angels" ', *Proc. Roy. Soc. B.*, **149**, 484–502.

HARPER, W. G. (1958) 'An unusual indicator of convection', *Proc. Seventh Weather Radar Conference*, Miami, Nov. 1958.

HARPER, W. G. (1959) 'Roosting movements of birds and migration departures from roosts as seen by radar', *Ibis*, **101**, 201–8.

HARPER, W. G. & BEIMERS, J. G. D. (1958) 'The movement of precipitation belts as observed by radar', *Quarterly Journal*, Roy. Met. Soc., July 1958, 242.

HAURWITZ, B. (1941) 'Dynamic meteorology', McGraw-Hill, New York.

HOFMANN, H. (1956) 'Plover on the radar screen', *Orn. Beob.*, **53**, 79–81.

S

HOUGHTON, E. W. (1963) 'Detection, recognition and identification of birds on radar', R. R. E. Memorandum No. 2047.

HOUGHTON, E. W. (1964) 'Detection, recognition and identification of birds on radar', *Eleventh Weather Radar Conference*, 14.

HOUGHTON, E. W. & COULTAS, F. W. (1958) 'A spring passage of "angels" at Malvern in 1958', *Roy. Radar Establ. Jour.*, 42, 1–9.

HOUGHTON, E. W. & LAIRD, A. G. (1967) 'A preliminary investigation into the use of radar as a deterrent of bird strikes on aircraft'. R.R.E. Memorandum.

KLOMP, H. (1956) 'The altitude of chaffinch migration', *Ardea*, 44, 235–9.

KNORR, O. A. (1954) 'The effect of radar on birds', *Wilson Bull.*, 66, 264.

KRAMER, G. (1950) 'Weitere Analyse der Faktoren welche die Zugaktivität des gekafigten Vogels orientieren', *Naturwiss*, 37, 377–8.

KRAMER, G. (1951) 'Eine neue Methode zur Erforschung der Zugorientierung und die bisher damit erzielten Ergebnisse', *Proc. 10th Int. Orn. Congr.* Upsala, 269–80.

KRAMER, G. (1951) 'Researches on the perception of ultra short waves by birds', *Vogelwarter*, 16, 55–9.

KRAMER, G. (1952) 'Experiments on bird orientation', *Ibis*, 94, 265–85.

KRAMER, G. (1957) 'Experiments on bird orientation and their interpretation', *Ibis*, 99, 196–228.

LACK, D. (1956) *Swifts in a Tower*, Methuen, London.

LACK, D. (1958) 'Migrational drift of birds plotted by radar', *Nature*, 182, 221–3.

LACK, D. (1959) 'Migration across the North Sea studied by radar. Part 1. Survey through the year', *Ibis*, 101, 209–34.

LACK, D. (1960a) 'The height of bird migration', *Brit. Birds*, 53(1), 5–10.

LACK, D. (1960b) 'Migration across the North Sea studied by radar. Part 2. The spring departure, 1956–59', *Ibis*, 102(1), 26–57.

LACK, D. (1960c) 'The influence of weather on passerine migration'. A review. *Auk*, 77, 171–209.

LACK, D. (1962a) 'Migration across the southern North Sea studied by radar. Part 3. Movements in June and July', *Ibis*, 104, 74–85.

LACK, D. (1962b) 'Radar evidence on migratory orientation', *Brit. Birds*, 55, 139–58.

LACK, D. (1963a) 'Migration across the southern North Sea studied by radar. Part 4. Autumn', *Ibis*, 105, 1–54.

LACK, D. (1963b) 'Migration across the southern North Sea studied by radar. Part 5. Movements in August, winter and spring, and Conclusion', *Ibis*, 105, 461–92.

LACK, D. (1966) Personal communication.

LACK, D. & EASTWOOD, E. (1962) 'Radar films of migration over eastern England', *Brit. Birds*, 55, 388–414.

LACK, D. & PARSLOW, J. L. F. (1962) 'Falls of night migrants on the English east coast in autumn 1960 and 1961', *Bird Migration*, 2, 187–201.

LACK, D. & VARLEY, G. C. (1945) 'Detection of birds by radar', *Nature*, 156, 446.

LANE, J. A. (1964) 'Small-scale irregularities of the radio refractive index of the troposphere', *Nature*, 204, 438–440.

LEE, S. L. B. (1963) 'Migration in the Outer Hebrides studied by radar', *Ibis*, 105, 493–515.

LIGDA, M. G. (1958) 'Radar observations of Redwing Blackbird flights', *Texas J. Sci.*, 10, No. 3.

LOWERY, G. H. (1951) 'A quantitative study of the nocturnal migration of birds', *Univ. Kansas Publ. Mus. Nat. Hist.*, 2, 361–472.

LOWERY, G. H. & NEWMAN, R. J. (1955) 'Direct studies of nocturnal migration', *Recent Studies in Avian Biology*, ed. A. Wolfson, University of Illinois Press.

MACKENZIE, J. K. (1956) 'Sea Breeze front at Lasham', *Sailplane and Gliding*, Vol. 7, No. 6 (Dec.), p. 294.

MARPLES, B. J. (1932) 'Starling roosts and flight lines near Oxford', *Brit. Birds*, **25**, 314–18.

MARPLES, B. J. (1934) 'The winter starling roosts of Great Britain (1932–33)', *J. Anim. Ecol.*, **3**, 187–203.

MARSHALL, A. J. (1961) 'Breeding Seasons and Migration', *Biology and Comparative Physiology of Birds*, Vol. 2, p. 307–39, New York and London.

MASCHER, J. W., STOLT, B-O., & WALLIN, L. (1962) 'Migration in spring recorded by radar and field observations in Sweden', *Ibis*, **104**, 205–15.

MASSON, P. W. (1930–1) 'Night soaring of swifts', *Brit. Birds*, **24**, 48–50.

MATTHEWS, G. V. T. (1955) *Bird Navigation*. University Press, Cambridge, England.

MATTHEWS, G. V. T. (1961) ' "Nonsense" orientation in Mallard (*Anas platyrhynchos*) and its relation to experiments on bird navigation', *Ibis*, **103**, 211–30.

MCMEEKING, J. M. (1953) *Oxford Orn. Soc. Ann. Rep.* 1952, 14–17.

MEINERTZHAGEN, R. (1955) 'The speed and altitude of bird flight', *Ibis*, **97**, 81–117.

MITCHELL, K. D. G. (1955) 'Aircraft observations of birds in flight', *Brit. Birds*, **48**, 59–70.

MITCHELL, K. D. G. (1957) 'Further aircraft observations of birds in flight', *Brit. Birds*, **50**, 291–302.

MITCHELL, K. D. G. (1964) 'Further observations of birds from aircraft', *Brit. Birds*, **57**, 315–24.

MOREAU, R. E. (1961) 'Problems of Mediterranean–Saharan migration', *Ibis*, **103**, 373–427, 580–623.

MYRES, M. T. (1964) 'Dawn ascent and reorientation of migrants', *Ibis*, **106**, 7–51.

NISBET, I. C. T. (1959) 'Calculation of flight directions of birds observed crossing the face of the moon', *The Wilson Bulletin*, **71**, 237–43.

NISBET, I. C. T. (1963a) 'Quantitative study of migration with 23-centimetre radar', *Ibis*, **105(4)**, 435–60.

NISBET, I. C. T. (1963b) 'Measurements with radar of the height of nocturnal migration over Cape Cod, Massachusetts', *Bird Banding*, **34**, 57–67.

NORTH, M. E. W. (1933) 'The winter distribution of the starling in South Cambridgeshire', *Camb. Bird Club Rep.* 1932, 18–27.

NORTON, K. A., VOGLER, L. E., MANSFIELD, W. V., & SHORT, P. J. (1955) 'The probability distribution of the amplitude of a constant vector plus a Rayleigh-distributed vector', *Proc. I.R.E.*, **43**, 1354–61.

PALMER, J. D. (1963) 'Organismic spatial orientation in very weak magnetic fields', *Nature*, **198**, 1061–2.

PARSLOW, J. L. F. (1962) 'Immigration of night migrants into Southern England in spring 1962', *Bird Migration*, **2**, 160–75.

PETERS, S. P. (1938) 'Sea breezes at Worthy Down', *Prof. Notes, Met. Office*, Vol. 6, No. 86.

PHELP, N. R. & DOWNIE, G. (1962) 'Radar recording', *British Kinematography*, **40**, 4–14.

PLANK, V. G. (1959) 'Spurious echoes on radar: a survey', *Geophys. Res. Papers*, No. 62, Air Force Cambridge Research Center, Bedford, Mass.

RICHARDSON, R. E., STACEY, J. M., & KOHLER, H. M. (1957) 'Radar angels at South Truro, Mass', *Proc. Sixth Weather Radar Conference*, Camb. Mass., 17 suppl.

RICHARDSON, R. E., STACEY, J. M., KOHLER, H. M., & NAKA, F. R. (1958) 'Elimination of a type of natural clutter in L-band radars', *Tech. Report* No. 178, M.I.T.

RICHARDSON, R. E., STACEY, J. M., KOHLER, H. M., & NAKA, F. R. (1958) 'Radar observation of birds', *Proc. 7th Weather Radar Conf.*, Miami, D.1–8.

ROEBUCK, A. (1934) 'The starling roosts in the east midlands', *Brit. Birds*, **27**, 325–32.

SAUER, E. G. F. (1956) *Naturwissenschaften*, **43**, 231.

SAUER, E. G. F. (1957a) 'Die Sternorientierung nächtlich ziehender Grasmücken (*Sylvia atricapilla, borin und curruca*)', *Zeitschr. Tierpsychol. 14*, 29–70.

SAUER, E. G. F. (1957b) 'Astro-navigational orientation of a warbler (*Sylvia c. curruca*) under an artificial starry sky', *Naturwiss*, **44**, 71.

SAUER, E. G. F. (1961) 'Further studies on the stellar orientation of nocturnally migrating birds', *Psychol. Forschung*, **24**, 224–44.

SAUER, E. G. F. & SAUER, E. (1955) 'Zur Frage der nächtlichen Zugorientierung von Grasmücken', *Rev. suisse Zool.*, **62**, 250–9.

SAUER, E. G. F. & SAUER, E. (1960) 'Star navigation of nocturnal migrating birds', *Cold Spring Harbor Symposia on Quantitative Biology*, **25**, 463–473.

SAXTON, J. A., LANE, J. A., MEADOWS, R. W., & MATTHEWS, P. A. (1964) 'Layer structure of the troposphere', *Proc. I.E.E.*, *III*, 275–283.

SCHAEFER, G. W. (1966) 'The study of bird echoes using a tracking radar', *Proc. 14th Int. Ornith. Congress*.

SCORER, R. S. & RONNE, C. (1956) 'Experiments with convection bubbles', *Weather*, May 1956, 151.

SENN, H. V. & HISER, H. W. (1957) 'Tracking hurricanes with radar', *Proc. 6th Weather Radar Conference*.

SIMPSON, J. E. (1962) 'Sea breeze summer', *Sailplane and Gliding*, Vol. 13, No. 6, p. 376.

SIMPSON, J. E. (1964) 'Sea-breeze fronts in Hampshire', *Weather*, **19**, 208–20.

STEWART, J. S. (1963) Personal communication.

SUTTER, E. (1950) 'Uber die Flughöhe ziehender Vögel', *Orn. Beob.*, **47**, 174.

SUTTER, E. (1956) 'Dreizehenmöwen im Winter 1954/55', *Orn. Beob.*, **53**, 79–81.

SUTTER, E. (1957a) 'Radar-Beobachtungen über den Verlauf des nächtlichen Vogelzuges', *Rev. suisse Zool.*, **64**, 294–303.

SUTTER, E. (1957b) 'Radar als Hilfsmittel der Vogelzugforschung', *Ornith. Beob.*, **54**, 70–96.

SUTTER, E. (1958) 'Frequenz und Ablauf des Nachtzuges nach Radar-Beobachtungen', *Proc. 12th Int. Ornithol. Congr.*, 28–9.

SYMONDS, A. E. J. (1961) 'The counting of starlings at country roosts', *Bird Study*, **8**, 185–93.

SYMONDS, A. E. J. (1962) Personal communication.

TANNER, J. A. (1966) 'Effect of microwave radiation on birds', *Nature*, **210**, p. 636.

TEDD, J. G. & LACK, D. (1958) 'The detection of bird migration by high power radar', *Proc. Roy. Soc.*, *B.*, **149**, 503–10.

TINBERGEN, L. (1956) 'Field observations of migration and their significance for the problems of navigation', *Ardea*, **44**, 231–5.

VLEUGEL, D. A. (1948) 'Enkele waarnemingen over "vorstofluckt" en "randtrek" in het Sloe – Schengengebied tijdens de winters van 1935/1936 en 1936/1937', *Ardea*. **36**, 143–62.

VUILLEUMIER, F. (1963) 'Factors concentrating fall migrants at an alpine pass', *Proc. XIIIth Int. Ornith. Congress*, 485–492.

WALLINGTON, C. E. (1961) *Meteorology for Glider Pilots*. John Murray, London.

WEITNAUER, E. (1952) 'Uebernachtet der Mauersegler, in der Luft?', *Orn. Beob.*, **49**, 37–44.

WEITNAUER, E. (1954) 'Weitener Beitrag zur Frage des Nächtigens beim Mauersegler', *Orn. Beob.* **51**, 66–71.

WEITNAUER, E. (1955) 'Zur Frage des Nächtigens beim Mauersegler, IV Beitrag', *Orn. Beob.*, **52**, 38–9.

WEITNAUER, E. (1956) 'Zur Frage des Nächtigens beim Mauersegler. V. Beitrag', *Orn. Beob.*, **53**, 74–9.

WHITEHOUSE, H. L. K. (1937 & 1938) 'The starling roosts of south Cambridge-shire', *Camb. Bird Club Reps.* 1936, 17–29 and 1937, 23–31.

WILCOCK, J. (1965) 'Detection by radar of autumn migration in eastern Scotland', *Ibis*, **107**, 316–25.

WILCOCK, J. (1964) 'Radar and visible migration in Norfolk, England', *Ibis*, **106**, 101–7.

WITHERBY, H. F., JOURDAIN, F. C. R., TICEHURST, N. F., & TUCKER, B. W. (1940) 'The Handbook of British Birds', H. F. and G. Witherby, London.

WYNNE-EDWARDS, V. C. (1929) 'The behaviour of starlings in winter', *Brit. Birds*, **23**, 138–53, 170–80.

WYNNE-EDWARDS, V. C. (1931) 'The behaviour of starlings in winter', *Brit. Birds*, **24**, 246–353.

Books for further reading

BATTEN, L. J. (1959) *Radar Meteorology.* University Press, Chicago.

CHRISTIAN, G. (1961) *Down the Long Wind.* Newnes, London.

DARLING, L. & DARLING, LOIS (1963) *Bird.* Methuen, London.

DORST, J. (1962) *The Migration of Birds.* Heinemann, London.

FRY, D. W. & GOWARD, F. K. (1949) *Aerials for Centimetric Wavelengths.* University Press, Cambridge, England.

HANSFORD, R. F. (1960) *Radio Aids to Civil Aviation.* Heywood, London.

KERR, D. C. (1949) Propagation of Short Radio Waves (Vol. 13. *Radiation Lab. Series of the Mass. Inst. of Technology*). McGraw-Hill, New York.

LACK, D. (1956) *Swifts in a Tower.* Methuen, London.

LACK, D. (1965) *Enjoying Ornithology.* Methuen, London.

LANDSBOROUGH-THOMSON, SIR A. (Editor) (1964) *A New Dictionary of Birds.* Nelson, London.

LAWSON, J. L. & UHLENBECK, G. E. (1950) 'Threshold Signals' (Vol. 24. *Radiation Lab. Series of the Mass. Inst. of Technology*). McGraw-Hill, New York.

MATTHEWS, G. V. T. (1955) *Bird Navigation.* University Press, Cambridge, England.

RIDENOUR, L. N. (Editor) (1947) 'Radar System Engineering' (Vol. 1. *Radiation Lab. Series of the Mass. Inst. of Technology*). McGraw-Hill, New York.

SLATER, L. E. (Editor) (1963) *Bio-Telemetry.* Pergamon Press, London and New York.

TAYLOR, D. & WESTCOTT, C. H. (1948) *Principles of Radar.* The University Press, Cambridge, England.

WALLINGTON, C. E. (1961) *Meteorology for Glider Pilots.* John Murray, London.

Index